THE EXPLORATION OF
WESTERN AMERICA
1800–1850

An Historical Geography

by

E. W. GILBERT, B.LITT., M.A.

Formerly Exhibitioner of Hertford College, Oxford;
Lecturer in Geography in the University
of Reading

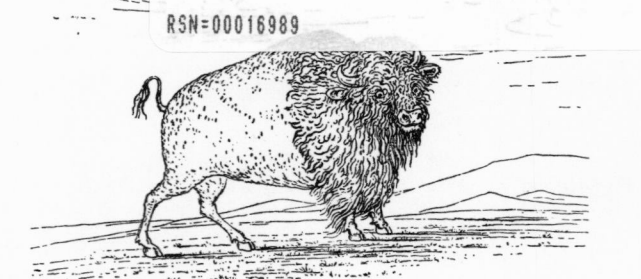

COOPER SQUARE PUBLISHERS, INC.
NEW YORK
1966

First Published 1933
Reprinted by Permission of Cambridge University Press

Published 1966 by
Cooper Square Publishers, Inc.
59 Fourth Avenue, New York, N. Y. 10003

Library of Congress Catalog Card Number: 65-26291

PRINTED IN THE UNITED STATES OF AMERICA
by SENTRY PRESS, NEW YORK, N. Y. 10019

CONTENTS

	PAGE
Preface	xi
Abbreviations	xv

HISTORICAL INTRODUCTION

Chap. I. The Early Exploration of Western America   1

II. The Purchase of Louisiana   14

PART I
A GEOGRAPHICAL ANALYSIS OF WESTERN AMERICA

Introduction   25

Chap. III.   The Physical Geography of the Region   27

IV. The Climate of the Region   36

V. The Natural Drainage of the Region   50

VI. The Natural Vegetation of the Region   65

VII. The Animals of the Region   77

VIII. The Indian Inhabitants of the Region   91

PART II
THE EXPLORATION OF WESTERN AMERICA
1800–1850

Introduction   101

Chap. IX. The Discovery of a Northern Trans-continental Route

(*a*) The Expedition of Lewis and Clark, 1803–1806   105

(*b*) The Fur-Traders, 1806–1811   124

PAGE

Chap. X. The Discovery of a Central Trans-continental Route

    (*a*) Astoria, 1810–1813   127

    (*b*) British Fur-Traders from the North, 1816–1829   131

    (*c*) The Rocky Mountains Fur Company, 1822–1836   133

    (*d*) The Discovery of South Pass   140

XI. The Discovery of Southern Trans-continental Routes

    (*a*) The Exploration of the Western Tributaries of the Mississippi, South of St Louis, 1803–1806   151

    (*b*) The Expedition of Pike, 1806–1807   153

    (*c*) The Expedition of Long and Bell, 1819–1820   158

    (*d*) The Santa Fé Trail   162

    (*e*) The Routes from Santa Fé to California   165

XII. The Discovery of the Great Basin and the Routes over the Sierra Nevada, 1832–1853   170

XIII. The Representation of Western America on Maps published between 1800 and 1850   192

XIV. Conclusion   204

Bibliography

    A. General Geographical Works   210

    B. The History of Exploration   212

Index   221

ILLUSTRATIONS

The Buffalo   *Title-page*
       George Catlin, *North American Indians.*

Fig.

1. A map of North America, by John Cary (1806)   *facing page* 1
       John Cary, *New Universal Atlas.*

2. The early exploration of Western America   *page* 10

3. A map of North America, by W. Winterbotham (1795)   11
       G. K. Warren, *Memoir of Exploring Expeditions.*

4. The unknown area of Western America (1800)   12
       John Cary, *New Universal Atlas.*

5. The settlements of Louisiana in 1800   17
       After K. Coman, *Economic Beginnings of the Far West.*

6. The natural boundaries of the Louisiana Purchase   22

7. The physiographic regions of the United States of
America   28
       After N. M. Fenneman.

8. The principal tectonic ranges of the Rocky Mountains   32
       After R. E. Flint.

9. The climatic regions of the United States of America   36
       After R. de C. Ward, *Climates of the United States.*

10. The mean annual rainfall of Western America   *facing page* 40
       After J. B. Kincer, *Atlas of American Agriculture.*

11. The average annual number of days with snow
cover   *page* 43
       After J. B. Kincer, *Atlas of American Agriculture.*

12. Snags in the Missouri   *facing page* 51
       Prince Maximilian of Wied, *Atlas.*

13. The drainage basins of Western America   64

14. A generalised vegetation map of Western America   *page* 66
       After B. E. Livingston and F. Shreve. *The Distribution
of Vegetation in the United States.*

15. Buffalo crossing the Missouri   83
       George Catlin, *North American Indians.*

Fig.

16. "Dog Town" or settlement of prairie dogs   *page* 87
    J. Gregg, *Commerce of the Prairies.*

17. The cultural regions of the Indian tribes   93
    Based on C. Wissler, *The American Indian.*

18. Meriwether Lewis
    N. Biddle's edition of the *History of the Expedition of Lewis and Clark.*

19. William Clark   *facing page* 106
    N. Biddle's edition of the *History of the Expedition of Lewis and Clark.*

20. The Great Falls of the Missouri, by W. Clark (1805)   *page* 113
    N. Biddle's edition of the *History of the Expedition of Lewis and Clark.*

21. A contoured map of the South Pass region   144

22. Zebulon Montgomery Pike
    Z. M. Pike, *Account of Expeditions* (1810).

23. John Charles Frémont   *facing page* 154
    J. Bigelow, *Life of J. C. Frémont.*

24. The Santa Fé trail   *page* 164
    Based on H. M. Chittenden, *History of the American Fur Trade of the Far West.*

25. Crossing the Sierra Nevada   *facing page* 181
    J. C. Frémont, *Report of Exploring Expedition.*

26. Part of a map entitled *Carte Génerale des Découvertes de l'Amiral de Fonte,* by J. N. de Lisle   *page* 193
    J. N. de Lisle, *Explication de la Carte des Nouvelles Découvertes* (1752).

27. A map of Western America, by Rector and Roberdeau (1818)   195
    G. K. Warren, *Memoir of Exploring Expeditions.*

28. A map of Western America, by A. Finley (1826)   197
    G. K. Warren, *Memoir of Exploring Expeditions.*

29. A map of Western America, by A. Gallatin (1836)   199
    Transactions of American Antiquarian Society, vol. II (1836). Reproduced in H. C. Dale, *The Ashley-Smith Explorations.*

30. A map of Western America, by B. L. E. Bonneville (1837)   200
    G. K. Warren, *Memoir of Exploring Expeditions.*

31. The principal western trails   206
    Based on H. M. Chittenden, *History of the American Fur Trade of the Far West.*

MAPS AT END

A. *Fig.* 32. The discovery of the northern and southern trans-continental routes.

Routes of Lewis and Clark, after Elliott Coues, *Expedition under the Command of Lewis and Clark*. Routes of Pike, Wilkinson and Malgares, after Elliott Coues, *Expeditions of Zebulon M. Pike*, Routes of Long and Bell, after E. James, *Account of an Expedition to the Rocky Mountains*, E.W.T. vol. XIV. Route of Colter and the Spanish Trail, after H. M. Chittenden, *History of the American Fur Trade of the Far West*.

B. *Fig.* 33. The discovery of central trans-continental routes.

Routes of Ashley and Smith, after H. C. Dale, *The Ashley-Smith Explorations*. Route of the Astorians, after H. M. Chittenden, *History of the American Fur Trade of the Far West*.

C. *Fig.* 34. The discovery of the interior basin and of the routes across the Sierra Nevada.

Route of Walker (1833), after H. M. Chittenden, *History of the American Fur Trade of the Far West*. Routes of Frémont, from J. C. Frémont, *Report*, and A. Nevins, *Frémont, the West's Greatest Adventurer*.

PREFACE

At the beginning of the nineteenth century a large part of the present territory of the United States that lies west of the Mississippi River was unexplored. By the year 1850, the main geographical features of this vast area had been revealed. This book is an attempt to reconstruct the geographical setting in which the explorers accomplished their work, and thus to estimate the influence of geographical factors on the history of the exploration of the region.

The first two chapters of the book are introductory in character. Chapter I is a brief historical summary of the exploration of North America before the nineteenth century, and shows that, in 1800, although the outline of the Pacific coast was known, inland exploration towards the west had not advanced far beyond the Mississippi River. Between that great river and the Pacific lay the Rocky Mountains and the interior basins, as yet untraversed by European explorers. The second chapter describes the purchase of Louisiana by the United States.

Part I is an analysis, in the light of modern geographical knowledge, of the region which remained unexplored in 1800. The geographical factors which influenced exploration have been emphasised. This part includes accounts of the physiography, climate, vegetation, animals, and human inhabitants of the area and correlates these geographical factors on a regional basis. The geographical conditions are illustrated by numerous extracts from the writings of the explorers themselves.

Part II is an account of the exploration of the region during the first half of the nineteenth century. This book does not attempt to give a detailed historical description of every expedition; it does attempt to draw a picture of the geographical setting of western America, as it appeared to the explorers of the time. The western America of a hundred years ago has passed away; the Africa of Livingstone exists no more. The systematic reconstruction of such geographical scenes, as they existed at given past periods of history, is the true function of historical geography.

I hope that the maps of routes will be of assistance to the reader in following the text, but they should be used in conjunction with a good atlas, as this book does not contain a detailed map of the relief, and many places mentioned in the text are not marked on the maps. All unnecessary details have been eliminated from the maps, in order that the routes of the explorers may be made as clear as possible.

The book has been compiled with the help of printed sources only, but I hope that it can claim some originality in its method of treatment of historical geography. Much valuable geographical matter lies buried in the journals of explorers, and I hope that the references quoted in this book will encourage students of Geography or History to use this material as an aid to the study of regional and historical geography.

I am indebted to the following for permission to make extracts from their books in copyright:

> John Wiley and Sons, Inc. for extracts from *Forest Physiography*, by I. Bowman;
>
> Ginn and Company (Boston) for extracts from *Climates of the United States*, by R. de C. Ward;
>
> The Carnegie Institute of Washington for extracts from *The Distribution of Vegetation in the United States*, by B. E. Livingston and F. Shreve;

and to Mr Paul A. F. Walter, Editor of *El Palacio*, for permission to reproduce a letter by J. L. Collins, which was first printed in *El Palacio*. Thanks are due to the Editor of the *Scottish Geographical Magazine*, for permission to reproduce two articles printed therein, which here form the substance of chapter VII and part of chapter X. For any inadvertent omission to acknowledge my sources, I here offer full apology.

I must express my thanks to many persons who have given me their help during the preparation of the book, especially to the following: to the late Mr H. O. Beckit, Reader in Geography in the University of Oxford, who advised me in the early stages of the work; to Professor R. McElroy, Harold Vyvyan Harmsworth Professor of American History in the University of Oxford, for much generous aid; to the late

Mr James Cossar; to Mr E. Heawood and the Library Staff
of the Royal Geographical Society; to Dr S. A. Peyton,
Librarian of the University of Reading; to Mr V. T. Harlow,
Keeper of Rhodes House Library, Oxford, and his assistants;
and to Mrs Robert Aitken. My grateful thanks are especially
due to Mr J. N. L. Baker, Lecturer in Geography in the
University of Oxford, who read the whole of the manuscript
with great care and made a large number of valuable sug-
gestions. Finally I must record my gratitude to my wife, who
has given me substantial help in the preparation of the maps,
and without whose constant encouragement this book would
not have been completed.

E. W. GILBERT

September 1932

ABBREVIATIONS

L. and C.: *History of the Expedition under the Command of Lewis and Clark*. Ed. by Elliott Coues. 4 vols. New York, 1893. In order to facilitate reference to other editions of the history of the expedition of Lewis and Clark, the date of each entry quoted from their journals is given in the footnotes.

Z. M. Pike, *Expeditions*: *The Expeditions of Zebulon Montgomery Pike*. Ed. by Elliott Coues. 3 vols. New York, 1895.

J. C. Frémont, *Report*: *Report of the Exploring Expedition to the Rocky Mountains in the year 1842, and to Oregon and North California in the years 1843–44* (28th Congress, 2d Session, Senate, 174). Washington, 1845.

J. C. Frémont, *Geog. Memo.*: *Geographical Memoir upon Upper California, in illustration of his Map of Oregon and California* (30th Congress, 1st Session, Senate, 148). Washington, 1848.

E.W.T.: *Early Western Travels, 1748–1846. A Series of Annotated Reprints of some of the best and rarest contemporary volumes of travel, descriptive of the Aborigines and Social and Economic Conditions in the Middle and Far West during the Period of Early American Settlement.* Ed. with notes by Reuben Gold Thwaites. Cleveland, 1904–6.

Full bibliographical references of all books quoted are included in the Bibliography at the end of the book.

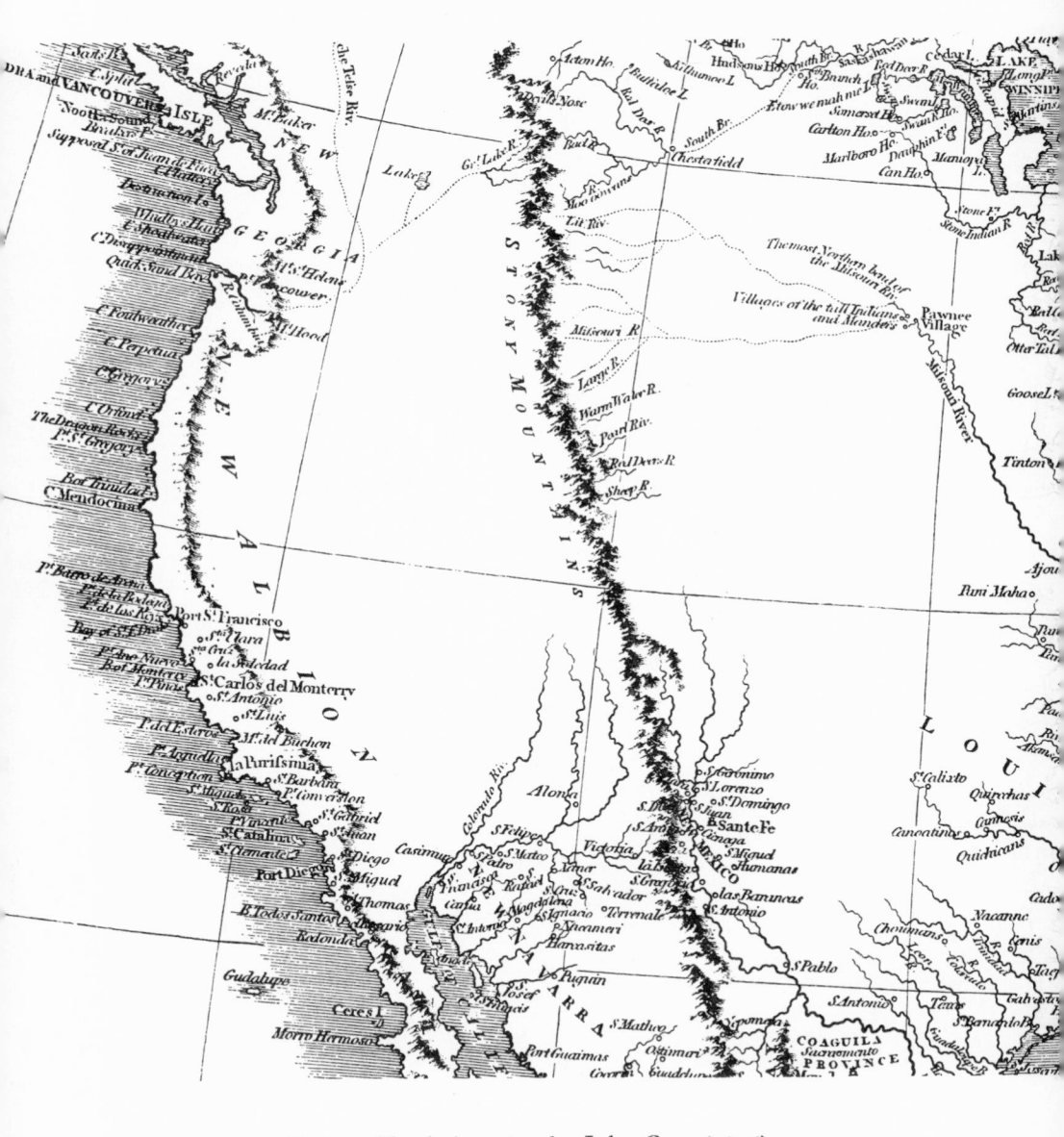

Fig. 1. North America, by John Cary (1806).

HISTORICAL INTRODUCTION

Chapter I

THE EARLY EXPLORATION OF
WESTERN AMERICA

In the year 1800 more than half the area that is now included in the United States was virtually unknown. In 1806 John Cary, the famous London cartographer, produced a "New Map of North America" (Fig. 1)[1], a large portion of which is almost devoid of geographical features or names, thus showing that a vast area in the west of the present United States was still unexplored. This map was compiled from "the latest authorities", and nothing was marked on the map unless Cary possessed reliable information concerning its existence. Other mapmakers had been content to draw on their imaginations when making maps of North America, but Cary did not attempt to fill up the blank spaces of his map with imaginary features. Cary's map reflects the stage which the exploration of America had reached at the beginning of the nineteenth century.

THE DISCOVERY OF THE PACIFIC COAST.[2] The outline of the Pacific coast was accurately indicated by Cary. The exploration of this coast had begun in the early years of the Spanish occupation of Mexico. In 1513 Balboa discovered the existence of the Southern or Pacific Ocean, and Cortés subsequently despatched several expeditions to explore the western coast of America. In 1533 one of these squadrons discovered lower California, which was at first believed to be an island. Cortés' last maritime expedition, led by Francisco de Ulloa in 1539, reached the head of the Gulf of California, doubled the southern

[1] John Cary, *New Universal Atlas*, sheet no. 51, A New Map of North America, dated December 1, 1806. The Atlas was not published until 1808.
[2] Fig. 2.

point of the peninsula, and sailed along its western coast as far as Cedros Island. Soon after America had been discovered, geographers evolved the theory that somewhere in the heart of the continent, there flowed a great waterway which connected the Atlantic with the Pacific. One of the main objects of the Spanish explorers of the Pacific coast was the discovery of this strait, which would provide them with a short route from Spain to China. The Spanish slowly ascended the coast and marked on their maps an imaginary strait, some distance north of their latest explorations. In 1542 an expedition of two ships under the command of Rodríguez, generally called Cabrillo, having coasted the western side of lower California, entered the Bay of San Diego, and then sailed through the Santa Barbara Channel. After the death of Cabrillo, Ferrelo the pilot continued the voyage, and having missed the entry into the Bay of San Francisco, passed Cape Mendocino, and may have sailed as far as lat. 42° 30'. In 1579 the English adventurer, Drake, traced the outline of the coast, possibly even further north, in a vain endeavour to find the passage. In 1602 Vizcaíno discovered Monterey Bay, and sailed as far north as lat. 43°, but no further exploration of the Pacific coast of America was undertaken by the Spaniards during the following one hundred and fifty years. They had become afraid lest the discovery of a passage should prove to be of greater value to their enemies than to themselves.

The Spaniards were roused from this policy of inaction by the news of Russian coastal exploration in the distant north. In 1774 Juan Pérez sailed as far north as lat. 55°, and on his return voyage entered the harbour afterwards known as Nootka Sound (lat. 49°), and named it San Lorenzo. In the following year, a second expedition under Heceta, with Bodega y Cuadra as second in command, was sent out with orders to sail as far north as possible. It seems probable that Bodega reached lat. 56° N., while Heceta is believed to have seen the mouth of the Columbia. In 1779 Arteaga and Bodega sailed as far as lat. 61° N., and obtained some information about Russian traders, who were already present in the region.[1]

---

[1] A useful account of the Spanish exploration of the Pacific coast can be found in C. E. Chapman, *A History of California: The Spanish Period*

As the result of Vitus Bering's discoveries, made in the years 1728 to 1729 and 1741 to 1742, the straits between the continents of Asia and North America, and the south coast of Alaska, were first revealed to Europeans. The Russian fur-traders at once exploited this area, and continually moved their headquarters further south, along the American coast, until in 1800 they were established at Sitka, on Baranof Island. In 1813 a Russian fortified trading post was built even further south at Bodega Bay, not far north of San Francisco. Spain considered these coasts and islands to be her own and protested against the Russian encroachments. Captain Cook's careful exploration, in 1778, of the coast between the latitudes of 43° and 60° N. added further intruders into the Spanish domains, as large numbers of English traders followed in the wake of Cook. The most notable of these men was Captain Robert Meares, who, in 1788, sailed into the strait between Vancouver Island and the Olympic Mountains,[1] and gave it the name of Juan de Fuca Strait, and also started an English settlement at Nootka Sound. The Spaniards, who regarded the coast as Spanish territory, seized several English ships, and it was only after a prolonged international controversy that Spain agreed to abandon Nootka Sound and all the coast north of the Columbia. Both countries sent representatives to undertake the transfer of the territory. Between the years 1792 and 1794, the British envoy, George Vancouver, an able navigator, made an accurate survey of an extensive part of the intricate coast, and his lieutenant, Broughton, sailed up the Columbia River and named Mounts Hood, Rainier and St Helens.[2] American fur-trading vessels from Boston appeared on the coast at the same time and in 1792 an American, Captain

(1923). For a fuller history of the earlier period see H. R. Wagner, *Spanish Voyages to the Northwest Coast of America in the Sixteenth Century* (1929), and H. E. Bolton, *Spanish Exploration in the Southwest 1542–1706* (1916).

[1] Meares gave the name of Mount Olympus to the mountain on the south of the strait, which Pérez had named Santa Rosalia in 1774.

[2] "Vancouver's task was carried out with a thoroughness rarely equalled in the history of maritime exploration." E. Heawood, *A History of Geographical Discovery in the Seventeenth and Eighteenth Centuries* (1912), p. 286.

Robert Gray, in the *Columbia* had preceded Broughton in the mouth of the Columbia, a river which he named after his ship. Thus, before the end of the eighteenth century, the coast-line of North America had been accurately mapped, and a flourishing fur trade had sprung up. A desire to carry on this trade by inland routes as well as by sea was one of the incentives for the exploration of the unknown interior of the continent.

EARLY ATTEMPTS TO CROSS THE CONTINENT FROM THE EAST. I. FRENCH AND ENGLISH.[1] Although so great a part of the interior of America was still unknown in 1800, it must not be imagined that there had been no attempts to cross the continent from the east. The French were the first to undertake this task, but they had no conception of the immense breadth of North America. The French, like the Spaniards, believed in the existence of a mythical trans-continental waterway, which would help them in their westward journey. In 1720 Father Charlevoix was sent out to draw up a report about the possibility of routes to the Pacific. He said that two courses were open to the French, either to send an expedition up the Missouri, or to establish a line of fur-trading posts among the Sioux, and gradually advance into the interior. The latter course was adopted by the authorities, and Pierre Gaultier de Varennes, Sieur de la Vérendrye, spent many years in endeavouring to find a way to the Pacific. During the years 1731–43, he established a chain of forts, known as the "Post of the Western Sea", which stretched from Lake Superior to the banks of the Assiniboine. From this river, one of La Vérendrye's parties pushed south to the Missouri and, in 1743, the Rocky Mountains were seen, probably in the neighbourhood of the Big Horn range. However, in spite of years of determined effort, the French did not find the western sea.

Early inland exploration by the English was confined to regions which lay north of French territory. The Hudson's Bay Company, at its formation, was entrusted with the duty of discovering a new passage to the South Sea, but did not expend much energy in endeavours to carry out explorations of this

[1] Fig. 2.

nature. When, in 1763, Great Britain obtained control of all the French empire in Canada, English adventurers were soon seeking a waterway across the continent. Among these men was Jonathan Carver, who, in 1766–8, attempted to find his way to the Pacific from the upper Mississippi. He explored the Elk and Minnesota tributaries of the Mississippi, but was unable to find the river which he described as the "Oregon, or the River of the West, that falls into the Pacific Ocean at the straits of Annian".[1] He did not make any substantial additions to geographical knowledge, but his account of his travels stimulated interest in the subject.

The northern part of the continent was now crossed three times by Englishmen. In 1771 Samuel Hearne, of the Hudson's Bay Company, reached the Coppermine River and followed it to the Arctic Ocean. Alexander Mackenzie, a member of the North-West Company, in 1789 reached the Great Slave Lake and descended the river which now bears the name of Mackenzie, until he sighted the Arctic Ocean. In 1793, on his second journey, Mackenzie crossed from the head of the Peace River to the Tacouche Tesse (afterwards called Fraser), and after descending that river for some miles, he made a direct western march and reached the ocean near Cape Menzies.

2. SPANISH. The Spaniards of New Mexico sent out many expeditions from their northern base at Santa Fé, in the Rio Grande valley. Some of these expeditions were undertaken as a means of protecting the province against invasion by foreign intruders, while other parties were sent out with the object of discovering overland routes from New Mexico to the Pacific. Westward exploration from Santa Fé was greatly stimulated by the establishment of Spanish settlements in upper California, as the result of coastal exploration. Missionaries played a leading part in this work and a Franciscan named Garcés in 1771 followed the course of the Gila and nearly reached the mouth of the Colorado. In 1774 Garcés and Captain J. B. de Anza made their way by the Gila and Colorado to the mission of San

[1] J. Carver, *Travels Through the Interior Parts of North-America, in the Years 1766, 1767, and 1768* (1778), Introduction, p. ix.

Gabriel, which had been established near the site of modern Los Angeles. In 1775 Anza was sent out with orders to establish a mission and Government post on the Bay of San Francisco. He was accompanied by Garcés, who explored the Colorado River as far as Mojave (lat. 35°) and undertook further exploration in this area. As a result of these and other expeditions, contact was established between New Mexico and upper California, both areas of Spanish colonisation, and a land route had been traced across the south of the continent of North America.[1]

The Spaniards did not neglect the possibilities of exploration in the regions which lay north of Santa Fé. As early as 1720 a party of Spanish explorers are said to have reached the Platte River and to have sought information about French traders, whose presence had been reported by Indians who were friendly to the Spanish.[2] The most important journey was undertaken, in 1776, by the Franciscan Fathers Dominguez and Escalante, who penetrated as far north as Utah Lake and returned by way of Sevier Lake. The results of these and other Spanish expeditions north of Santa Fé were not generally known, and the region remained unmapped.

After the Spanish had obtained possession of Louisiana from the French in 1763, they sent out men from St Louis to explore the possibilities of the Missouri as a western route. In 1793 the Lieutenant-Governor of Spanish Illinois (upper Louisiana), Zenon Trudeau, organised the "Compañia de Descubridores del Misuri" or Company of Explorers of the Missouri, for the purpose of developing the fur trade and to find a way to the Pacific Ocean. The first expedition of 1794, led by J. B. Truteau, a schoolmaster of St Louis, was a failure, and the expedition

[1] See H. E. Bolton, *Anza's California Expeditions*, 5 vols. (1930), and Elliott Coues, *On the Trail of a Spanish Pioneer. The Diary and Itinerary of Francisco Garcés in his Travels through Sonora, Arizona, and California.* 2 vols. (1900). Bolton describes Anza as the "first to open a route across the Sierras and first to lead a colony overland to the North Pacific shores." 1, Introduction, p. vi.

[2] Alfred B. Thomas, "The Yellowstone River, James Long and Spanish reaction to American intrusion into Spanish Dominions 1818–1819", *New Mexico Historical Review*, IV (April, 1929), 164–87. Thomas states that the expedition of 1720 "until 1819, so far as is known, remained 'the farthest north' of Spanish expansion activities from New Mexico".

under Lecuyer, in 1795, was also unsuccessful owing to the hostility of the Indians. The third expedition was under the command of James Mackay, a Scotchman who had become a Spanish subject. Mackay established three trading posts between the Platte and the Niobrara, and it seems probable that one member of his expedition, John Evans, a Welshman, reached the villages of the Mandans. President Jefferson is known to have possessed a copy of Mackay's instructions to Evans, and Evans' map of the Missouri. The map was sent to Lewis and Clark before they set out on their great journey.[1]

3. AMERICAN. Thomas Jefferson, long before he became President of the United States, did his utmost to promote the exploration of western America. He was keenly interested in all scientific questions, and was one of the first Americans to make a serious study of American geography.[2] On December 4, 1783, he wrote to George Rogers Clark, "I find they have subscribed a very large sum of money in England for exploring the country from the Missisipi to California. they pretend it is only to promote knolege. I am afraid they have thoughts of colonising into that quarter. some of us have been talking here in a feeble way of making the attempt to search that country. but I doubt whether we have enough of that kind of spirit to raise the money. how would you like to lead such a party? tho I am afraid our prospect is not worth asking the question".[3] This letter is of particular importance, because the great explorer of the West, William Clark, was a brother of George Rogers Clark. Clark refused Jefferson's proposal, and in his reply he asserted that "large parties will never answer the purpose. They will alarm the Indian Nations they pass through.

[1] F. J. Teggart, "Notes supplementary to any edition of Lewis and Clark", *Annual Report of the American Historical Association for the Year* 1908, I, 185–95, Washington, 1909. See also "Journal of Jean Baptiste Truteau on the Upper Missouri, 'Première Partie', June 7, 1794–March 26, 1795", *American Historical Review*, XIX (1914), 299–333.

[2] G. T. Surface, "Thomas Jefferson: A Pioneer Student of American Geography", *Bulletin of the American Geographical Society*, XLI (December, 1909), 743–50.

[3] *American Historical Review*, III (July, 1897), 673.

Three or four young Men well qualified for the Task might perhaps compleat your wishes at a very tryfling Expence".[1]

In 1786 Jefferson, when serving as American Minister in Paris, made serious proposals to an adventurer named John Ledyard and suggested that he should carry out the exploration of western America. The history of this incident is described by Jefferson himself as follows:

While I resided in Paris, John Ledyard of Connecticut arrived there, well known in the United States for energy of body and mind. He had accompanied Captain Cook in his voyage to the Pacific ocean, and distinguished himself on that voyage by his intrepidity. Being of a roaming disposition, he was now panting for some new enterprise. His immediate object at Paris was to engage a mercantile company in the fur trade of the western coast of America, in which, however, he failed. I then proposed to him to go by land to Kamschatka, cross in some of the Russian vessels to Nootka Sound, fall down into the latitude of the Missouri, and penetrate to and through that to the United States. He eagerly seized the idea, and only asked to be assured of the permission of the Russian government. I interested myself in obtaining that of M. de Semoulin, M.P. of the Empress at Paris, but more especially the Baron de Grimm, M.P. of Saxe-Gotha, her more special agent and correspondent there, in matters not immediately diplomatic. Her permission was obtained, and an assurance of protection while the course of the voyage should be through her territories. Ledyard set out from Paris and arrived at St Petersburg after the Empress had left that place to pass the winter (I think) at Moscow. His finances not permitting him to make unnecessary stay at St Petersburg, he left it with a passport from one of the ministers, and at two hundred miles from Kamschatka, was obliged to take up his winter quarters. He was preparing in the spring to resume his journey, when he was arrested by an officer of the Empress, who, by this time, had changed her mind, and forbidden his proceeding. He was put into a close carriage and conveyed day and night, without ever stopping, till they reached Poland, where he was set down and left to himself. The fatigue of this journey broke down his constitution, and when he returned to Paris, his bodily strength was much impaired. His mind, however, remained firm; and after this he undertook the journey to Egypt. I received a letter from him, full of sanguine hopes, dated at Cairo, the 15th of November, 1788, the day before he was to set out for the head of the Nile, on which day, however, he ended his career and life; and thus failed the first attempt to explore the western part of our northern continent.[2]

    [1] Quoted by Temple Bodley, *George Rogers Clark* (1926), p. 238. See also J. A. James, *The Life of George Rogers Clark* (1928), p. 305.
    [2] *Writings of Thomas Jefferson*, ed. H. A. Washington, VIII, 482–3, in a biographical sketch of Meriwether Lewis.

In 1792 Jefferson persuaded the American Philosophical Society to finance an expedition, with orders to accomplish its purpose "by ascending the Missouri, crossing the Stony mountains, and descending the nearest river to the Pacific".[1] André Michaux, a French botanist, was chosen as leader of the party; unfortunately he became involved in political intrigues, and his expedition had no considerable geographical results, as he did not venture far into unexplored territory.[2] Jefferson's third plan had come to nothing, and the Americans made no further attempts to explore the country west of the Mississippi until they had purchased Louisiana.

Winterbotham's History,[3] published in 1795, contains an interesting map (Fig. 3), which shows the prevalent conceptions of the time. The most striking feature of the map is a large inland sea above lat. 42°. To the south-east of the sea is a smaller lake with a large stream flowing into it from the west. The main authority for marking these lakes must have been the vague reports of Indians.

Cary's map of 1806 is a more reliable illustration of the stage which exploration had reached, because Cary was exceedingly careful in the compilation of his maps. These two maps prove that very little was known of the area west of the Mississippi. The little French villages are marked by Cary on the upper Missouri, but the source of that river was a mystery. The plains of the Platte, Little Missouri and Yellowstone and the country that lay between them and the Pacific were absolutely unknown. The Rocky Mountains were not known to exist in the present area of the United States, although, under the name of the Stonies, the northward extension of the Rockies in British America was known, and Cary tentatively extends this range southward.

In 1800, although the Pacific coast had been explored and the

[1] *Ibid.* VIII, 483.

[2] *Journal of André Michaux*, 1793–1796, reprinted in Early Western Travels Series, 1748–1846, vol. III, ed. R. G. Thwaites, Cleveland, 1904. The series are cited below as E.W.T.

[3] W. Winterbotham, *Historical, Geographical, Commercial and Philosophical View of the American United States and of the European Settlement in America and the West Indies* (1795), 4 vols.

continent had been crossed in the south by the Spanish and in
the north by Hearne and Mackenzie, there had been no trans-

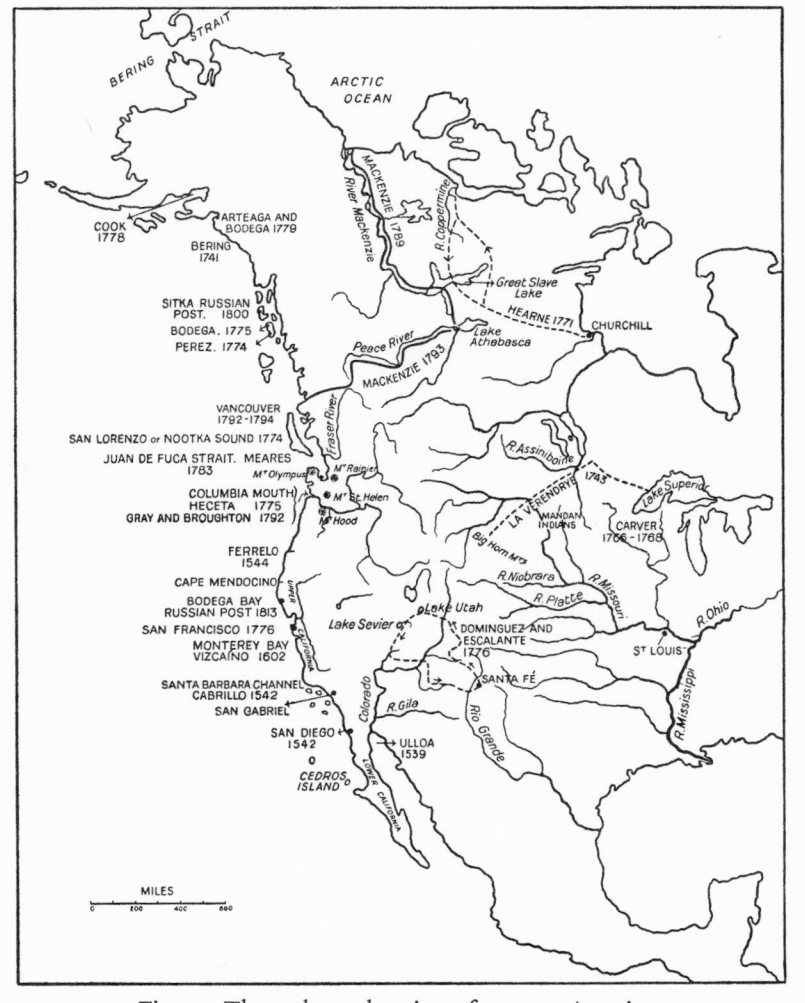

Fig. 2. The early exploration of western America.

continental journey across the central part of North America
(Fig. 2). The greater part of the area that the United States was

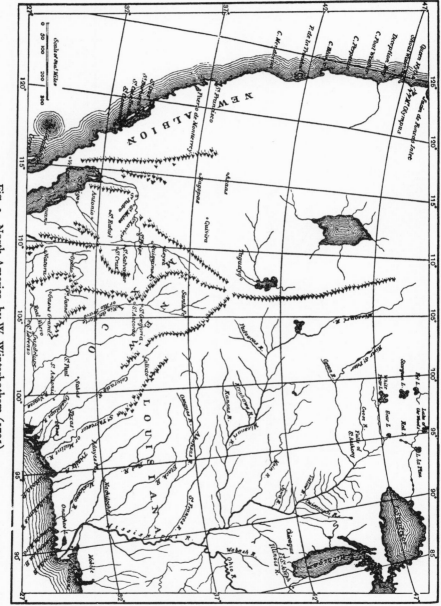

Fig. 3. North America, by W. Winterbotham (1795).

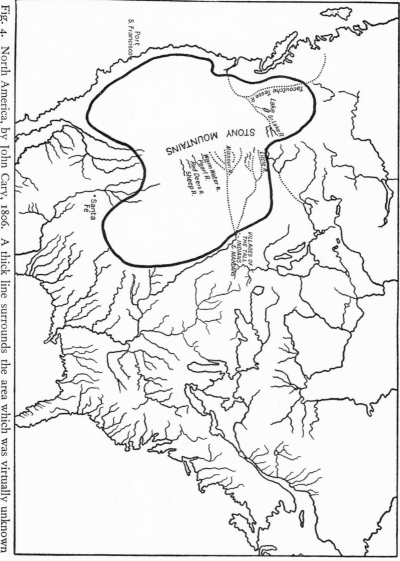

Fig. 4. North America, by John Cary, 1806. A thick line surrounds the area which was virtually unknown in 1800. The names marked within the line are the only names marked by Cary on this part of the map.

to purchase, under the name of Louisiana, was still unmapped, and is shown as a blank part of Cary's map.

Fig. 4 shows the approximate area which was still unknown in 1800. The work of unveiling this immense *terra incognita* was one of the great achievements of exploration of the early nineteenth century. Americans like Jefferson were eager to accomplish this task, but no effective exploration could be undertaken until the region became a part of the political area of the United States. The extraordinary succession of events, by which a large part of the unknown region passed into the hands of the United States, must now be described.

Chapter II

THE PURCHASE OF LOUISIANA

AMERICAN SETTLEMENT IN THE MISSISSIPPI BASIN. In November, 1762, before the end of the Seven Years' War, when it had become obvious that France would inevitably lose all her American possessions, Louis XV ceded to Spain the town and neighbourhood of New Orleans and all that part of Louisiana which lay west of the Mississippi. In the following year, France lost to England all her territories east of the Mississippi, and the great river became the boundary between Spanish Louisiana and the American dominions of England. When the American colonies gained their independence, they succeeded to this western boundary with Spain, and American settlers poured westward over the Appalachians into the area drained by the eastern tributaries of the Mississippi. The growth of population was very rapid; by 1790 there were over one hundred thousand settlers in the western area and it became necessary to divide it into political divisions. Kentucky and Tennessee became States in 1792 and 1796 respectively; the Territory of Mississippi was organised in 1798,[1] and in 1803 the State of Ohio was created (Fig. 6).

The settlers of these new states were compelled to use the Mississippi and its tributaries as their principal means of communication with their markets. The waterways were consequently of great importance and large numbers of boats carried various kinds of produce downstream to New Orleans. Not only river-craft but also sea-going vessels were built at Pittsburgh and other places in the Ohio valley. These ships sailed down the river and sometimes continued their voyage across the Atlantic. Most of the larger American settlements were ports of call for the boatmen.

The American pioneers were soon pressing against the restraints of the Spanish boundaries; very few of them attempted

[1] The Territory of Mississippi was considerably enlarged in 1804.

to move north into Canada. The tendency of the Americans was to move west and south-west, and here they came into contact with French and Spanish speaking peoples. The Mississippi, the political frontier, was not an effective barrier to westward movement, and many Americans crossed the river and settled in St Louis and the other small French towns. They joined parties of French traders and ascended the Missouri to traffic with the Indians. The famous pioneer, Daniel Boone, in 1798 received from the Spanish Government a grant of 850 acres in the Femme Osage district. In 1800 he was appointed a syndic or magistrate, a title which he held until the cession of Louisiana to the United States.[1] Nevertheless the Spanish did not welcome the arrival of large numbers of American settlers; especially as they were usually not of the Roman Catholic faith. It became certain that there would be a conflict as soon as the Americans were sufficiently numerous. The immediate objective of the Americans was to control the commerce of the Mississippi and to obtain possession of New Orleans. The western American settlers regarded Spain as their natural enemy because she possessed New Orleans, the main outlet of their trade.[2] However, in 1795 Thomas Pinckney made a treaty with Spain, by the provisions of which the right of free navigation of the Mississippi and the right of deposit of goods at New Orleans were granted to the Americans for a period of three years. In 1798 the Spanish authorities made no attempt to discontinue the treaty and western American trade continued to prosper.

[1] H. A. Bruce, *Daniel Boone and the Wilderness Road* (1910), and R. G. Thwaites, *Daniel Boone* (1903).

[2] Professor Paxson has described the importance of the Mississippi at this period as follows: "The surplus crops of the West were finding their way to a market. From the farm where they were grown, which was often on a stream navigable to light craft in early spring, the cargoes of wheat and corn, meal and flour, pork, bacon and whiskey found their way to the broad waters of the Ohio and Mississippi. In flat-boats and barges, manned by local talent at the sweeps, they were floated south. In the long trip, drifting by day, and tied to some convenient shore at night, the farmer boatmen had time to gossip over the trade in which they ventured. The Mississippi dominated not their whole lives but their balance of profit". F. L. Paxson, *History of the American Frontier*, 1763–1893 (1924), p. 130.

FRENCH AND SPANISH SETTLEMENT IN LOUISIANA.[1] Although Louisiana was politically under the Spanish flag, it did not contain many Spanish inhabitants, the population being principally of French extraction. The settlements which existed in Louisiana, in the year 1800, can be divided into two groups, those on the lower Mississippi with New Orleans as the capital, and those in the neighbourhood of the junction of the Missouri and Mississippi—a region known as upper Louisiana (Fig. 5). A Spanish census of 1799 records that 42,375 persons (of whom two-thirds were white) lived in the settlements of lower Louisiana, along the Mississippi and Red Rivers. The town of New Orleans contained ten thousand persons. The French Acadians, who had been banished from Nova Scotia, had taken refuge in Baton Rouge, Iberville and Point Coupée,[2] while most of the

[1] Information concerning the condition of Louisiana at this period is to be found in the following works:

An Account of Louisiana. Being an Abstract of Documents in the Offices of the Departments of State and of the Treasury, Philadelphia, 1803. Reprinted in Old South Leaflets, vol. v, no. 105, pp. 89–116, Boston, n.d. This "account" of Louisiana was compiled by order of President Jefferson.

M. de Vergennes, ministre de Louis XVI, *Mémoire Historique et Politique sur la Louisiane* (1802). M. de Vergennes, who died in 1787, wrote his book during the war of American Independence. He argued that Louisiana should be restored to France, because he feared that the United States, after the war, would invade the territory of France and Spain. "La restitution de Louisbourg, du Canada, et de la Louisiane, sont les seuls moyens pour empêcher les invasions que j'appréhende...La Louisiane couvre la Mexique et est à portée de secourir la Floride", p. 28.

F. M. Perrin du Lac, *Voyage dans les deux Louisianes, et chez les nations sauvages du Missouri, par les États-Unis, l'Ohio et les Provinces qui le bordent, en 1801, 1802 et 1803* (1805). Reprinted in Sir Richard Phillips' *Collection of Modern and Contemporary Voyages and Travels*, 1st series, vol. VI, translated from the French (1807). Perrin du Lac left St Louis in May, 1802, ascended the Missouri as far as the White River, and collected a large amount of information about trading conditions in that region. It is interesting to notice that he regarded Louisiana as "a barrier to preserve the rich Spanish possessions in Mexico" (Phillips, *op. cit.* p. 58). H. R. Wagner, in his bibliography, *The Plains and the Rockies* (1921), has described Perrin du Lac's map as "the earliest published map of the trans-Missouri region which can be said to display even the faintest resemblance to accuracy".

[2] *Account of Louisiana*, Old South Leaflets, vol. v, no. 105, pp. 98–9.

other settlements contained the descendants of the original French colonists (Fig. 5).

Spanish Illinois, or upper Louisiana, contained a total population of about six thousand persons, who were scattered in a number of small settlements, all situated along the banks of the rivers. St Louis, the capital, only contained about nine hundred and twenty-five inhabitants. Petite Prairie, Ste Généviève, Cap

Fig. 5. The settlements of Louisiana in 1800 (after Coman).

Girardeau, Corondelet, St Charles, and St André were the most important of the other villages (Fig. 5). There were as many as thirty American families in St André. Jefferson's account of Louisiana states that "at least two-fifths, if not a greater proportion of all the settlers on the Spanish side of the Mississippi, in the Illinois country are...supposed to be Americans".[1]

[1] *Account of Louisiana*, Old South Leaflets, vol. v, no. 105, p. 99.

The products of lower Louisiana were sugar cane, cotton, indigo, and tobacco. The cultivation of sugar had been abandoned when the Spanish took over the province, but had been revived in 1796. Vergennes describes the products of the country as follows:

L'Indigo qui était inférieur à celui de Saint Domingue ne l'était que par défaut de culture et ignorance des habitants. Les Cannes de Sucre commençaient à réussir, et l'on serait parvenu à les établir. Le tabac y venait à profusion...Les Montagnes qui bornaient les possessions de la France d'avec celles du royaume de Mexique dont la chute des eaux viennent par diverses petites rivières se perdre dans celle des Akancas, nous indiquaient par les morceaux de minéraux trouvés sur les bords des rivières, qu'elles sont remplies de ces riches métaux, et aussi abondantes que celles de possession du roi d'Espagne.[1]

The chief products of upper Louisiana were furs, while lead, lumber, horses, and cattle were of a secondary importance.

THE PURCHASE OF LOUISIANA.[2] Spain continued to hold the two Louisianas, until Napoleon conceived the idea of building a second New France in the western half of America. After considerable diplomatic negotiation, Napoleon induced the Spanish Government to retrocede Louisiana to France. By the preliminary treaty of San Ildefonso, which was made in October of 1800, it was agreed that Spain should receive the kingdom of Etruria in exchange for Louisiana. There was a long delay before the Spaniards completed the transaction, as they refused to hand over Louisiana, unless France gave a pledge that she would never alienate the province. In spite of Napoleon's requests, the Spaniards obstinately refused to include the Floridas in the territory which was to be transferred to France. It was not until October, 1802, that the King of Spain finally signed the order by which Louisiana was to be surrendered to France.

In the early part of the year 1802 Napoleon sent a large expedition to occupy the island of San Domingo. This army

[1] M. de Vergennes, *Mémoire*, p. 179.
[2] An excellent condensed account of the political events, which resulted in the purchase of Louisiana, can be found in Edward Channing, *A History of the United States* (1926), vol. IV, chaps. XI and XII. For a longer account see Henry Adams, *History of the United States of America*, 9 vols. (1889–1911). Vol. II contains the history of the Louisiana purchase.

had to face not only a native negro rebellion, led by Toussaint l'Ouverture, but also a virulent outbreak of yellow fever. Napoleon lost twenty generals and thirty thousand men in his San Domingo adventure. The French occupation of New Orleans was delayed, but the display of military activity by the French in the West Indies was viewed with some anxiety by the American President, Jefferson. Americans were still further alarmed, when, in October, 1802, the Spanish Intendant closed the mouth of the Mississippi to American traders by withdrawing the right of deposit, which had been granted in 1795. It was generally believed that the Spanish official had acted under instructions received from the French. Great indignation and excitement prevailed among western Americans, who demanded that their Government should take strong action.

Jefferson regarded the cession of Louisiana to France as contrary to the interests of the United States. As early as May 14, 1801, he had written: "We fear that Spain is ceding Louisiana to France, an inauspicious circumstance to us".[1] On May 26, 1801, Jefferson, in a letter to Monroe, stated that "there is considerable reason to apprehend that Spain cedes Louisiana and the Floridas to France. It is a policy very unwise in both, and very ominous to us".[2] He saw very clearly that a hostile New Orleans could block the growing American trade of the Mississippi and Ohio valleys, and in a letter to R. R. Livingston, dated April 18, 1802, he wrote:

The cession of Louisiana and the Floridas[3] by Spain to France, works most sorely on the United States.... There is on the globe one single spot, the possessor of which is our natural and habitual enemy. It is New Orleans, through which the produce of three-eighths of our territory must pass to market, and from its fertility it will ere long yield more than

[1] Collections of the Massachusetts Historical Society, 7th series, I, 95, Thomas Jefferson to Thomas Mann Randolph, Boston, 1900.
[2] Writings of Thomas Jefferson, ed. P. L. Ford (1893), VIII, 58.
[3] It must be remembered that the Spanish Government believed that no part of Florida had been ceded to France by the treaty of San Ildefonso. After the United States had bought Louisiana, Jefferson asserted that west Florida was included in the area purchased. A prolonged dispute with Spain on this question was eventually settled in 1819, when the United States purchased the Floridas, although they had forcibly taken possession of parts of west Florida in 1810 and 1813.

half of our whole produce, and contain more than half of our inhabitants. France, placing herself in that door, assumes to us the attitude of defiance. Spain might have retained it quietly for years.... The day that France takes possession of New Orleans, fixes the sentence which is to restrain her forever within her low-water mark. It seals the union of two nations, who, in conjunction, can maintain exclusive possession of the ocean. From that moment, we must marry ourselves to the British fleet and nation.[1]

When the news of the closure of New Orleans reached Washington, Jefferson at once took steps to recover the right of deposit. On January 11, 1803, James Monroe was appointed as Minister Plenipotentiary and Envoy Extraordinary to France and Spain. Monroe's instructions were to endeavour to purchase New Orleans and the Floridas and thus secure the free navigation of the Mississippi.

Before Monroe had arrived in Paris, Napoleon was considering the possibility of selling the whole province of Louisiana. Napoleon saw that another war with England was inevitable, and realised that the British fleet could easily capture New Orleans as soon as the struggle began. He therefore considered that it was better to raise some money for the war by the sale of Louisiana than to allow the province to fall into the hands of England. He may have hoped that a more powerful United States would be England's rival.[2] On April 10, Napoleon, when discussing the possibility of disposing of the whole of Louisiana with his Finance Minister Barbé-Marbois, said : "Ils ne me demandent qu'une ville de la Louisiane ; mais je considère déjà la colonie comme perdue tout entière, et il me semble que dans les mains de cette puissance naissante elle sera plus utile à la politique, et même au commerce de la France, que si je tentais

---

[1] *Writings of Thomas Jefferson*, ed. H. A. Washington, IV, 431–2.
[2] For a discussion of the motives which led Napoleon to dispose of Louisiana, see Chapter IV and the Appendix of Robert M. McElroy's *The Pathway of Peace. An Interpretation of some British-American Crises* (1927). It appears to be impossible to discover the real reason which made Napoleon willing to sell Louisiana. After discussing several possible motives, Professor McElroy has suggested that Napoleon "designed his cession to be merely a convenient method of guarding France's cherished American province until European victories should enable him to occupy it", and that "England disposed of, he would again seek to reclaim the lost province of Louisiana", pp. 191–2.

de la garder".[1] On the following day, April 11, Talleyrand surprised Robert R. Livingston, the American Minister at Paris, by asking him how much the United States would pay for the whole of Louisiana.

Monroe, who arrived in Paris on April 12, was astonished by the proposal, as he had only received authority to negotiate for New Orleans and the Floridas. Napoleon demanded that the matter should be settled as soon as possible, because he wanted the money. After much haggling about the price to be paid, a treaty was eventually signed on May 2 (although the documents were antedated to April 30), by which Louisiana, with no precise boundaries, was sold to the United States for sixty million francs. The United States also agreed to pay the debts owed by France to American citizens, a sum which was not to exceed twenty million francs. Thus, at a cost of about fifteen million dollars, the territory of the United States was virtually doubled (Fig. 6). The news of these negotiations did not reach Washington until July, and Congress ratified the treaty in October.

Spain had provisionally agreed to cede Louisiana to France in October, 1800, but the French had never taken possession of the province. Spanish officials were still ruling the scattered population of French and Americans, some of whom had become naturalised Spanish subjects. Two ceremonies of legal transfer were now carried out. On November 30, 1803, the Spanish surrendered New Orleans to the French, who handed it over to the Americans on December 20. On March 9, 1804, the purchase was finally completed, when St Louis and upper Louisiana were transferred to the representatives of the United States.

BOUNDARIES OF LOUISIANA (Fig. 6). The boundaries of Louisiana had never been very precise. The Americans did not know the exact limits of the area which they purchased. In the official *Account of Louisiana*, published in 1803, it is stated that

the precise boundaries of Louisiana, westwardly of the Mississippi, though very extensive, are at present involved in some obscurity. Data are equally

[1] F. Barbé-Marbois, *Histoire de la Louisiane et de la cession de cette Colonie par la France* (1829), p. 287.

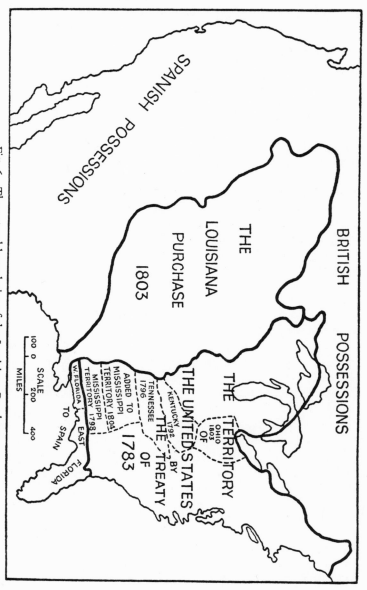

Fig. 6. The natural boundaries of the Louisiana Purchase.

wanting to assign with precision its northern extent. From the source of the Mississippi, it is bounded eastwardly by the middle of the channel of that river to the thirty-first degree of latitude: thence it is asserted upon very strong grounds that according to its limits, when formerly possessed by France, it stretches to the east, as far, at least, as the river Perdigo, which runs into the bay of Mexico, eastward of the river Mobille.[1]

When Louisiana was ceded to Spain in November, 1762, the boundaries of the province were not defined. In 1800, by article III of the secret treaty of San Ildefonso, Spain promised to return to France "the colony or province of Louisiana with the same extent it now has in the hands of Spain, and had while in the possession of France, and such as it ought to be in conformity with the treaties subsequently concluded between Spain and other states".[2]

The treaty, by which Louisiana was ceded to the United States, described the territory as being the same as that ceded by Spain to France by the treaty of San Ildefonso.[3] The American commissioners in Paris did not object to the vague definition of boundaries, which was given in the treaty, as they probably realised that the indefinite nature of this clause would be an asset to them in future negotiations. In the later disputes with Great Britain concerning the north-western boundary, the United States actually claimed the area now forming the States of Oregon, Washington, and Idaho, on the ground that it formed a part of the Louisiana purchase. That there was no ground for such an extensive claim is proved by the evidence of M. Barbé-

[1] *Account of Louisiana*, Old South Leaflets, vol. v, no. 105, p. 89. See J. A. Robertson, *Louisiana under the Rule of Spain, France and the United States*, 1785–1807 (1911), II, 137–215, for a discussion of the complicated question of the boundary between Louisiana and Florida.

[2] W. H. Malloy (ed.), *Treaties, Conventions, International Acts, etc. between The United States of America and other Powers*, 1776–1909 (1910), I, 506.

[3] By article I of the treaty of cession "The First Consul of the French Republic, desiring to give to the United States a strong proof of his friendship, doth hereby cede to the said United States, in the name of the French Republic, forever and in full sovereignty, the said territory with all its rights and appurtenances as fully and in the same manner as they have been acquired by the French Republic in virtue of the abovementioned Treaty concluded with his Catholic Majesty". Treaty of April 30, 1803. Malloy, *op. cit.* I, 509.

Marbois, who signed the treaty with Livingston and Monroe. Marbois concluded that "les côtes de la mer de l'Ouest n'étaient certainement pas comprises dans la cession ; mais déjà les États-Unis y sont établis".[1] He also constructed a map, on which he marked the western extent of Louisiana by a line, which corresponds to the one hundred and tenth meridian ; on the area now comprising Oregon, Washington, and Idaho, he wrote : "Territoires et Pays occupés par les États-Unis à la suite du traité de cession de la Louisiane".[2] Marbois considered that the action of the Americans in not asking for more precise definitions was justified by events. "Il importe en effet de ne pas introduire dans les traités des clauses ambigues ; cependant les plénipotentiaires américains ne firent plus d'objections, et si, en paraissant se résigner à ces termes généraux comme à une nécessité, ils les trouvèrent en effet préférables à des stipulations plus précises, il faut convenir que l'événement a justifié leur prévoyance."[3] Although it is quite clear that the purchase did not include any land on the west of the Rocky Mountains, it is certain that Oregon fell into the hands of the United States as a natural consequence of the great purchase. The Government of the United States now proceeded to send out expeditions to survey their newly acquired territory.

[1] Barbé-Marbois, *Histoire de la Louisiane*, p. 311.
[2] *Ibid.* p. 109.
[3] *Ibid.* p. 311.

PART I

A GEOGRAPHICAL ANALYSIS OF WESTERN AMERICA

INTRODUCTION

The first part of this book is a geographical description of the portion of western America which was still unexplored in 1800. Regional divisions have been used, where possible, as a means of description. The area has been divided into physiographic regions, climatic regions, drainage basins, vegetation regions, and regions which differentiate the cultures of the Indian tribes. Only in the chapter on animals was it found unnecessary to attempt a regional treatment. This regional analysis has been made in the light of modern geographical knowledge, but the actual words of the explorers themselves have been used to explain the positive statements of modern geographers.

The influence which geography exerts on the course of history can be most clearly seen in the earliest stages of the historical development of a region. In the "old" continents, human development has become so complex that it is very difficult to disentangle the geographical factors which most closely concern their organisation at the present day. The history of exploration has, therefore, a peculiar value to the geographer, because it reveals a vivid picture of man when nature's influence over his movement and settlement is most obvious. Unfortunately for the geographer, it is almost impossible to draw such a picture for some regions of the world at certain periods of history, because the documentary and other evidence is so scanty. In the case of North America in the nineteenth century, however, the student is overwhelmed by a mass of geographical material which exists in the journals of traders and explorers. Extracts from the writings of men such as Lewis and Clark, Pike and Frémont have been used in the

following chapters to illustrate the means by which the exploration of the area was influenced by nature. Nevertheless, the aim of the historical geographer must not be limited to mere geographical determinism. The real object of historical geography is, in Professor P. M. Roxby's words, "the reconstruction of the physical setting of the stage in the different phases of development".[1] The following chapters endeavour to apply this principle and describe the geography of western America in the early nineteenth century, before civilised man had begun to alter the face of the country with the scars of mines, towns, and railways.

[1] P. M. Roxby in his Presidential Address to Section E (Geography) at the Bristol meeting of the British Association for the Advancement of Science, September, 1930. Reprinted in *Scottish Geographical Magazine*, XLVI (September, 1930), 289.

Chapter III

THE PHYSICAL GEOGRAPHY
OF THE REGION

The Continent of North America can be divided into eight
major physical regions, all of which are represented in the
United States.[1] These major divisions of America are the
Laurentian Upland, the Coastal Plains, the Appalachian High-
lands, the Interior Plains, the Interior Highlands, the Rocky
Mountain system, the Intermontane Plateaux, and the Pacific
Mountain system (see Fig. 7). In the area at present under
consideration the first three of these regions are not represented
(Fig. 7).

The *Interior Plains* consist of the interior of the continent
and contain only small differences of local relief. The major
unit can be divided into two parts, the *Central Lowlands*, sometimes known as the Prairies, and the *Great Plains*. Both regions
are underlain by rocks in nearly horizontal beds. In the east the
age is mainly Palaeozoic, but in the west large areas are covered
by younger sediments. The northern part of these plains has
been heavily glaciated while the southern part has not felt the
influence of ice. The boundary between the Central Lowlands
and the Great Plains is an escarpment facing east, and usually
not more than a few hundred feet in height. The chief differences
between the two regions are differences of rainfall and natural
vegetation rather than differences of topography. The boundary
between the two regions corresponds very closely to the
20-inch isohyet, which is almost the same as the hundredth

[1] The most useful division of the United States into physiographic
regions is by N. M. Fenneman, "Physiographic Divisions of the
United States", *Annals of the Association of American Geographers*, VI
(1915–16), 19–98; revised and enlarged in XVIII (1928), 261–353. See also
N. M. Fenneman, *Physiography of Western United States* (1931), I. Bowman, *Forest Physiography* (1911), and W. L. Joerg, "Subdivisions of
North America into Natural Regions", *Annals Ass. Am. Geog.* IV
(1913–14), 55–83.

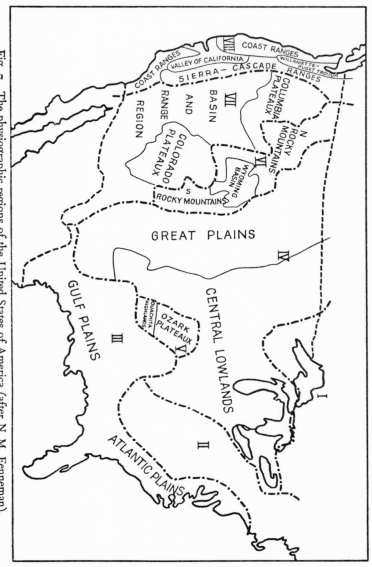

Fig. 7. The physiographic regions of the United States of America (after N.M. Fenneman).
Major physical divisions.

I. Laurentian Upland. II. Appalachian Highlands. III. Coastal Plains. IV. Interior Plains. V. Interior Highlands. VI. Rocky Mountain System. VII. Intermontane Plateaux. VIII. Pacific Mountain System.

meridian. The line marks a definite change from a well-watered lowland to a higher and semi-arid plateau. When the traveller crossed this line from the east and entered the Great Plains, he entered the land of the buffalo and the Indian.

The region of the *Great Plains* is a true plateau rising from a level of 1000 to 2000 feet, on the western border of the Central Lowlands, to a height of 5000 to 6000 feet at the eastern base of the Rocky Mountains. These plains are about 1200 miles in length and about 300 miles broad, and are sharply distinguished from the mountains of the west. The plateau is sufficiently high to allow dissection by rivers and this fact clearly differentiates it from the lower plains on the east. The northern part of the Great Plains is well described by Lewis and Clark in the following words:

The country is here spread into wide and level plains, swelling like the ocean, in which the view is uninterrupted by a single tree or shrub, and is diversified only by the moving herds of buffalo. The soil consists of a light-colored earth, intermixed with a large proportion of coarse gravel without sand, and is by no means so fertile as either the plains of the Columbia or those lower down the Missouri. When dry it cracks, and is hard and thirsty, while in its wet state it is as soft and slimy as soap. The grass is naturally short, and at this time is still more so from the recent passage of the buffalo.[1]

The whole of the southern part of the area was covered with a deep covering of waste from the western mountains in recent geological times. The central section, usually called the High Plains, is the remnant of this flat smooth surface. These high plains extend northward from central Texas (Llano-Estacado) to Nebraska and are still covered with late tertiary beds.

Thus it will be clearly understood that the explorers who proceeded westward from the Mississippi had to cross the two areas called the Central Lowlands and the Great Plains before they reached the Rocky Mountains. They were hindered by no great physical obstacles of relief, but proceeded by a gentle rise

[1] Elliott Coues, *History of the Expedition under the Command of Lewis and Clark*, 4 vols. New York, 1893 (hereafter cited as *L. and C.*), III, 1085–6, July 17, 1806. The dates of entries in the journals of Lewis and Clark are given in order to facilitate reference to other editions.

to the foot of the mountains. The *Interior Highlands* do not form a real barrier to movement. They consist of two parts, the *Ozark Plateau* and the *Ouachita Highlands*, separated one from the other by the valley of the Arkansas. These mountains are of the Appalachian type of folding and it has been suggested that they may be a continuation of the southern Appalachians. Several of the early western expeditions followed the course of the Arkansas. South of these mountains the Mississippi flows through a region called the *Gulf Plains*, which is really the south-eastern portion of the plains which stretch from the Rio Grande, round the Appalachians, and along the Atlantic coast to Maine.

The *Rocky Mountains* are the eastern flank of the great Cordillera which stretches with more or less continuity from Alaska to central New Mexico. Nevertheless, the system is characterised by great variety of structure.[1] The mountains can be divided into three regions, the *northern* and *southern Rocky Mountains* and the *Wyoming Basin*. In Alaska and Canada the system consists of a series of parallel ridges and this system is continued over the border into Montana. In central Montana the Rockies are represented by irregular mountain groups such as the Bridger, Big Snowy, Big and Little Belt Mountains (see Fig. 8). In Canada and Montana a definite eastern "front" can be traced, but almost ceases to exist in the central part of the Rockies or Wyoming Basin. The northern Rockies consist of many mountain ranges, differing in structure, but forming a continuous expanse of mountain country broken by inter-montane valleys, extending north into Canada and including the Wasatch range in the south.

The two mountain regions, the northern and southern Rockies, are not a continuous range but are separated by the *Wyoming Basin*. A plateau-like surface is virtually continuous

[1] R. E. Flint states that in Canada and northern Montana the structure of the eastern border of the Rockies is governed by great overthrust faults. On the other hand he considers that from southern Wyoming to the southern end of the Rockies open folding is the dominating structure. He concludes that compression has been the chief factor in the building of these mountains. R. E. Flint, "A Brief View of Rocky Mountain Structure", *Journal of Geology*, XXXII (1924), 410–31.

from the Great Plains through the Wyoming Basin to the Colorado Plateaux, but the structure of the Wyoming Basin is similar to the structure of the Rockies. Isolated mountains rise from the horizontal beds of the Wyoming Basin and indicate the continuity of structure. In central Wyoming the basin is 250 miles broad.

The *southern Rockies* are mainly in the State of Colorado. They rise to altitudes of 10,000 to 14,000 feet and consist of several ranges all running north to south, but partly enclosing high grass areas called Parks. The eastern range is called the Front range and rises over 6000 feet above the Great Plains, culminating in Pike's Peak. The explorer, Pike, wrote the following description of his first view of these mountains on November 15, 1806:

When our small party arrived on the hill they with one accord gave three cheers to the Mexican mountains. Their appearance can be easily imagined by those who have crossed the Alleghenies; but their sides were whiter, as if covered with snow, or a white stone. These were a spur of the grand western chain of mountains which divide the waters of the Pacific from those of the Atlantic ocean; and it [the spur] divides the waters which empty into the Bay of the Holy Spirit from those of the Mississippi, as the Alleghenies do those which discharge themselves into the latter river and the Atlantic. They appear to present a natural boundary between the province of Louisiana and New Mexico, and would be a defined and a natural boundary.[1]

The exploration of the Rockies was governed by these three great divisions. In the north explorers such as Lewis and Clark found the greatest difficulty in crossing the series of parallel ranges and valleys (Fig. 8). In many parts of the southern

[1] Elliott Coues, *The Expeditions of Zebulon M. Pike*, 3 vols. New York, 1895 (hereafter cited as Z. M. Pike, *Expeditions*), II, 444. Pike's description can be compared with the following, written by N. M. Fenneman in 1915: "Except near the south end, the entire eastern boundary of this mountain province is easily traced on the contour map of the United States (scale 40 miles to one inch), and may be seen as a mountain front by an observer standing a few miles distant on the Great Plains. In southern Colorado and northern New Mexico, such observations are less satisfactory. This portion of the Great Plains Province is itself very rugged, a high and deeply dissected plateau.... Views of the mountain front must therefore be had from high points on the plateau". N. M. Fenneman, *op. cit. Annals Ass. Am. Geog.* VI, 76–7.

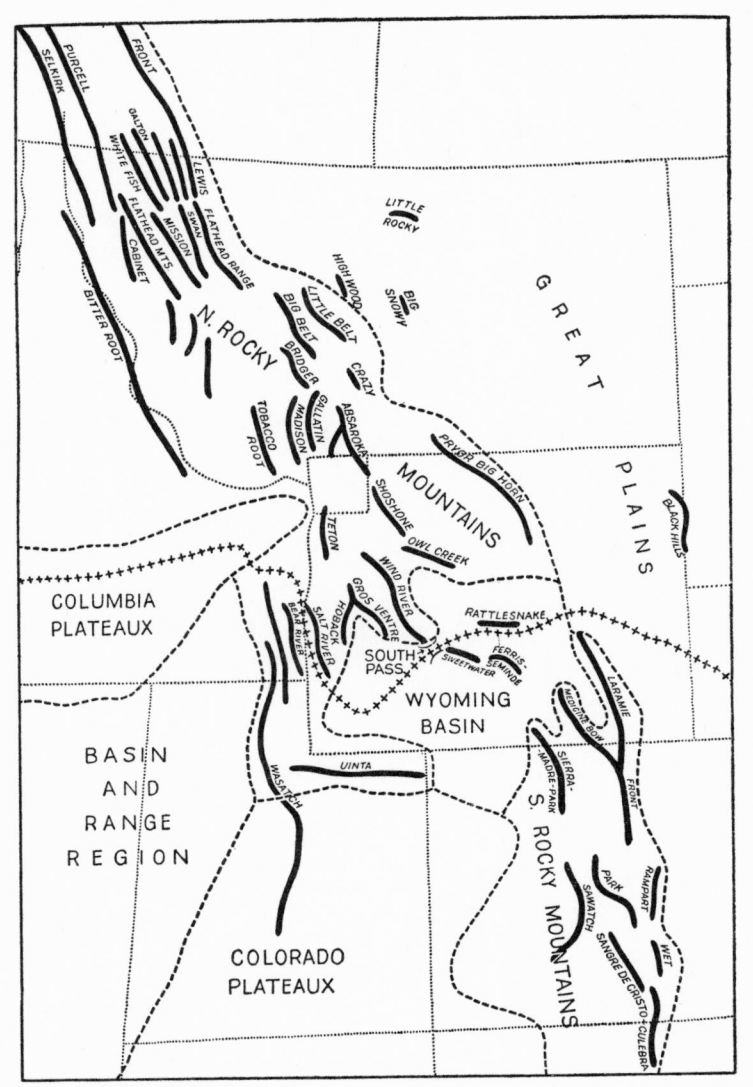

Fig. 8. The principal tectonic ranges of the Rocky Mountains (after R. E. Flint). The Oregon Trail, the central route through the Rocky Mountains, by way of the South Pass, is shown by a line of crosses.

Rockies the mountains presented the appearance of an unscaleable wall. In the centre, in the Wyoming Basin, there was an easy route across the mountains. The gentle gradients of this route resulted in the discovery of South Pass and the road afterwards traversed by thousands of emigrants, the Oregon trail. Fig. 8 shows this central route through the Rockies and also indicates the large number of ranges which had to be crossed on the northern border of the United States.

To the west and south of the Rocky Mountain system is a great area generally known by the name of the *Intermontane Plateaux*. In this region mountains exist only as small ranges separated by desert plains. The region can be divided into three parts, the Columbia Plateaux, the Colorado Plateaux, and the Basin and Range region.

The major portion of the *Columbia Plateaux* consists of the drainage basin of the Columbia River, while the eastern section is in the basin of the Snake River, the main tributary of the Columbia. The old topography of the region was covered with flows of lava which came from different centres. Lakes were formed after these outpourings and the present soil is a result of the disintegration of the lava. The rivers flow in ravines several thousand feet deep, thus exposing the horizontal beds of the lava. This area, a plateau of horizontal rocks, is a marked contrast to the mountains on its eastern and western sides.

The *Colorado Plateaux* occupy the basin of the Colorado River and vary in altitude from 6000 to 10,000 feet. These greatly elevated strata are made up of horizontal sediments sometimes covered by lava flows, and are very deeply dissected. The region consists of several plateaux separated by faults and deep cañons, the chief being the Grand Cañon, 100 miles long. These cañons formed an almost insuperable barrier to human movement. The general character of the Plateaux is interrupted by a few volcanic mountains.

The *Basin and Range region* can be divided into two parts. The northern half is approximately the area of internal drainage, named by the explorer, John C. Frémont, the Great Basin. The south-western portion is a continuation of the Sonoran district of Mexico, while the south-eastern is a continuation of the

Mexican highlands. This region includes the most arid portions of the United States. The dominant physical characteristic common to the whole of the vast area is the existence of isolated but nearly parallel mountain ranges. Wide desert plains, consisting of the deposits of waste from the mountains, exist between the mountain ranges. The deposits are frequently very deep. This combination of local desert basins and mountain ranges is the cause of the regional name of "Basin and Range". Frémont describes a part of the region in the following words : "The interior of the Great Basin, so far as explored, is found to be a succession of sharp mountain ranges and naked plains. These ranges are isolated, presenting summit lines broken into many peaks, of which the highest are between ten and eleven thousand feet above the sea".[1]

The explorer, having crossed the Rocky Mountains, entered one of the three interior plateaux. The discovery of the great arid interior and of the inland drainage basin was one of the most important events in the history of American discovery. The existence of this immense interior was entirely unsuspected by the early explorers.

The last major region to be considered is the *Pacific mountain system*. This consists of two parts, the *Sierra-Cascade range* and the *Pacific border*. The Sierra-Cascade range, which forms a continuous belt of mountainous country stretching from north to south, is the western rampart of the series of interior plateaux. The Sierra Nevada are from 10,000 to 15,000 feet in altitude, but the Cascade range is broader and lower. The two ranges have a different geological history. The southern part of the Cascade Mountains is composed of a line of volcanic cones of various heights, while the Sierra Nevada are composed of old sedimentary rocks which have been subjected to uplift. The Cascades are breached by the Columbia River, which affords an easy route for explorers. The gap was used by Lewis and Clark, who had crossed the Rockies in their most difficult part,

[1] J. C. Frémont, *Geographical Memoir upon Upper California, in illustration of his Map of Oregon and California* (U.S. Govt. Doc. 30th Congress, 1st Session, Senate, Miscel. Doc. no. 148), Washington, 1848 (hereafter cited as J. C. Frémont, *Geog. Memo.*), pp. 11–12.

and by others who had discovered the easier crossing of South Pass. The Sierra Nevada were a more formidable obstacle to communication than the Cascades. No river flows directly across the range and travellers were compelled to use difficult passes. The easiest pass across the Sierra Nevada, namely the Truckee Pass, was not discovered until 1844.

The Pacific border region is composed of two parts. On the west there is a range of *Coastal mountains* consisting of the Olympic Mountains, the Oregon coast ranges, the Californian coast ranges and the Los Angeles range. This series of mountain ranges is separated from the Sierra-Cascade range by the *Californian valley*, the *Willamette valley* and the *Puget Sound valley*. In about lat. 42° there is no great valley, as the two mountain ranges are joined by the Klamath Mountains.

It will be obvious that explorers from the east, once they had crossed the Sierra-Cascade range, entered one of the three great valleys, and emigrants found here the goal of their journeys. These great valleys are separated from the coast by the coastal ranges. The Pacific washes the foot of the coastal mountains and there are only four gateways from the sea through these ranges. In the north are the openings of Juan de Fuca Strait and the Columbia River, which were the termini of the earliest overland routes from the east. Astor's expedition of 1810–12 sent parties by both land and sea to the mouth of the Columbia River. The third opening in the coastal ranges is the famous Golden Gate of San Francisco, not so easily accessible from the interior as the northern openings. Finally, there is the gateway of Los Angeles, which was developed as the terminus of a land route, the Spanish trail, rather than as an entry from the sea.

Chapter IV

THE CLIMATE OF THE REGION

The whole area under consideration can be divided into three main climatic regions, the Plains, the Plateau, and the Pacific border, and each of these may be subdivided into northern and southern districts (Fig. 9).

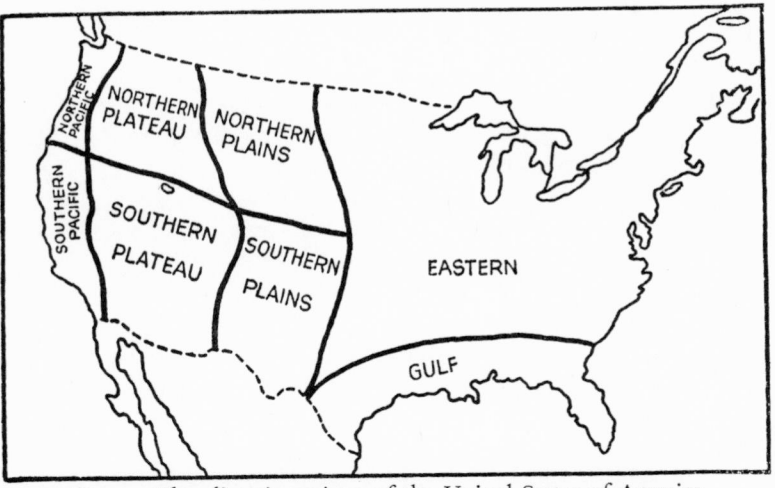

Fig. 9. The climatic regions of the United States of America
(after R. de C. Ward).

TEMPERATURE. The Plains have what is essentially a continental climate. They are cut off from the Pacific Ocean by a great mountain barrier and do not feel the influence of any large body of water.[1] When compared with the east of the United States,

[1] Ward gives the following table of the temperatures of the Plains:

	Mean Annual	January	July	Absolute maximum	Absolute minimum
North	40° F.	0°–10° F.	65°–70° F.	105°–110° F.	− 50° to − 60° F.
South	65° F.	40°–50° F.	80°–85° F.	105°–110° F.	about zero

R. de C. Ward, *Climates of the United States* (Ginn and Co. 1925), p. 433.

the Plains have a greater amount of sunshine, a greater daily range of temperature, and more wind. The winds have been described as having a monsoonal character, north and north-west in winter, and south and south-east in summer. Cold winds are a feature of the climate of the Plains, and explorers frequently complained of frost-bite. On December 12, 1804, Lewis and Clark wrote in their journal, "the wind is still from the north, the thermometer being at sunrise 38° below zero".[1] The Plains have a very clear atmosphere, the importance of which is explained by Brackenridge in the following passage : "The height of this western region, and the open plains which compose it, cause it to possess a pure elastic air. The sky has a more delightful blue than I ever saw any where else ; the atmosphere in a serene calm evening is so clear, that a slight smoke can be discerned at the distance of many miles ; and it is of great importance to the Indians in detecting their enemies, and in giving warning ; but it also exercises their caution in the highest degree. In point of health it is unnecessary to say any thing ; such a country must necessarily be salubrious".[2]

The great Interior or Plateau region has a very varied relief. Temperature is therefore largely a reflection of altitude and general statements are of little value.[3] The summers in the lower plateaux of the south are very hot, but low humidity makes very high temperatures endurable. The southern winters are mild. In the north the heat of summer is less severe and winters are colder. The whole area, north and south, enjoys a great number of hours of sunshine. Perhaps the most important factor affecting explorers living in the open is the extraordinary diurnal range of temperature which prevails throughout the

---

[1] *L. and C.* I, 211. Degrees of temperature in Fahrenheit.

[2] H. M. Brackenridge, E.W.T. VI (1816), 158–9.

[3] Ward, *Climates of the United States*, p. 437, gives the following table of the temperatures of the Plateau:

	Mean Annual	January	July	Absolute maximum	Absolute minimum
North	50° F.	20°–30° F.	65°–70° F.	100°–105° F.	– 10° to – 30° F.
South	60°–70° F.	40°–50° F. +	80°–90° F. +	110°–115° F. +	zero to 20° F.

whole region, particularly in the west. These conditions are well described by Lewis and Clark when travelling near the Snake River. "The weather", says Clark, "was very cold; the water which stood in the vessels exposed to the air being covered with ice a quarter of an inch thick. Ink freezes in the pen, and the low grounds are perfectly whitened with frost. After this the day proved exceedingly warm".[1]

The Pacific border region can be divided into two parts. The climate of the northern portion resembles that of north-western Europe, while the south enjoys a climate which is similar to that of the Mediterranean. In both parts diurnal and seasonal ranges of temperature are slight, because the influence of the ocean is everywhere predominant. "The mean temperature in the Joaquin valley, during the journey from the middle of December to the middle of January, was at sunrise 29° and at sunset 52°, with generally a faint breeze from the snowy mountains in the morning, and calm weather at the evening".[2] Owing to the high winter temperature, the harbours of the Pacific do not freeze.[3]

RAINFALL. Fig. 10, a map of the annual rainfall of the western United States, reveals the fact that rainfall increases with altitude. This increase is not uniform and does not always continue to the highest altitudes. The maximum rainfall in the Sierra Nevada occurs at an altitude of 4000 to 6000 feet, but in the Rockies the maximum annual rainfall occurs at much greater altitudes. Cyclones increase the amount of rainfall, and regions which lie in the track of frequent cyclonic disturbances receive very heavy rainfall. On the northern Pacific coast and in the northern Rocky Mountains the rainfall is largely due to the influence of cyclones.

[1] *L. and C.* II, 541, August 21, 1805.
[2] J. C. Frémont, *Geog. Memo.* p. 19.
[3] Ward, *Climates of the United States*, p. 439, gives the following table of the temperatures of the Pacific border region:

	Mean Annual	January	July	Absolute maximum	Absolute minimum
North	50°–55° F.	35°–40° F.	60°–65° F.	90°–100° F.	10°–0° F.
South	65° F. ±	50° F.	65°–70° F.	105°–110° F.	20° F. ±

In the Gulf States a third factor increases the rainfall. In this area the great heating of the surface causes many thunderstorms.

There is a gradual decrease in the amount of annual rainfall from the Atlantic and Gulf towards the west. On the eastern side of the Plains the annual rainfall is between 20 and 25 inches, while on the western side it is less than 15 inches. In some parts of Montana, relief causes a larger amount of rainfall. The rainfall varies very greatly from year to year, but agriculture is impossible without irrigation where the rainfall is under 20 inches.

The Plateau region receives a small annual rainfall, which is everywhere less than 20 inches, frequently below 10 inches, and over a considerable portion of the south-west less than 5 inches. The largest amounts occur in the regions of greatest altitude. The whole area is in the rain shadow of the Pacific ranges and arid conditions are the natural result. In the north, the western mountain barrier is not so effective, and the higher parts of the northern Plateau region receive a plentiful rainfall. Nevertheless, the difference between the eastern and western sides of the Pacific ranges is very marked. Lewis and Clark, on their return journey from the Pacific, were much impressed by the sudden change of climate which occurred when they had reached the eastern side of the Cascade Mountains. "The climate too," says Clark, "though we are only on the border of the plains, is here very different from that we have lately experienced. The air is drier and more pure, and the ground itself is as free from moisture as if there had been no rain for the last ten days."[1] Even in the south of this region, where the rainfall is smaller, mountainous regions receive an adequate rainfall. The Rocky Mountains are so far from the Pacific that, except in the north they do not obtain a very heavy rainfall.

The rainfall is as much as 100 inches on the north-west coast of the Pacific border region, and decreases to about 10 inches on the south coast. In the extreme north-west rain falls on half the days in the year and there is a marked decrease in the number of rainy days from north to south.

[1] *L. and C.* III, 952, when near the Dalles, April 16, 1806.

SEASONAL DISTRIBUTION OF RAINFALL.[1] The Plains have a well-marked seasonal rainfall. The area of this type extends from the extreme south of the United States to northern Canada. The rain is heaviest in summer with a maximum in June. Winter is dry, but no month is entirely rainless. This *régime* is well illustrated by Gregg in his classic, *The Commerce of the Prairies*. When he was near Independence on May 16, 1831, he wrote the following account of the weather :

On the following day we had a foretaste of those protracted, drizzling spells of rain, which at this season of the year, so much infest the frontier prairies. It began sprinkling about dark and continued pouring without let or hinderance for forty-eight hours in succession; and as the rain was accompanied by a heavy north-wester, and our camp was pitched in the open prairie, without a stick of available timber within a mile of us, it must be allowed that the whole formed a prelude anything but flattering to valetudinarians.[2]

The summer rainfall which Gregg describes is due to convectional action, when the ground is very rapidly heated. Gregg gives the following reason for the comparative aridity of the Plains :

The great elevation of all the plains about the Rocky Mountains, is perhaps the principal cause of the extraordinary dryness of the atmosphere. There is but little rain throughout the year, except from July to October—known as the *rainy season*; and as the Missouri traders usually arrive about its commencement, the coincidence has given rise to a superstition, quite prevalent among the vulgar, that the Americans bring the rain with them. During seasons of drought, especially, they look for the arrival of the caravans as the harbinger of speedy relief.[3]

Frémont describes the summer rainfall, when he was on the Plains near the junction of the rivers Missouri and Kansas on June 11, 1842, in the following words : " Shortly after midnight it began to rain heavily, and, as our tents were of light and thin cloth, they offered but little obstruction to rain ; we were all well

---

[1] See W. G. Kendrew, *Climates of the Continents* (2nd ed. 1927), pp. 291 ff.
[2] J. Gregg, *Commerce of the Prairies* (1845), E.W.T. xix, 193.
[3] *Ibid.* xix, 286–7.

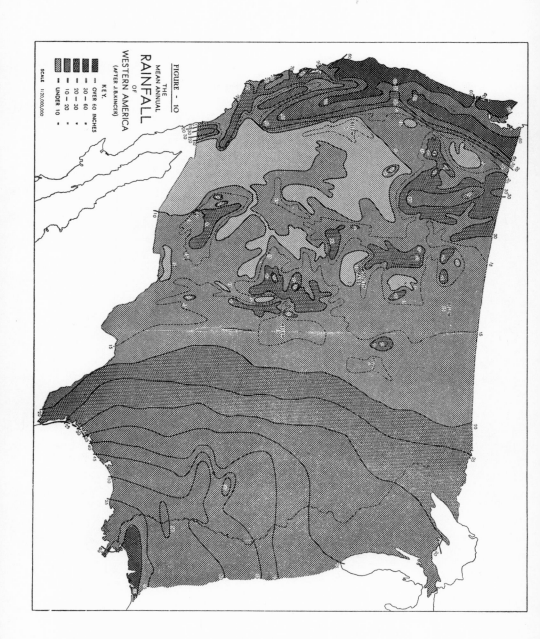

soaked, and glad when morning came. We had a rainy march on the 12th".[1]

The Plateau can be divided into two parts. In the northern portion there is more rain in the winter than in the summer, December and January being the rainiest months. Nevertheless, the whole area is comparatively arid. The southern portion is the most arid part of the United States, the meagre rainfall occurring mainly in the winter, but the intense heat of the summer causes convectional showers.

The Pacific border region can be divided by the Klamath Mountains into two parts. In the northern region there is a winter maximum, but there is also abundant rain in the summer. The rainfall is partly due to the relief and partly to the succession of cyclones and is similar to the rainfall of north-western Europe.[2] In the southern region the rain also falls in winter, but the rainless summer is more marked. The Californian coast is subject to fogs. Frémont speaks of the Californian coastal climate, north of San Francisco, in the following terms : "I learned from Captain Smith, a resident at Bodega, that the winter months make a delightful season—rainy days (generally of warm showers) alternating with mild and calm, pleasant weather, and pure bright skies—much preferable to the summer, when the fogs and strong northwest winds, which prevail during the greater part of the year, make the morning part of the day disagreeably cold".[3]

Explorers travelling west from the Mississippi crossed the area of the Plains in which rainfall falls largely in summer. The rainfall diminished in amount as they went towards the west. After crossing the Rockies, they reached two arid regions in which the rain falls mainly in the winter. Finally they would cross the Sierra-Cascade range of mountains and reach one of the coastal regions with a very marked winter maximum of

---

[1] J. C. Frémont, *Report of the Exploring Expedition to the Rocky Mountains in the year* 1842, *and to Oregon and North California in the years* 1843–44 (28th Congress, 2d Session, Senate 174), Washington, 1845 (hereafter cited as J. C. Frémont, *Report*), pp. 10–11.

[2] See *infra*, pp. 116–7, for Lewis and Clark's records of the weather experienced in this region.

[3] J. C. Frémont, *Geog. Memo.* p. 35.

rainfall. The Cascades and the Sierra Nevada form one of the most definite and clearly marked climatic boundaries in the world. Frémont, when describing the Cascade Mountains, says :

The lofty range of the Cascade mountains forms a distinct boundary between the opposite climates of the regions along its western and eastern bases. On the west, they present a barrier to the clouds of fog and rain which roll up from the Pacific ocean and beat against their rugged sides, forming the rainy season of the winter in the country along the coast. Into the brighter skies of the region along their eastern base, this rainy winter never penetrates; and at the Dalles of the Columbia the rainy season is unknown, the brief winter being limited to a period of about two months, during which the earth is covered with the slight snows of a climate remarkably mild for so high a latitude.[1]

The same author also lays great emphasis on the difference between the climates of the eastern and western sides of the Sierra Nevada. He says :

The two sides of the Sierra exhibit two distinct climates. The state of vegetation, in connection with some thermometrical observations made during the recent exploring expedition to California, will establish and illustrate this difference. In the beginning of December, 1845, we crossed this Sierra, at latitude 39° 17′ 12″, at the present usual emigrant pass, at the head of the Salmon Trout river, 40 miles north of New Helvetia, and made observations at each base, and in the same latitude, to determine the respective temperatures; and two bases being, respectively, the *western* about 500, and the *eastern* about 4000 feet above the level of the sea; and the pass, 7200 feet. The mean results of the observations were, on the *eastern* side, at sunrise, 9°; at noon, 44°; at sunset, 30°; the state of vegetation and the appearance of the country being at the same time (second week in December) that of confirmed winter; the rivers frozen over, snow on the ridges, annual plants dead, grass dry, and deciduous trees stripped of their foliage. At the *western* base, the mean temperature during a corresponding week was, at sunrise, 29°, and at sunset, 52°, the state of the atmosphere and of vegetation that of advancing spring; grass fresh and green, four to eight inches high, vernal plants in bloom, the air soft, and all the streams free from ice. Thus December, on one side of the mountain, was winter; on the other side it was spring.[2]

SNOWFALL. North America has been described as "the snowiest of the continents", and the snowfall had a considerable influence on the exploration of the region.

[1] J. C. Frémont, *Report*, p. 194, November 14, 1843.
[2] J. C. Frémont, *Geog. Memo.* p. 7. Degrees of temperature in Fahrenheit.

It is almost impossible to construct an adequate cartographical representation of snowfall. Possibly a map showing the average annual number of days with snowcover (Fig. 11) is a more useful representation of snowfall than a map showing the number of inches which are supposed to have fallen. Although both maps are likely to deviate from the truth for want of sufficient data, they both show that latitude is the controlling factor of snowfall on the Plains. The lines of equal depth and

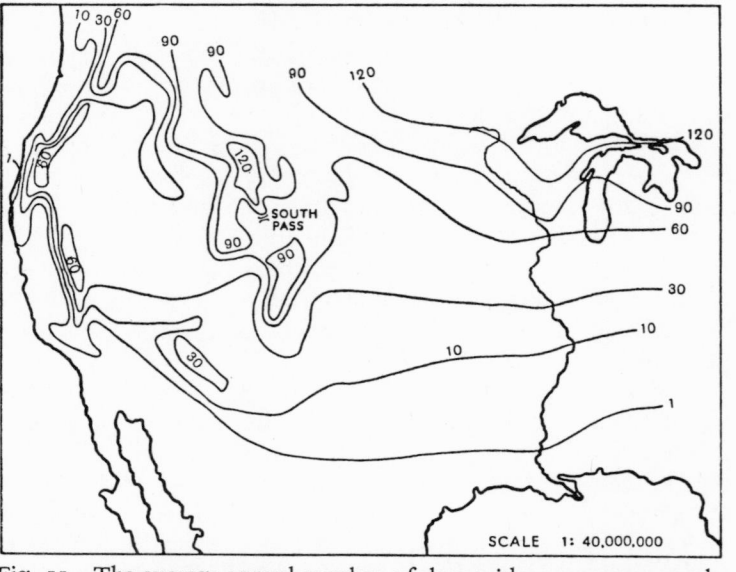

Fig. 11. The average annual number of days with snow cover: under 1 day, 1–10 days, 10–30 days, 30–60 days, 60–90 days, 90–120 days, over 120 days, (after J. B. Kincer, *Atlas of American Agriculture*), based on records of about 200 full reporting stations, 1895–1914.

the lines of number of days snow-cover extend in an east to west direction. The total annual snowfall on the Great Plains is small, but a considerable amount falls in the spring and summer. On May 2, 1805, Lewis and Clark, when moving across the Plains, write that "at daylight it began to snow, and did not stop till ten o'clock when the ground was covered an inch deep, forming a striking contrast with the vegetation, which is now

considerably advanced, some flowers having put forth and the cottonwood leaves being as large as a dollar".[1] In the extreme north the snowfall of the Plains is between 30 and 40 inches.

In the Rocky Mountains snowfall is not so heavy as in the Sierra Nevada, but there are very heavy falls, particularly on the western slopes. In the mountains of Colorado the snowfall sometimes exceeds 25 feet, occurring chiefly in the spring months, and in Wyoming 17 feet. The two areas of heavy fall in the Rockies correspond to the northern and southern Rocky Mountains; they are divided by an area of low fall, which corresponds to the Wyoming Basin and includes the South Pass. The lighter fall of snow helped to make this the easiest crossing of the Rockies.

The whole of the Plateau province is in the snow shadow of the western mountain barrier. Thus there is a great decrease in the amount of snowfall in the lower part of the Plateau. About 20 to 30 inches of snow falls in the northern part of the area and sometimes less than 1 inch in the southern part. The mountains of the Plateau have a heavier snowfall. In most parts of the Great Basin the ground is only covered with snow for a short period.

The snowfall of the Pacific mountains is very heavy. The western flanks of the Cascades and the Sierra Nevada receive an average fall of 33 to 41 feet. The western slopes of the Cascades receive about 33 feet every year, while on the east of the mountains 20 inches is the maximum. In one place in the Sierra Nevada the fall was as high as 58 feet in one year and a fall of 25 feet in one month has been recorded. Frémont's crossing of the Sierra Nevada in January, 1844,[2] was rendered more difficult by the heavy snowfall, which he found in places to be as deep as 20 feet (Fig. 25).

Heavy snow often delayed movement, even on the Plains. On November 29, 1804, Lewis and Clark stated that "the snow which fell yesterday and last night is 13 inches in depth".[3] However, the snow on the Plains generally melted quickly and

[1] L. and C. I, 292.
[2] See infra, p. 181 and Fig. 25.
[3] L. and C. I, 203.

extreme cold was a greater hindrance to travellers than the actual depth of snow. On December 8, 1804, Lewis and Clark made the following entry: "the snow was generally 6 or 8 inches deep and sometimes 18, in consequence of which two of the party were hurt by falls, and several had their feet frost-bitten".[1]

Even in the south of the Plains the snow which fell on the Santa Fé trail was often a very real danger. A certain James L. Collins, an experienced pioneer of the Santa Fé trail, was asked by the Governor of New Mexico to give his opinion on the advisability of crossing the Plains from Missouri to Santa Fé during the winter months. The Governor wanted the information in order to make a communication to the legislature, then in session at Santa Fé. Collins' letter forms an appendix to Governor Lane's message read to the legislature in December, 1852. This letter is reproduced below.

Santa Fé, N.M., December 10, 1852.

Dear Sir,

In answer to your inquiry on the subject of the practicability of a winter trip across the plains from the frontier of Missouri to New Mexico, I have to say that my acquaintance with the route in question commenced in the year 1827. Previous to that date, I believe, but one attempt was made to cross the plains in the winter, and that was in the year 1824 or 1825, by a small party from St Louis, at the head of which Messrs Faulkner and Anderson. They reached a forest on the Arkansas River, near Choteau's Island, where they were met by a heavy fall of snow, in which nearly all their horses and mules perished and they were compelled to winter on an island that has since been known as "Log Island" from the quantity of timber cut for the subsistence of the few remaining animals, and to shelter the men from the storm.

After this it was for a number of years deemed impracticable to attempt the trip in the winter, but since the road has become better known it has been frequently traveled, often, however, resulting in great destruction of property and of human life. In the month of December, 1841, Don Manuel Alvarez, an experienced and enterprising traveler, with a small party, was caught in a snow storm on Cottonwood creek, near Council Grove. In a few hours, two men and all his mules were frozen to death, and the snow drifted in such torrents as to extinguish the fires in a very few minutes. All hope seemed to be at once shut out from the party; everything of life had perished, and they themselves seemed fast sinking into an everlasting sleep. Two of the number, the stoutest among them, had sank to rise no more, and the remainder would unquestionably have

[1] *L. and C.* I, 210.

shared the same fate, but for the energy of Mr Alvarez himself, who, by absolutely driving the men into motion, was enabled to keep them alive until the storm had abated. Many of them, however, were badly frozen.

Few scenes have been presented to the view of men more terrific than the one encountered by the little party on that dreadful night.

About the same period another party under the charge of Don Ant. Roubidoux, met a snow storm at the same place. They lost in one night over 400 mules and horses, and one or two men, and narrowly escaped the loss of the entire party.

In 1844, Dr H. Connelly and Mr Spyre, as early in the season as the 12th of October, encountered a storm near the Arkansas River, in which a number of mules perished, and the remainder were saved by running them into the timber in the river, a distance of some fifteen miles.

The same party, a few days later, met a second storm on the Cimarron, in which they lost in one night over 300 mules, and were compelled to remain until mules were sent from Santa Fé to their relief.

In 1848, Messrs Waldo, McCoy and Co., government freighters, on their return to Missouri lost nearly all their cattle, amounting to 800 or 900 head. The wagons were left on the plains until spring.

In 1849, Messrs Brown, Russell and Co., in crossing the Jornada, from the Arkansas to the Cimarron, with a train of some twenty wagons, were overtaken by a storm of snow and sleet accompanied with a terrific wind. The men retreated to their covered wagons leaving their cattle to wander whither they would; but they instinctively kept within the inclosure formed by the wagons; they perished, however, in a few hours. The snow drifted into the wagons through every crevice until they were filled nearly to the top of the bows, this fortunately sheltered the men beneath from the piercing cold without. Two of the men ventured, about day light, to get out of their wagon for the purpose of kindling a fire, but in a few minutes became so stiffened with the intense cold that they were unable to get into their wagon again without assistance. The others prudently kept beneath their blankets and canopy of snow during the whole day and succeeding night, not venturing to change their position, wisely determining to endure the pangs of hunger rather than run the risk of sharing the same fate of their unfortunate animals.

On the second day the storm abated, though the cold was still intense. They ventured from their coverts to look upon the sad wreck of life around them and to think upon the awful condition in which they were placed—a condition which none can realize but those who have experienced it. Hundreds of miles from any civilized habitation, in the midst of a desert waste producing not a stick of timber in a range of many miles, and no animal left, they seemed to be shut up by an inexorable destiny.

One consolation was left them, the train was loaded with provisions and they could use the wagons for fuel. But for this they must all soon have perished; they were, however, enabled thus to sustain themselves until succor arrived in the spring.

In 1850, the same company with a large train of wagons with Govern-

ment freight encountered a snow-storm between this place and San Miguel, in which they lost over a thousand head of cattle. For this loss they have a claim now pending before the Congress of the United States.

In the year 1851 the Cottonwood creek was again the scene of a terrible destruction of life. A Government train that had been started to the States by Col. Sumner, was overtaken by one of those destructive storms so frequently met with at that ill-fated spot; in a single night nearly three hundred mules perished; one man was also lost, and several others badly frozen. In the same storm, the party in charge of the mail lost all their animals near Fort Atkinson, but were fortunately picked up by a train that had been more fortunate than themselves, and brought on to the Fort.

Other losses of life and property could be recited if it were deemed necessary, and to this, I could also add a detail of the destruction of the lives and property of our fellow-citizens by the marauding savage tribes that have infested the rout for the last thirty years, that would astonish the minds of the public that the attention of the Government had not long since been directed to the subject.

Trusting that the representations of your Excellency may arrest the immediate attention of Congress, to the end that further and more ample protection may be given to this route, not only against the depredations of the Indians, but against the inclemency of the season.

I remain with high consideration,

Your ob't serv't,

J. L. COLLINS.

His Excellency Wm. Carr Lane,
    Gov. of Ter. of N.M.[1]

REGIONAL DESCRIPTIONS OF CLIMATE. The climate of the Plains region has been discussed and illustrated by the accounts of the explorers, but the climates of the Plateau and Pacific border regions have not been so fully described. Frémont wrote good general accounts of the climates of the Plateau region (the Great Basin) and of the Pacific border (maritime California), which are given below.

The Great Basin

The climate of the Great Basin does not present the rigorous winter due to its elevation and mountainous structure. Observations made during the last expedition, show that around the southern shores of the Salt lake, latitude 40° 30', to 41°, for two weeks of the month of October, 1845, from the 13th to the 27th, the mean temperature was 40° at sunrise, 70° at

1 Benjamin M. Read, "Perils of the Santa Fé Trail in its Early Days (1822–1852)", *El Palacio*, XIX (1925), 206–11 (reproduced by kind permission of the Editor).

noon, and 54° at sunset; ranging at sunrise, from 28° to 57°; at noon, from 62° to 76°; at four in the afternoon, from 58° to 69°; and at sunset, from 47° to 57°.

Until the middle of the month the weather remained fair and very pleasant. On the 15th, it began to rain in occasional showers, which whitened with snow the tops of the mountains on the south-east side of the lake valley. Flowers were in bloom during all the month. About the 18th, on one of the large islands in the south of the lake, *helianthus*, several species of *aster, erodium cicutarium*, and several other plants, were in fresh and full bloom; the grass of the second growth was coming up finely, and vegetation, generally, betokened the lengthened summer of the climate.

The 16th, 17th, and 18th, stormy with rain; heavy at night; peaks of the Bear river range and tops of the mountains covered with snow. On the 18th, cleared, with weather like that of late spring, and continued mild and clear until the end of the month when the fine weather was again interrupted by a day or two of rain. No snow within 2000 feet above the level of the valley.

Across the interior, between latitudes 41° and 38°, during the month of November (5th to 25th), the mean temperature was 29° at sunrise, and 40° at sunset; ranging at noon (by detached observations) between 41° and 60°. There was a snow storm between the 4th and 7th, the snow falling principally at night, and sun occasionally breaking out in the day. The lower hills and valleys were covered a few inches deep with snow, which the sun carried off in a few hours after the storm was over.

The weather then continued uninterruptedly open until the close of the year, without rain or snow; and during the remainder of November, generally clear and beautiful; nights and mornings calm, a light breeze during the day, and strong winds of very rare occurrence. Snow remained only on the peaks of the mountains.

On the western side of the basin, along the base of the *Sierra Nevada*, during two weeks, from the 25th *November* to the 11th *December*, the mean temperature at sunrise was 11°, and at sunset, 34°; ranging at sunrise from zero to 21°, and at sunset from 23° to 44°. For ten consecutive days of the same period, the mean temperature at noon was 45°, ranging from 33° to 56°.

The weather remained open, usually very clear, and the rivers were frozen.[1]

Maritime California

The climate of maritime California is greatly modified by the structure of the country, and under this aspect may be considered in three divisions— the *southern*, below Point Concepcion and the Santa Barbara mountain, about latitude 35°; the *northern*, from Cape Mendocino, latitude 41°, to the Oregon boundary; and the *middle*, including the bay and basin of San Francisco and the coast between Point Concepcion and Cape Mendocino.

[1] J. C. Frémont, *Geog. Memo.* pp. 12–13.

Of these three divisions, the rainy season is longest and heaviest in the north and lightest in the south. Vegetation is governed accordingly—coming with the rains—decaying when they fail. Summer and winter, in our sense of the terms, are not applicable to this part of the country. It is not heat and cold, but wet and dry, which mark the seasons; and the winter months, instead of killing vegetation, revive it. The dry season makes a period of consecutive drought, the only winter in the vegetation of this country, which can hardly be said at any time to cease. In forests, where the soil is sheltered; in low lands of streams and hilly country, where the ground remains moist, grass continues constantly green and flowers bloom in all the months of the year. In the southern half of the country the long summer drought has rendered irrigation necessary, and the experience of the missions in their prosperous day, has shown that, in California, as elsewhere, the dryest plains are made productive, and the heaviest crops produced by that mode of cultivation. With irrigation a succession of crops may be produced throughout the year. Salubrity and a regulated mildness characterize the climate; there being no prevailing diseases, and the extremes of heat during the summer being checked by sea breezes during the day, and by light airs from the Sierra Nevada during the night. The nights are cool and refreshing, as is the shade during the hottest day.[1]

Note

The following weather records will be found useful:

Coues, Elliott, *History of the Expedition under the Command of Lewis and Clark*, III, 1264–81, Appendix IV, Meteorological Register.

Frémont, J. C. *Geographical Memoir upon Upper California, in illustration of his Map of Oregon and California* (1848). Appendix IV contains a record of meteorological observations, made in the Great Basin, from December 17, 1843, to February 21, 1844.

Ross, A. *Adventures of the First Settlers on the Oregon or Columbia River* (1849), E.W.T. VII, Appendix, a table of weather at the mouth of the Columbia from March 22 to July 22, 1811.

[1] J. C. Frémont, *Geog. Memo.* pp. 42–3.

Chapter V

THE NATURAL DRAINAGE OF
THE REGION

The navigable rivers had a very real importance in the exploration of the region, as they were routes of travel by boat and
canoe. In the great plains, where many rivers were unnavigable,
the traveller was nevertheless obliged to follow the course of
the river to obtain water and the cottonwood tree which supplied him with wood fuel. The main expeditions were undertaken by traders, and along the rivers they found not only their
prey, the valuable beaver, but also the settlements of the Indians
with whom they traded.[1]

The continental divide between the rivers flowing to the
Atlantic and the Pacific Oceans is indicated on Fig. 13. It will
be seen that most of the rivers take their rise in the Rocky
Mountains and flow across either the Plains or the Interior
Plateaux.

The drainage on the east of the Rocky Mountains can be
divided into four systems, the upper Missouri, the Platte and
the Kansas, the Arkansas and the Red, and the Rio Grande and
Pecos (Fig. 13). The first three systems contain tributaries of
the Mississippi, but the Rio Grande and Pecos flow indepen-
dently into the Gulf of Mexico.

Upper Missouri. The most important of the rivers flowing on
the eastern side of the Rockies is the Missouri. This river, rising
in the northern mountains, a region of heavy rainfall and snowfall, has a larger supply of water than the streams which rise
farther south. The river flows through the dry plains, where
the rainfall is less than 20 inches. Evaporation decreases the
volume of water but the river does not disappear. The Missouri

[1] The *Water-Supply Papers* of the United States Geological Survey
provide valuable modern descriptions of the drainage. See nos. 241–52,
Surface Water-Supply of the United States, 1907–8. Prepared under the
direction of M. O. Leighton (1909–10).

Fig. 12. Snags in the Missouri.

eventually flows south, and is joined by other rivers which rise in the Rocky Mountains, thus obtaining a whole series of additional sources of water supply. The river is navigable for a distance of 2285 miles from the sea, as far as Fort Benton, 37 miles below the Great Falls, which prevent any further navigation upstream. Owing to its navigability, the Missouri became the first line of advance into the unknown west, and was used by Lewis and Clark.

The right banks of the Missouri and the Mississippi below St Louis are joined by two types of stream which have crossed the Great Plains. The headwaters of one type are in the mountains and the headwaters of the other type are in the plains. The streams which rise in the mountains have a regular supply of water from rain or snow, and although they may sometimes become very low, they generally flow for the whole year. Several of them have two floods in the year, a spring flood as the result of the melting of the snows in the mountains, and a summer flood as the result of the thunderstorms in the plains. The flow of the streams which rise in the plains is exceedingly uncertain, as their main supply of water is obtained from the summer rains. If the summer is dry, the river may completely disappear or be reduced to a series of pools.[1]

The basin of the upper Missouri was the most important basin in the early stages of exploration, because of the navigability of the main stream. It must not be imagined that the navigation of the river was an easy task. The course of the river was constantly changing and the bed was often filled with trees, which formed a dangerous obstacle to boats (Fig. 12). On July 2, 1804, Lewis and Clark record that "here for half an hour the river became covered with drift-wood, which rendered navigation dangerous, and was probably caused by the giving way of some sand-bar, which had detained the wood."[2] It was often necessary to throw the greatest weight on the bows of the boat, as a precaution against the quantities of concealed timber.[3] Sand-banks frequently caused slow progress. Lewis and Clark say that they "with great difficulty were enabled to struggle

[1] I. Bowman, *Forest Physiography* (1911), p. 409.
[2] *L. and C.* I, 36.   [3] *Ibid.* I, 5, May 15, 1804.

through the sand-bars, the water being very rapid and shallow,
so that we were several hours making a mile. Several times the
boat wheeled on a bar, when the men were obliged to jump out
and prevent her from upsetting; at others, after making a way
up one channel, the shoalness of the water forced us back to
seek the deep channel. We advanced only four miles in the
whole day".[1] The sand-bars were sometimes used as camps,
and their sudden disappearance proved very inconvenient to
the explorer. "Between one and two o'clock", write Lewis and
Clark, "the sergeant on guard alarmed us, by crying that the
sand-bar on which we lay was sinking. We jumped up and
found that both above and below our camp the sand was under-
mined and falling in very fast. We had scarcely got into the
boats and pushed off, when the bank under which they had been
lying fell in, and would certainly have sunk the two periogues
if they had remained there".[2] The innumerable meanders of the
river made navigation lengthy and tedious. On August 5, 1804,
Captain Clark relates that, "in pursuing some game in an
eastern direction, (he) found himself at the distance of 370 yards
from the camp, at a point of the river where we had come
twelve miles. When the water is high this peninsula is overflowed; and, judging from the customary and notorious changes
in the river, a few years will be sufficient to force the main
current of the river across and leave the great bend dry".[3] The
navigation of the river was described as a "science by itself".
At certain periods of the year ice was a great danger. Washington Irving says: "The Missouri, flowing from high and cold
latitudes, and through wide and open plains, exposed to chilling
blasts, freezes early. The winter may be dated from the 1st of
November; there was every prospect, therefore, that it would
be closed with ice long before Mr Hunt could reach its upper
waters".[4]

The three source rivers of the Missouri are the Jefferson, the

[1] *L. and C.* I, 115, September 12, 1804. See also p. 16 and pp. 25–6 for
accounts of delays caused by sand-bars.
[2] *Ibid.* I, 124–5, September 21, 1804.
[3] *L. and C.* I, 68. An interesting description of the formation of ox-bow
lakes is given on the same page.
[4] Washington Irving, *Astoria; or, Enterprise Beyond the Rocky Mountains* (1839), p. 108.

Madison, and the Gallatin. From the three forks the river flows almost due north until it is joined by Maria's River. At the Great Falls of the Missouri, which are 150 miles below the three forks, the water falls 500 feet, in 8 miles. The head of navigation on the Missouri is 37 miles below the Great Falls, near the mouth of Maria's River. Fort Benton grew up near the head of navigation, while Fort Union sprang up near the junction of the Missouri and the Yellowstone, the next important tributary. The valleys of the Yellowstone, and of its principal tributary the Big Horn, formed useful routes for fur-traders. After the junction of the Yellowstone and the Missouri, the main stream flows steadily south. The river then changes its course from south to south-east, and at this point there arose the station of Fort Pierre, in the heart of the district inhabited by the Sioux tribe of Indians. The junction of the Missouri and the Platte is the next strategic point. "The passing of the mouth of the Nebraska (Platte), therefore, was equivalent among boatmen to the crossing of the line among sailors, and was celebrated with like ceremonials of a rough and waggish nature practised upon the uninitiated; among which was the old nautical joke of shaving".[1]

The second drainage basin to be considered is the *Basin of the Platte and the Kansas*, the central tributaries of the Missouri. The length of the Platte is about 1000 miles. It was useless for navigation, and has been described as "a thousand miles long and six inches deep". Washington Irving speaks of it as "the most magnificent and the most useless of rivers". Long gives the following description of the river: "The Platte, called by the Otoes, Ne-braska (Flat river, or water), is, as its name imports, almost uniformly broad and shoal. It is fordable at almost any place, except when swollen by freshets, which occur in the spring season from the melting of the snow, and occasionally during the other portions of the year, from excessive rain".[2] John Hunter described the river in the following words:

The river La Platte rises in the Rocky Mountains, runs nearly east, is about one thousand six hundred miles in length; broad, shoal and not navigable,

[1] W. Irving, *Astoria*, p. 126.
[2] E. James, *Expedition under Command of Major S. H. Long* (1823), E.W.T. xv, 230.

I believe, even during the prevalence of its floods. It is exceedingly winding for more than half the distance from its heading sources, and flows principally through sandy barrens, and over a sandy bed, occasionally interrupted by rocks. At times it is almost dry, and may be forded in particular places with almost dry feet; while, at others, it is difficult to conceive of the volume of water that seeks a level, with astonishing rapidity, through its wide cut channels.[1]

Nevertheless, though boats could not navigate its course, the river led the traveller by a gentle rise to the summit of the divide. By means of a tributary of the north fork of the Platte, called the Sweetwater, the river leads to the South Pass, the easiest route across the central part of the Rocky Mountains. The Oregon trail followed the Platte and Sweetwater Rivers to South Pass. If it had been possible to use boats there is no doubt that the route would have been used earlier than it was. John Hunter compares the respective values of the Missouri and the Platte in the following words: "The route of the Missouri is widely circuitous, the river of difficult ascent, and the mountains next to impassable for loaded teams, even though human art and means should be exhausted in the construction of roads. That of the La Platte from the seat of government, is perhaps the most direct communication; but then, as before remarked, this river is not navigable, nor can it be made so, for any expence at present justifiable by the object in view".[2] Only when the "Prairie Schooner", or covered wagon, came into use could this route be utilised. On June 28, 1842, Frémont met a party of fourteen men making their way by the side of the Platte, on foot. Frémont's description of their adventures explains the difficulty of navigating the Platte and is worth quoting in full.

A brief account of their fortunes will give some idea of navigation in the Nebraska. Sixty days since, they had left the mouth of Laramie's Fork, some three hundred miles above, in barges laden with the furs of the American Fur Company. They started with the annual flood, and, drawing but nine inches water, hoped to make a speedy and prosperous voyage to St Louis; but, after a lapse of forty days, found themselves only one

[1] John D. Hunter, *Memoirs of a Captivity among the Indians of North America* (1823), p. 157. Hunter, when a child, was captured by Indians and remained with them until he was nineteen years of age. His book is an interesting account of the manners and customs of the Indians.

[2] John Hunter, *op. cit.* p. 159.

hundred and thirty miles from their point of departure. They came down rapidly as far as Scott's bluffs, where their difficulties began. Sometimes they came upon places where the water was spread over a great extent, and here they toiled from morning until night, endeavouring to drag their boat through the sands, making only two or three miles in as many days. Sometimes they would enter an arm of the river, where there appeared a fine channel, and, after descending prosperously for eight or ten miles, would come suddenly upon dry sands, and be compelled to return, dragging their boat for days against the rapid current; and at others, they came upon places where the water lay in holes, and getting out to float off their boat, would fall into water up to their necks, and the next moment tumble over against a sandbar.[1]

The Indians navigated the river in "small flat canoes made of hides",[2] but when Frémont attempted to imitate them, he was compelled to abandon his bull-boat, after dragging it over the sands for three or four miles.[3] The river itself formed a useful guide to the west and was sometimes actually used as a road.[4]

Between the junction of the Kansas with the Missouri and the town of St Louis, the Missouri is joined by the Osage. The Osages, a powerful Indian tribe, inhabited this valley, which was explored by Pike in 1806.

[1] J. C. Frémont, *Report*, p. 17. Parkman wrote a similar account of the difficulties which attended any attempt to navigate the Platte. "They had reason to haste, for already the voyage from Fort Laramie had occupied a full month, and the river was growing daily more shallow. Fifty times a day the boats had been aground; indeed those who navigate the Platte usually spend half their time upon the sand-bars. Two of these boats, the property of private traders, afterwards separating from the rest, got hopelessly involved in the shallows, not very far from the Pawnee villages, and were soon surrounded by a swarm of the inhabitants. They carried off everything that they thought valuable, including most of the robes." F. Parkman, *The Oregon Trail* (1925 ed.), p. 88.

[2] *L. and C.* 1, 52, July 21, 1804.

[3] J. C. Frémont, *Report*, p. 78, September 15, 1842.

[4] "The water in the Platte was extremely low; in many places, the large expanse of sands, with some occasional stunted trees on the banks, gave it the air of the sea coast; the bed of the river being merely a succession of sandbars, among which the channel was divided into rivulets a few inches deep. We crossed and recrossed with our carts repeatedly and at our pleasure; and, whenever an obstruction barred our way, in the shape of precipitous bluffs that came down upon the river, we turned directly into it, and made our way along the sandy bed, with no other inconvenience than the frequent quicksands, which greatly fatigued our animals." J. C. Frémont, *Report*, p. 77.

In the south-west there are two drainage basins, the first being that of the *Arkansas and the Red Rivers*. These rivers are separated from the central Missouri basin by the Ozark plateau. The second drainage basin of the south-west, the *Rio Grande and Brazos Basin*, contains streams which flow direct into the Gulf of Mexico, the chief of which are the Rio Grande and its tributary the Pecos, the Colorado, and the Brazos.

All the rivers of the south-west are long and have drainage basins that are very small in relation to the length of the streams. The existence of such small basins in an arid region results in the drying up of the streams for long periods of the year.

The Arkansas formed for a 100 miles the main line of the Santa Fé trail, and a branch of the trail followed the river right up to the mountains. The trail followed the Cimarron for 90 miles. The Cimarron was always dry, but the few springs which existed along its banks were of great importance on the journey. The Canadian River was at first supposed to be the upper course of the Red River, and in 1820 Major Long discovered the distinction between the two rivers. Pike gives the following accounts of the Arkansas River:

The Arkansaw, on the party's arrival, had not water in it six inches deep, and the stream was not more than 20 feet wide; but the rain of the two days covered all the bottom of the river, which in this place is 450 yards from bank to bank. These are not more than four feet in height, bordered by a few cottonwood trees; on the north side is a low swampy prairie; on the south, a sandy sterile desert at a small distance. In the afternoon the doctor and myself took our horses and crossed the Arkansaw, in order to search for some trees which might answer the purpose to make canoes; found but one, and returned at dusk.[1]

The Arkansaw river, taking its meanders agreeably to Lieutenant Wilkinson's survey of the lower part, is 1981 miles from the entrance into the Mississippi to the mountains, and from thence to its source 192 miles, making its total length 2173 miles: all of which may be navigated with proper boats, constructed for the purpose, except the 192 miles in the mountains. It has emptying into it several small rivers navigable for 100 miles and upward. Boats bound up the whole length of the navigation should embark at its entrance on the 1st of February, when they would have the fresh (high water) quite to the mountains, and meet with no detention. But if they should start later, they would find the river 1500

[1] The Arkansas at its great bend. Z. M. Pike, *Expeditions*, II, 427-8, October 18, 1806.

miles up nearly dry. It has one singularity which struck me very forcibly at first view, but which, on reflection, I am induced to believe is the same case with all the rivers which run through a low, dry, sandy soil in warm climates, as I observed it to be the case with the Rio del Norte, viz.: for the extent of 400 or 500 miles before you arrive near the mountains, the bed of the river is extensive and a perfect sand-bar, which at certain seasons is dry, or at least the water is standing in ponds not affording sufficient to procure a running course; but when you come nearer the mountains you find the river contracted, a gravelly bottom, and a deep, navigable stream. From these circumstances it is evident that the sandy soil imbibes all the (not evaporated) waters which the sources project from the mountains, and renders the river in dry seasons less navigable 500 than 200 miles from its source.[1]

The *Rio Grande* is a typical river of the plains. It flows down in great torrents from the mountains and disappears in the plains, except at flood season. It is impossible to navigate this river. From the upper part of the valley, the overland trail left for California, and the valley was of great importance to the Santa Fé trail, as it contained the Spanish towns of Santa Fé and Taos.

When the Rockies had been crossed, the explorers would enter one of the three basins, the Columbia Basin, the Great Basin of Interior drainage, or the Colorado Basin.

The *Columbia Basin* extends southwards to include the great tributary of the Snake. The sources of the Snake are very much mixed with those of the Missouri and the Yellowstone. The Snake rises in Yellowstone Park at about the same height as the Missouri and reaches the ocean in half the distance. It is therefore a much more rapid stream than the Missouri, possesses a strong current, and is exceedingly difficult to cross.[2] Frémont gives a graphic account of the river on September 24, 1843.

The river here enters between low mural banks, which consist of a fine vesicular trap rock, the intermediate portions being compact and crystalline. Gradually becoming higher in its downward course, these banks of

[1] Z. M. Pike, *Expeditions*, II, 517–22.

[2] "The present valley of Snake River extends across Idaho in a semicircular course about 80 miles wide. Its course is underlain by lake beds and intercalated flows of basalt that slope gently from the bordering mountains to the axis of the valley. Into these beds the river has cut a sharp canyon 400 to 1000 feet deep, thus exposing the structure." I. Bowman, *Forest Physiography*, p. 197. This and five other passages in the next few pages are reprinted by permission from *Forest Physiography*, by Isaiah Bowman, published by John Wiley and Sons, Inc.

scoriated volcanic rock form, with occasional interruptions, its characteristic feature along the whole line to the Dalles of the Lower Columbia,
resembling a chasm which had been rent through the country, and which
the river had afterwards taken for its bed. The immediate valley of the
river is a high plain, covered with black rocks and artemisias. In the south
is a bordering range of mountains, which although not very high, are
broken and covered with snow....[1]

The constant succession of rapids makes the river unnavigable.
The Portneuf is an important tributary on the left bank, and
joins the main stream 15 miles above the American Falls. The
Oregon trail passed from the Bear River valley to the Snake by
means of the Portneuf, and the valley of this small river is used
by the railway to-day. Fort Hall was a key point, situated at
the junction of the Portneuf and the Snake. The Oregon trail
followed a right bank tributary, the Boisé, and then crossed the
Snake on its way over the Blue Mountains and so to the Columbia. The Snake is joined on the right by the Salmon and the
Clearwater Rivers, both good hunting grounds for beaver.
Near its junction with the Salmon River, the Snake passes
through an immense cañon 3000 feet deep. Only after its
junction with the Clearwater does the Snake become navigable.

The upper basin of the Columbia, part of which lies in
Canada, is a very complicated drainage system. The Columbia,
which flows in a deep gorge,[2] receives Clark's fork, and, lower
down, the Spokane.

When the Columbia has united with the Snake River, it
turns abruptly to the west. At the elbow, the river receives two
small tributaries from the south. These are the Walla-Walla and
the Umatilla, whose valleys were used by the Oregon trail. The
Columbia is joined by three further tributaries before it reaches
the sea, the John Day, the Deschutes, and the Willamette
Rivers. The Willamette drains the valley between the coast and
the Cascade ranges of mountains. The junction of this river
with the main stream was very important, and a British fort

[1] J. C. Frémont, *Report*, p. 164, near the American Falls.
[2] "The greatest difficulty in the utilization of the water of the Snake
and the Columbia arises from the fact that large stretches of these rivers
occur at great depths below the general level of the country. The Columbia
flows in a canyon with fairly abrupt walls sunk from 100 to 1000 feet below
the broad stretches east of it in Washington." I. Bowman, *op. cit.* p. 205.

(Fort Vancouver) was established here in the early years of the fur trade. The Columbia expands into a great estuary and finally passes over a dangerous bar into the Pacific. "The Columbia, or Oregon," says Washington Irving, "for the distance of thirty or forty miles from its entrance into the sea, is, properly speaking, a mere estuary, indented by deep bays so as to vary from three to seven miles in width; and is rendered extremely intricate and dangerous by shoals reaching nearly from shore to shore, on which, at times, the winds and currents produce foaming and tumultuous breakers. The mouth of the river proper is but about half a mile wide, formed by the contracting shores of the estuary."[1]

The Columbia is not continuously navigable throughout its course in the same way as the Missouri. Ocean vessels can ascend the river for 100 miles. Above this point there are a series of rapids,[2] the most famous of which are the Dalles and the Priest rapids, which compelled the use of difficult portages. It was possible to ascend the Snake River to about 30 miles above the junction with the Clearwater. Chittenden has estimated that there are in the basin more than 2000 miles of waterways navigable for small craft.

Interior Basin. To the west of the Colorado Basin lies an immense area of inland drainage, usually called the Great Basin, and covering an area of over 200,000 square miles (Fig. 13). Its most striking feature is the Great Salt Lake, which is exceedingly saline and has an area of about 2000 square miles. The lake is estimated to contain 400 million tons of common salt.[3] The present lake is a remnant of a lake which existed in quaternary times, and is known by geologists as Lake Bonneville. This lake was ten times the size of the present lake, and drained northwards to the Snake River. The following account of Great Salt Lake, written by Frémont in 1843, is of interest:

Carrying with us the barometer and other instruments, in the afternoon we ascended to the highest point of the island—a bare rocky peak, 800 feet

[1] W. Irving, *Astoria*, p. 63.
[2] For an account of these rapids, see W. Irving, *Astoria*, pp. 78–9, and *L. and C.* II, 670 ff.
[3] I. C. Russell, *North America* (1904), p. 142.

above the lake. Standing on the summit, we enjoyed an extended view of the lake, enclosed in a basin of rugged mountains, which sometimes left marshy flats and extensive bottoms between them and the shore, and in other places came directly down into the water with bold and precipitous bluffs. Following with our glasses the irregular shores, we searched for some indications of a communication with other bodies of water, or the entrance of other rivers; but the distance was so great that we could make out nothing with certainty. To the southward, several peninsular mountains, 3000 or 4000 feet high, entered the lake, appearing, so far as the distance and our position enabled us to determine, to be connected by flats and low ridges with the mountains in the rear. Although these are probably the islands usually indicated on maps of this region as entirely detached from the shore, we have preferred to represent them, in the small map on the preceding page, precisely as we were enabled to sketch them on the ground, leaving their more complete delineation for a future survey. The sketch, of which the scale is nearly sixteen miles to an inch, is introduced only to show clearly the extent of our operations, which, it will be remembered, were made when the waters were at their lowest stage. At the season of high waters in the spring, it is probable that all the marshes and low grounds are overflowed, and the surface of the lake considerably greater.[1]

The rivers which enter the Great Salt Lake all flow into its eastern shore. The Bear is the largest tributary;[2] its valley was used by the Oregon trail and is used by the railway at the present day. Weber River is another tributary on the eastern side of the lake, while the Jordan flows into it from Utah Lake, a body of fresh water lying to the south of Great Salt Lake. "The Utah", says Frémont, "is about thirty-five miles long, and is remarkable for the numerous and bold streams which it receives, coming down from the mountains, on the southeast, all fresh water."[3]

To the south of Utah Lake is Sevier Lake with its long tributary, the Sevier. The course of the Sevier is very similar to that of the Bear River. The lake is very shallow and very salt and formed a part of Lake Bonneville.

[1] J. C. Frémont, *Report*, p. 155, September 9, 1843. See also J. C. Frémont, *Geog. Memo.* pp. 8–9.

[2] "The Bear River, on the east, rising in the massive range of the Timpanogos mountains and falling into the Great Salt lake, after a doubling course through a fertile and picturesque valley, two hundred miles long." J. C. Frémont, *Geog. Memo.* p. 11.

[3] *Ibid.* p. 8.

On the eastern side of the Sierra Nevada are a series of lakes, Humboldt Lake, Pyramid Lake,[1] Carson Lake, Lake Tahoe, Mono Lake, Owen's Lake, and many others. "The number of small lakes is very great, many of them more or less salty, and all, like the rivers which feed them, changing their appearance and extent under the influence of the season, rising with the melting of the snows, sinking in the dry weather, and distinctly presenting their high and low water mark."[2]

The largest and most important river of the Great Basin is the Humboldt, which flows into Humboldt Lake. The California trail from South Pass passed along the banks of this river, which led directly to the Salmon Trout (Truckee) River. Frémont named this river Humboldt after the great scientist and gives the following description of it:

It is a very peculiar stream, and has many characteristics of an Asiatic river—the Jordan, for example, though twice as long—rising in mountains and losing itself in a lake of its own, after a long and solitary course. It rises in two streams in mountains west of the Great Salt Lake, which unite, after some fifty miles, and bears westwardly along the northern side of the basin towards the Great Sierra Nevada, which it is destined never to reach, much less to pass. The mountains in which it rises are round and handsome in their outline, capped with snow the greater part of the year, well clothed with grass and wood, and abundant in water. The stream is a narrow line, without affluents, losing by absorption and evaporation as it goes, and terminating in a marshy lake, with low shores, fringed with bulrushes, and whitened with saline encrustations. It has a moderate current, is from two to six feet deep in the dry season, and probably not fordable anywhere below the junction of the forks during the time of melting snows, when both lake and river are considerably enlarged. The country through which it passes (except its immediate valley) is a dry, sandy plain, without grass, wood, or arable soil; from about 4700 feet (at the forks) to 4200 feet (at the lake) above the level of the sea, winding among broken ranges of mountains, and varying from a few miles to twenty in breadth. Its own immediate valley is a rich alluvion, beautifully covered with blue grass, herd grass, clover, and other nutritious grasses; and its course is marked through the plain by a line of willow and cotton-

[1] "Pyramid Lake is thirty-five miles long, between four and five thousand feet above the sea, surrounded by mountains, is remarkably deep and clear, and abounds with uncommonly large salmon trout.... Lake Walker affords great numbers of trout and is a place of resort for Indians in the fishing season." *Ibid.* p. 9.

[2] J. C. Frémont, *Geog. Memo.* p. 9.

wood trees, serving for fuel. The Indians in the fall set fire to the grass and destroy all trees except in low grounds near the water.[1]

A number of rivers collect their water from the Sierra Nevada, flow down the eastern side of the mountains into the Great Basin, and find no outlet to the sea. In addition to Salmon Trout River, there are Carson and Walker Rivers, "both handsome clear water streams, nearly one hundred miles long, coming down the eastern flank of the Sierra Nevada, and joining lakes of their own name at its base".[2] Owen's River "is a large bold stream about one hundred and twenty miles long, gathering its waters in the Sierra Nevada, flowing to the southward and forming a lake about fifteen miles long at the base of the mountain".[3] Owen's Lake is between 4 and 15 feet deep.[4]

The southern section of the Great Basin is a natural desert where all water is carried away by evaporation. This is the region of Death Valley and the Mohave desert.

Colorado Basin. The sources of the Colorado are of interest. The Big Sandy River flowed from South Pass and formed a part

---

[1] J. C. Frémont, *Geog. Memo.* p. 10.

[2] *Ibid.* p. 11.

[3] *Ibid.* p. 11.

[4] Bowman explains the way in which the rivers of the Great Basin receive their water in the following words: "The chief rivers of the Great Basin receive their principal supply of water not from rainfall in their middle or lower courses but from melting snows in the mountains, as on the eastern and western borders of the basin. The stream discharge of the region is characteristic, the maximum occurring in the late spring or early summer, and a minimum during the winter months. The streams receive little or no additions after leaving the mountains, and diminish in size and often cease to flow at the surface. The streams which discharge eastward from the Sierra Nevada, such as the Carson and the Truckee, have an immense run-off, during the late spring, although the snows accumulate to a great depth in their thickly forested headwater regions and a considerable quantity is stored in natural lakes which supply water gradually to the streams into which they discharge....

"Those streams that are supplied by melting snows have great changes in volume from season to season, especially if the supply from springs is exceptionally deficient. Thus the Humboldt River derives its supply from the melting of snows in headwater regions, and the run-off during the spring and summer months is very heavy; but as soon as the snow is gone the rivers are left practically without a source of supply and their channels gradually become dry". I. Bowman, *op. cit.* pp. 216–17.

of the Oregon trail, while the upper basin of the Green River contained valuable supplies of furs. When the Green River has crossed the southern boundary of Wyoming, it flows due east, and on entering the State of Colorado, it turns abruptly to the south-west. The course of the Green River and of the Colorado (as Green River is called after its junction with Grand River), passes through a series of cañons, which are almost impossible to cross. The only important crossing was the one used by the Spanish trail to Los Angeles and is now used by a railway. The nature of the valley of the Colorado made it impossible as a route until it leaves the Grand Cañon near the mouth of Virgin River. However, the eastern tributaries of the Colorado, the San Juan, the Little Colorado and the Gila, provided service-able routes. From Santa Fé the crossing of the watershed between the Rio Grande and the Gila Basins was comparatively easy, and the Gila provided a direct route to San Diego. The more northern Spanish trail followed the upper waters of the Colorado, the Sevier River, and the Virgin River. The Grand Cañon itself proved to be an insuperable barrier to movement.

Sacramento and San Joaquin Basins. The great valley of California is drained by the Sacramento and the San Joaquin. These two streams unite and emerge in San Francisco Bay. The San Joaquin was described by Frémont in the following words: "To-day we touched several times the San Joaquin river—here a fine-looking, tranquil stream, with a slight current, and ap-parently deep. It resembled the Missouri in color, with occa-sional points of white sand; and its banks, where steep, were a kind of sandy clay; its average width appeared to be about eighty yards. In the bottoms are frequent ponds, where our approach disturbed multitudes of wild fowl, principally geese".[1]

One of the tributaries of the Sacramento, the Bear River, flows down from the Sierra Nevada. This river leads to the Truckee Pass (7017 feet), which was used by the California trail. Frémont describes the valley of the Sacramento as follows: "The valley of the Sacramento is divided into upper and lower— the lower two hundred miles long, the upper about one hundred;

---

[1] J. C. Frémont, *Report*, p. 250, April 3, 1844.

and the latter not merely entitled to the distinction of upper as being higher up on the river, but also as having a superior elevation of some thousands of feet above it".[1] The upper valley of the Sacramento or Pitt River led to Lassen's Pass, one of the passes which were used by the "forty-niners".

In the history of the exploration of the world, rivers have always been of primary importance as a controlling factor of the routes of pioneers. In no other region can this conclusion be so clearly proved as in the western half of the United States.

[1] J. C. Frémont, *Geog. Memo.* p. 25.

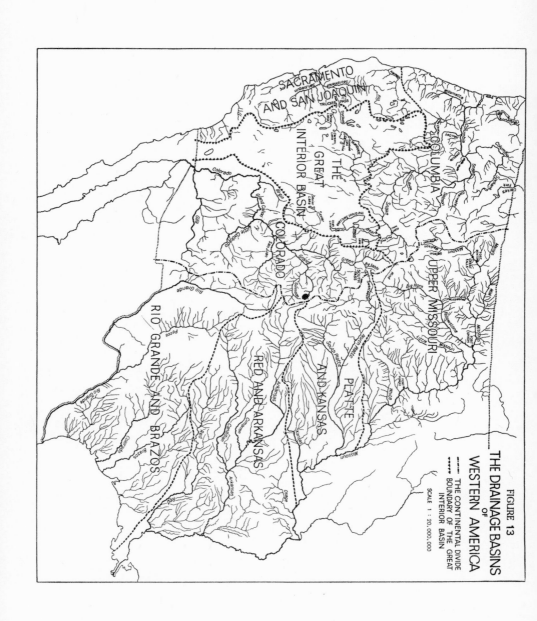

FIGURE 13
THE DRAINAGE BASINS
OF
WESTERN AMERICA

—·—·— THE CONTINENTAL DIVIDE
✦✦✦✦ BOUNDARY OF THE GREAT
INTERIOR BASIN

SCALE 1 : 20,000,000

Chapter VI

THE NATURAL VEGETATION OF THE REGION

The United States can be divided into three forest belts, Atlantic, Rocky Mountain and Pacific. The central or Rocky Mountain forest is separated from the other forests by a belt of desert on the west and a belt of grassland on the east.[1]

B. E. Livingston and F. Shreve have constructed a generalised map of the vegetation of the United States of America,[2] which forms a useful basis for a discussion of the distribution of vegetation. A generalised map of this kind is particularly valuable in a study of the influence of vegetation on the history of the exploration of the area, as the great mass of information contained on a detailed map is apt to obscure the main influences. The area under consideration in this book is shown on Fig. 14, and the vegetation regions are numbered. On the east there are three distinct areas of forest, none of which greatly concern this book and can be summarily treated.

REGION I. THE SOUTH-EASTERN EVERGREEN FOREST. This forest region is not very dense and is largely composed of evergreen needle-leaved trees with an admixture of deciduous broad-leaved trees.[3]

[1] This general arrangement is well described by Bowman in the following words: "A single unbroken forest belt extends across North America, the spruce forest of Canada... southward from this broad transcontinental forest belt are an Atlantic forest, a Pacific forest and a Rocky Mountain forest. The two intervening belts of country—the Great Plains and the Great Basin—are forestless though not treeless. This distribution is controlled largely by rainfall, though the distribution of species within each region is also controlled by insolation, temperature, wind velocity, water supply and geographic relation to postglacial centers of dispersal". I. Bowman, op. cit. p. 123.

[2] B. E. Livingston and F. Shreve, The Distribution of Vegetation in the United States as related to the Climatic Conditions (1921), plate 2, p. 47.

[3] The pinelands of the Gulf region are said "to present a very clean floor, carpeted by grasses, palmetto, pitcher-plants, and a multitude of other herbaceous species". B. E. Livingston and F. Shreve, op. cit. p. 40.

REGION II. DECIDUOUS FOREST. This forest formerly occupied a considerable part of the Mississippi valley and extended to the southern Appalachians. Before the settlement of the area by whites, it formed an unbroken forest of deciduous trees. A few prairies occurred in the southern part of the area, and evergreen needle-leaved trees occupied areas of shallow soil. The common trees are oak, hickory, chestnut, beech, maple, walnut, and ash.

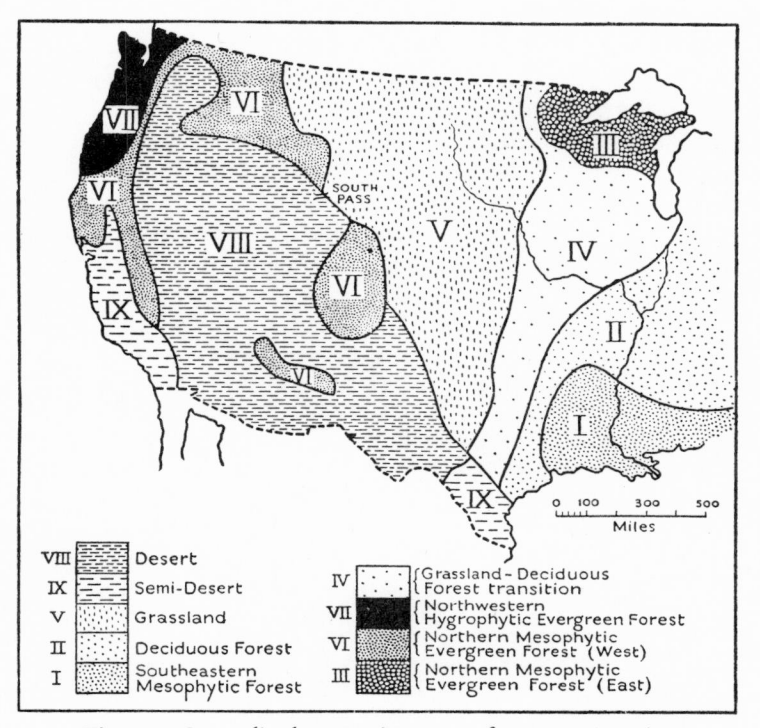

Fig. 14. Generalised vegetation map of western America
(after B. E. Livingston and F. Shreve)

REGION III. THE NORTHERN EVERGREEN FOREST (East) consists of the States of Michigan, Wisconsin and northern Minnesota. This forest is composed chiefly of needle-leaved trees with an admixture of broad-leaved trees. The common

trees are white pine, jack pine, black and white spruce, bur oak, basswood, and sugar maple.

The explorers left one of these three forest regions behind them as they moved towards the west and crossed REGION IV, the transition area between Deciduous forest and Grassland. This region is an ill-defined area in which deciduous forest occupies a part of the upland. On the western side of the belt there is a very large proportion of grassland while on the eastern side deciduous forest is predominant, the principal trees being bur oak and black oak.

REGION V. GRASSLAND. The vast area of the Plains is covered by a more or less closed sod of perennial grasses, becoming more open towards the south and towards the north-west. A scattered representation of desert forms is present, particularly in the "bad lands". Deciduous trees advance from the east into the area along the valleys of the largest streams, while evergreen forests encroach on it from the west. Neverthe-less, the vegetation is characterised by great uniformity.[1]

The origin of the Prairies has been hotly disputed. The explorer Pike explains the origin of the "vast tract of untimbered country which lies between the waters of the Missouri, Missis-sippi and the Western Ocean, from the mouth of the latter river to 40° north Latitude", in the following words:

In that vast country of which I speak, we find the soil generally dry and sandy, with gravel, and discover that the moment we approach a stream the land becomes more humid, with small timber. I therefore conclude that this country never was timbered; as from the earliest age the aridity of the soil, having so few water-courses running through it, and they being principally dry in summer, has never afforded moisture sufficient to support the growth of timber. In all timbered land the annual discharge of the leaves, with the continual decay of old trees and branches, creates a manure and moisture, which is preserved from the heat of the sun not being per-mitted to direct his rays perpendicularly, but only to shed them obliquely through the foliage. But here a barren soil, parched and dried up for eight months in the year, presents neither moisture nor nutrition sufficient to nourish the timber. These vast plains of the western hemisphere may

[1] The monotony of nature was reflected by a monotony of human life. "Rarely an incident occurred to vary the monotonous resemblance which one day on the prairies here bears to another, and which scarcely require a particular description." J. C. Frémont, *Report*, pp. 107–8.

become in time as celebrated as the sandy deserts of Africa; for I saw in my route, in various places, tracts of many leagues where the wind had thrown up the sand in all the fanciful forms of the ocean's rolling wave, and on which not a speck of vegetable matter existed.

But from these immense prairies may arise one great advantage to the United States, viz.: the restriction of our population to some certain limits, and thereby a continuation of the Union. Our citizens being so prone to rambling and extending themselves on the frontiers will, through necessity, be constrained to limit their extent on the west to the borders of the Missouri and Mississippi, while they leave the prairies incapable of cultivation to the wandering and uncivilised aborigines of the country.[1]

Pike's conclusions have been entirely falsified by events.

After reviewing all the different theories[2] which have been brought forward to explain the origin of the prairies, Harshberger concludes:

that the prairie soils, however, originating as loess, were at once tenanted by grass vegetation, because in proximity in nearby plant formations. Once a prairie soil was formed, trees were unable to encroach upon it, except where by erosion in the stream valleys the dense turf was broken, or at the base of cliffs, and elsewhere, where loose talus, or stony ground prevented the grass vegetation from making a close mat.... Another cause that operated in the past to prevent trees from extending in the prairies was the presence of millions of buffaloes in the region. The buffalo severely grazed the grasses and kept them in close mats. The buffaloes likewise attracted the Indians, who set fire to the grass, thus confining the trees to the river banks, mountains, and broken lands.[3]

Fires were frequently caused by the carelessness of white travellers,[4] as well as by the Indians.

[1] Z. M. Pike, *Expeditions*, II, 524–5.

[2] The cause of prairies has been "traced to the fineness of the loess, the direction of the strong prevailing southwest winds, inimic to tree growth; the occupancy of a recent submerged area by grass vegetation after the recession of the water; the peculiar chemic character of the soil; the character of the climate; the underlying geologic formations". J. W. Harshberger, *Phytogeographic Survey of North America*, vol. XIII of *Die Vegetation der Erde*, ed. A. Engler and O. Drude (1911), p. 516.

[3] J. W. Harshberger, *op. cit.* pp. 516–7. The burning of the prairie is mentioned by Lewis and Clark. "The ground, having been recently burnt by the Indians, is covered with young green grass." *L. and C.* I, 119, September 16, 1804.

[4] "Our fire was carelessly permitted to communicate with the prairie grass. As there was a head-wind blowing at the time, we very soon got out of the reach of the conflagration: but the next day, the wind having changed, the fire was again perceived in our rear approaching us at a very brisk pace." J. Gregg, *Commerce of the Prairies*, E.W.T. XX, 205.

The grass is longer in the east than in the west, and grows earlier in the east.[1] The shorter grass of the west does not grow until the summer rains.[2] Travel over these plains was unhindered by any obstacles of natural vegetation. "Eastward of that meridian" (Fort Laramie), says Frémont, "the principal objects which strike the eye of a traveller are the absence of timber, and the immense expanse of prairie, covered with the verdure of rich grasses, and highly adapted for pasturage. Wherever they are not disturbed by the vicinity of man, large herds of buffalo give animation to this country."[3] According to Frémont the "prairie" extended "almost directly to the bases"[4] of the Rocky Mountains. When at a distance of 40 miles from Pike's Peak, Frémont describes the prairies in the following words: "An immense and comparatively smooth and grassy prairie, in very strong contrast with the black masses of timber and the glittering snow above them.... With occasional exceptions, comparatively so very small as not to require mention, these prairies are every where covered with a close and vigorous growth of great variety of grasses, among which the most abundant is the buffalo grass".[5]

REGION VI. THE NORTHERN EVERGREEN FOREST (WEST) consists of part of the Pacific coast (north of San Francisco), the Sierra Nevada and Cascades, all but the Alpine portion of the Rocky Mountains, above 6000 to 7000 feet, and the higher summits of all the coastal and inland mountain ranges of the western States. This large area is characterised throughout by a pure stand of needle-leaved evergreen trees, although deciduous trees may be present in small numbers. Virgin stands of this

[1] "The buffalo are usually found much further east early in the spring, than during the rest of the year, on account of the long grass, which shoots up earlier in the season than the short pasturage of the plains." J. Gregg, op. cit. E.W.T. XIX, 205.

[2] "The country which, when we passed up, looked as if the hard winter frosts had passed over it, had now assumed a new face, so much of vernal freshness had been given to it by the late rains." J. C. Frémont, Report, p. 77, August 27, 1842.

[3] J. C. Frémont, Report, p. 49.

[4] Ibid. p. 114.

[5] Ibid.

forest range from 60 to 125 feet in height and vary from open formation to heavy forest with a completely shaded floor. The forest is made up of a very large number of species of trees. Some extensive areas are formed of one single species and others of three or four species only. In the western half of the area, the yellow pine, the red fir, and the lodge-pole pine are the dominant trees.

In the Rocky Mountains spruce grows luxuriantly at heights of between 8000 and 10,000 feet and at lower altitudes yellow pine and red fir are predominant.[1] The difficulty of crossing the northern Rocky Mountains was increased by the timber. Lewis and Clark frequently complained of the fallen timber as a cause of delay. When near the source of Clark's River they write that "the road had been very bad during the first part of the day, but the passage of the mountain, which was eight miles across, was very painful to the horses, as we were obliged to go over steep, stony sides of hills and along the hollows and ravines, rendered more disagreeable by fallen timber, chiefly pine, spruce-pine, and fir".[2] When snow remained in the trees the difficulty of travel was still further accentuated and Lewis and Clark say: "The road was, like that of yesterday, along steep hillsides, obstructed with fallen timber and a growth of eight different species of pine, so thickly strewed that the snow fell from them as we passed; this kept us continually wet to the skin, and so cold that we were anxious lest our feet should be frozen, as we had only thin moccasins to defend them".[3]

The forests of Colorado are not continuous with the forests of the northern Rocky Mountains. The zone between the two areas of forest contained the South Pass, the absence of trees

---

[1] The forest "is much broken into forest islands by the restricted areas of mountain land which are sufficiently high to provoke an adequate rainfall from the prevailing westerly winds". I. Bowman, *op. cit.* p. 126.

[2] *L. and C.* II, 593, September 12, 1805. When crossing the Bitter Root Mountains by the Lo Lo Pass the explorers wrote the following description: "The mountains which we crossed to-day were much more difficult than those of yesterday; the last was particularly fatiguing, being steep and stony, broken by fallen timber, and thickly overgrown by pine, spruce, fir, hackmatack and tamarac". *L. and C.* II, 596, September 14, 1805.

[3] *L. and C.* II, 598, September 16, 1805.

being one of the main reasons for the early pre-eminence of that pass. In the south, in New Mexico, there are considerable areas of isolated forest on the mountains,[1] but only in the north are the forests of the Sierra-Cascade Mountains continuous with the forests of the Rockies. The northern Rocky Mountains have a considerable westward extension of forest, namely the forest of the Blue Mountains, which Frémont describes in the following words: "Resuming our journey, we commenced the ascent of the mountain through an open pine forest of large and stately trees, among which the balsam pine made its appearance".[2] Frémont also gives the following account of the forests of the Sierra Nevada, which he crossed in 1844:

The forest here has a noble appearance: the tall cedar is abundant; its greatest height being 130 feet, and circumference 20, three or four feet above the ground; and here I see for the first time the white pine, of which there are some magnificent trees. Hemlock spruce is among the timber, occasionally as large as 8 feet in diameter four feet above the ground; but, in ascending, it tapers rapidly to less than one foot at the height of 80 feet. I have not seen any higher than 130 feet, and the slight upper part is frequently broken off by the wind. The white spruce is frequent; and the red pine (*pinus colorado* of the Mexicans) which constitutes the beautiful forest along the flanks of the Sierra Nevada to the northward, is here the principal tree, not attaining a greater height than 140 feet, though with sometimes a diameter of 10. Most of these trees appeared to differ slightly from those of the same kind on the other side of the continent.[3]

Frémont's journey was considerably delayed by the forest and by the snow retained by the trees. In his *Geographical Memoir*, Frémont describes the western side of the Sierra Nevada in the following words: "Timber holds the first part in the advantages of this slope, the whole being heavily wooded, first with oaks, which predominate to about half the elevation of the mountain; and then with pines, cypress, and cedars, the pines predominating; and hence, called the pine region, as that below is called

---

[1] "The lower elevations of the mountains of the Trans-Pecos region cause the forest to disappear or to become restricted to a few higher ranges." I. Bowman, *op. cit.* p. 126.

[2] J. C. Frémont, *Report*, p. 180.

[3] *Ibid.* p. 233.

the oak region, though mixed with other trees. The highest summits of the Sierra are naked, massive granite rock, covered with snow, in sheltered places, all the year round".[1]

REGION VII. THE NORTH-WESTERN EVERGREEN FOREST.[2] This forest occupies the central region of Washington, Oregon, and northern California and is characterised by the density of the stand and the size of the trees, which are generally 100 to 125 feet in height and often greater.[3] The floor of the forest is heavily shaded and supports very few deciduous undertrees. Nevertheless, there is usually a rich growth of shrubs, ferns, mosses, and other herbaceous plants. The characteristic tree is the Douglas fir associated with red fir, redwood, black hemlock, red cedar, and white fir.[4] The shaded floor of the forest is frequently covered with fallen trunks and boughs overgrown with mosses, which were a great obstacle to movement. The whole area was one in which travel was exceedingly difficult as the undergrowth was in many places almost impenetrable. In the words of Lewis and Clark:

The whole lower country was covered with almost impenetrable thickets of small pine, with which is mixed a species of plant resembling arrowwood, 12 or 15 feet high, with a thorny stem, almost interwoven with each other, and scattered among the fern and fallen timber. There is also a red berry, somewhat like Solomon's seal, which is called by the natives solme and used as an article of diet. This thick growth rendered travelling almost impossible, and it was made more fatiguing by the steepness of the mountain, which was so great as to oblige him to draw himself up by means of

[1] J. C. Frémont, *Geog. Memo.* p. 28.

[2] *L. and C.* III, 821–39, contains a comprehensive account of the vegetation of this region.

[3] Lewis and Clark describe the forest in the following words: "The hills along the coast are high and steep; the general covering is a growth of lofty pines of different species, some of which rise more than 200 feet, and are 10 or 12 feet in diameter near the root. Besides these trees we observe on the point a species of ash, the alder, the laurel, one species of wild crab, and several kinds of underbrush, among which rosebushes are conspicuous". *L. and C.* II, 724, November 30, 1805.

[4] *L. and C.* III, 829–33, describe the following seven species of pines on the Pacific Coast: (1) *Abies nobilis* (red fir), (2) *Tsuga mertensiana* (hemlock spruce), (3) *Thuja gigantea*, (4) probably *Abies grandis* (great white fir), (5) *Pseudotsuga douglasi* (Douglas fir), (6) *Pinus lambertiana* (giant white pine), (7) *Picea sitchensis* (spruce).

the bushes. The timber on the hills is chiefly of a large tall species of pine, many of them 8 or 10 feet in diameter at the stump, and rising sometimes more than 100 feet in height.[1]

REGION VIII. DESERT lies between the Rocky Mountain forests and the Sierra Nevada. The desert contains two principal types of vegetation, creosote-bush and sage-bush.

The sage-bush (*Artemisia*) occupies the floor and low mountains of the Great Basin and extends from southern Washington to southern Nevada and east to Colorado. The *Artemisia* is a small evergreen shrub, which is sometimes only a few inches high, but generally covers the ground to a height of 4 feet or more. Lewis and Clark describe the northern part of this area where the Snake joins the Columbia in the following words: "There is on this plain no tree, and scarcely any shrubs, except a few willow-bushes; even of smaller plants there is not much more than the prickly-pear, which is in great abundance, and is even more thorny and troublesome than any we have yet seen".[2] The valley of the Snake was chiefly composed of sage-bush desert.[3] The Great Basin itself consists of mountain ranges and valleys between them. The ranges are "thinly wooded with some varieties of pine, (*pinus monophyllus* characteristic), cedar, aspen, and a few other trees; and afford an excellent quality of bunch grass, equal to any found in the Rocky mountains".[4] In the Basin these scattered patches of forest contain trees between 25 and 50 feet in height, the chief type being Juniper. "Sterility", says Frémont, "is the absolute characteristic of the valleys between the mountains [in the Great Basin], no wood, no water, no grass; the gloomy artemisia the prevailing shrub—no animals".[5]

The creosote-bush occupies the southern part of Nevada and the interior of California. In the Californian desert the creosote-bush and the sand-bur are the dominant plants. Short-lived

---

[1] *L. and C.* II, 706–7, November 13, 1805.
[2] *L. and C.* II, 637, October 17, 1805.
[3] "We were now about to leave the valley of the great southern branch of the Columbia river, to which the absence of timber, and the scarcity of water, give the appearance of a desert." J. C. Frémont, *Report*, p. 175.
[4] J. C. Frémont, *Geog. Memo.* p. 12.   [5] *Ibid.*

annuals are abundant in the spring months. Frémont illustrates this in his account of the Mohave Desert, which he describes thus: "The country had now assumed the character of an elevated and mountainous desert; its general features being black, rocky ridges, bald, and destitute of timber, with sandy basins between.... But, throughout the nakedness of sand and gravel, were many beautiful plants and flowering shrubs, which occurred in many new species, and with greater variety than we had been accustomed to see in the most luxuriant prairie countries; this was a peculiarity of this desert".[1]

REGION IX. SEMI-DESERT is represented by two disconnected areas. In southern Texas it consists of an open or closed stand of small trees and shrubs, chiefly deciduous, with local areas of grassland, the dominant tree being mesquite. The Pacific semi-desert is a region in which the vegetation varies from encinal (open oak forest) through chaparral to desert. The chaparral is sometimes a very low shrub and sometimes 6–7 feet in height. These trees were generally so close together that the region could only be traversed with difficulty.

It is interesting to consider the value of the natural vegetation to the explorer. Before leaving Regions I, II and IV, on a westward journey, the traveller usually obtained what timber he required. On the Santa Fé trail the last point for obtaining good wood was Council Grove. "During our delay at the Council Grove", says Gregg, "the laborers were employed in procuring timber for axle-trees and other wagon repairs, of which a supply is always laid in before leaving this region of substantial growths; for henceforward there is no wood on the route fit for these purposes; not even in the mountains of Santa Fé do we meet with any serviceable timber."[2] When travelling up the Missouri the traveller laid in a stock of ash for oars before passing the mouth of the Platte, as ash could not be obtained higher up the river. Lewis and Clark describe the country between St Louis and the junction of the Platte with the Missouri in the following words: "The country on the north of the river

[1] J. C. Frémont, *Report*, pp. 261–2.
[2] J. Gregg, *Commerce of the Prairies*, E.W.T. XIX, 201.

is rich and covered with timber; among which we procured the ash for oars. At two miles it changes into extensive prairies, and at seven or eight miles' distance becomes higher and waving. The prairie and high lands on the south commence more immediately on the river; the whole is well watered and provided with game, such as deer, elk, and bear".[1]

The cottonwood tree grew along the banks of the Missouri and its western tributaries for a great distance across the plains and was the only vegetation of any value to the traveller.[2] "In the meadows and along the shore", say Lewis and Clark, "the tree most common is the cottonwood, which, with the willow, forms almost the exclusive growth of the Missouri".[3] The cottonwood provided shelter, fuel, logs for huts, and food for horses.[4] The bark of the cottonwood was frequently the only food of the animals, while its timber was used in the construction of log canoes. It was an inferior wood but, as it was the only timber available, necessity compelled the traveller to use it.

The pines of the Rocky Mountains made a good fuel, but they were chiefly important as a hindrance to travel. They generally contained no game and the fact that they still held the winter snow in the spring made them a considerable obstacle.

The sage-bush of the Interior Basin was not a good fuel, but

[1] *L. and C.* I, 26–7, June 17, 1804. See also W. Irving, *Astoria*, p. 127: "After passing the Nebraska [Platte], the party halted for part of two days on the bank of the river, a little above Papillion Creek, to supply themselves with a stock of oars and poles from the tough wood of the ash, which is not met with higher up the Missouri".

[2] The cottonwood "deserves to be called the tree of the desert—growing in sandy soils, where no other tree will grow; pointing out the existence of water, and furnishing to the traveller fuel, and food for his animals". J. C. Frémont, *Report*, p. 115.

[3] *L. and C.* II, 516, August 18, 1805.

[4] "When the round leaf or sweet-bark cottonwood can be had abundantly, horses may be wintered but with little inconvenience. They are very fond of this bark, and, judging by the effect produced from feeding it to my horses last winter, I suppose it almost, if not quite, as nutricious as Timothy hay." Ashley, 1827, in H. C. Dale, *Ashley-Smith Explorations* (1918), pp. 137–8.

could be used as a shelter in a storm. The prickly pear injured the feet of travellers and their animals but it was often used as a food.

In the history of the exploration of the region, the vegetation must primarily be counted as an obstacle to human movement. With few exceptions, the most important being the cottonwood, the natural vegetation was not a great material assistance to the explorer.

Chapter VII

THE ANIMALS OF THE REGION[1]

"Animals are *par éminence* the communities of the Prairies."[2]
GREGG, Commerce of the Prairies.

The distribution of animals exerted a considerable influence on the exploration of western America. The main object of many of the explorers of this region was the collection of furs, a trade which brought great wealth to the successful. Animals, particularly the buffalo, provided the explorer with food, while bears were a source of danger to human movement. Thus the animals may be considered in the following categories: the beaver as wealth, the buffalo as food, and the bear as a hindrance.

THE BEAVER (*Castor canadensis*). In the year 1800 the whole of America, west of the Mississippi, was swarming with beavers. "The Beaver seems to have chosen this country for his own", says de Smet.[3] The animal lived along the banks of the rivers and streams, wherever there was any vegetation. As each animal was worth anything between four and eight dollars, the trapping of these animals was an extraordinarily remunerative occupation and a powerful incentive to exploration. The beaver lived in houses constructed along the banks of streams, with passages which opened into the water. If the water was too shallow to conceal the opening, the beaver constructed dams to increase the depth of the water. On September 5, 1804, when near the junction of the Niobrara and Missouri Rivers, Lewis and Clark recorded that "near the mouth of this creek the beaver had made a dam across so as to form a large pond, in which they

[1] This chapter is reprinted, with slight modifications, from an article entitled "Animal Life and the Exploration of Western America", which appeared in *Scottish Geographical Magazine*, XLVII (January, 1931), 19–28.
[2] J. Gregg, *Commerce of the Prairies*, E.W.T. XX, 259.
[3] P. J. de Smet, S.J., *Letters and Sketches* (1843), E.W.T. XXVII, 260.

built their houses ".[1] They also described how effective this dam may be in altering the course of a river.

We saw many otter and beaver to-day. The latter seem to contribute very much to the number of islands and the widening of the river. They begin by damming up the small channels of about 20 yards between the islands; this obliges the river to seek another outlet, and as soon as this is effected the channel stopped by the beaver becomes filled with mud and sand. The industrious animal is then driven to another channel, which soon shares the same fate, till the river spreads on all sides, and cuts the projecting points of the land into islands.[2]

The beaver could cut down quite large trees to make his dam and build his home.

Captain Bonneville gives an excellent account of some hours which he spent watching beaver making a dam, but he concludes that they have not the great skill in cutting the trees with which they are sometimes credited.

I have often [says Captain Bonneville] seen trees measuring eighteen inches in diameter, at the places where they had been cut through by the beaver, but they lay in all directions, and often very inconveniently for the after purposes of the animal. In fact, so little ingenuity do they at times display in this particular, that at one of our camps on Snake River, a beaver was found with his head wedged into the cut which he had made, the tree having fallen upon him and held him prisoner until he died.[3]

The trappers naturally acquired a complete knowledge of the life of these animals, and were very expert at capturing them by means of their steel traps.

Practice [says Captain Bonneville] has given such a quickness of eye to the experienced trapper in all that relates to his pursuit, that he can detect the slightest sign of beaver, however wild; and although the lodge may be concealed by close thickets and overhanging willows, he can generally, at a single glance, make an accurate guess at the number of its inmates. He now goes to work to set his trap; planting it upon the shore, in some chosen place, two or three inches below the surface of the water, and secures it by a chain to a pole set deep in the mud. A small twig is then stripped of its bark, and one end is dipped in the "medicine", as the trappers term the peculiar bait which they employ.[4]

[1] *L. and C.* I, 108.
[2] *Ibid.* II, 436–7, July 24, 1805.
[3] W. Irving, *Adventures of Captain Bonneville* (1850), p. 142.
[4] *Ibid.* p. 143.

The only part of the beaver which was used as food was the tail, but this was one of the greatest delicacies. Beaver pelts were exported to Europe at the rate of 200,000 per annum, and the animals were rapidly being exterminated. With a change of fashions in Europe the price of beaver fell, and as trapping did not remain so profitable the animal was not so completely exterminated as was the buffalo. Many other animals were hunted for their fur, especially the muskrat, the skins of which were exported to England in large numbers.

THE BUFFALO OR AMERICAN BISON (*Bos americanus*) (see Title-page). The buffalo provided almost everything that the Indians and trappers required. They were distributed over the whole area of the plains, but "seldom range beyond the South Pass, and never west of Green river".[1] Pike found these animals in the mountains of Colorado in the winter, so that it appears that they were not troubled by snow.[2]

Every part of the buffalo was used by the Indian, and a whole volume could be written on this subject. Gregg says "the animal furnishes almost the exclusive food of the prairie Indians, as well as covering for their wigwams and most of their clothing; also their bedding, ropes, bags for their meat, etc.; sinews for bowstrings, for sewing moccasins, leggins, and the like".[3] To the white explorer the buffalo was valuable as food, as a means of making boats, and as fuel. "The flesh of the buffalo", says Gregg, "is, I think, as fine as any meat I ever tasted: the old hunter will not admit that there is anything equal to it."[4] The references in the accounts of expeditions to shooting of buffalo for daily food are innumerable. The tongue of the buffalo was the best part of the animal for eating, but several other parts of its body were regarded as delicacies.

Frémont gives an account of the way in which boats were constructed from the animal. He says that they

spent two days in the construction of a bull boat. Men were sent out on the evening of our arrival, the necessary number of bulls killed, and their

[1] Joel Palmer, *Journal of Travels over the Rocky Mountains* (1847), E.W.T. xxx, 260.
[2] Z. M. Pike, *Expeditions*, II, 472, December 24, 1806.
[3] J. Gregg, *op. cit.* E.W.T. xx, 264.   [4] *Ibid.* xx, 263.

skins brought to the camp. Four of the best of them were strongly sewed together with buffalo sinew, and stretched over a basket frame of willow. The seams were then covered with ashes and tallow, and the boat left exposed to the sun for the greater part of one day, which was sufficient to dry and contract the skin, and make the whole work solid and strong. It had a rounded bow, was eight feet long and five broad, and drew with four men about four inches water.[1]

In regions where wood was scarce, the dry excrement of the buffalo formed an admirable fuel, and there are frequent references to its use in the journals of explorers. On July 19, 1805, Lewis and Clark wrote: "Such was the want of wood in the neighborhood that he was unable to procure enough to make a fire, and was therefore obliged to substitute the dung of the buffalo, with which he cooked his breakfast".[2] Frémont on July 3, 1842, when near the junction of the north and south Platte Rivers, wrote: "Our fires were partially made of the *bois de vache*, the dry excrement of the buffalo, which, like that of the camel in the Arabian deserts, furnishes to the traveller a very good substitute for wood, burning like turf".[3]

The buffalo hunt was an important event in the lives of the Indians and trappers. The animals were not fierce beasts despite their appearance. They moved about in great herds, and when in movement they terrified the inexperienced observer. Gregg says: "Their advance is somewhat frightful—their thundering rumble over the dry plain—their lion-like fronts and dangling beards—their open mouths and hanging tongues—as they come on, puffing like a locomotive engine at every bound, does at first make the blood settle a little heavy about the heart".[4]

METHODS OF HUNTING BUFFALO. The Indians had various methods of hunting the animal. One method was to hunt on horseback, and to surround the animals by an attack on all sides. Another method was to decoy a great herd to the edge of a precipice. The buffalo would then push each other over the edge, large numbers being killed. The "surround" method of hunting is described in the following passage:

[1] J. C. Frémont, *Report*, p. 78.   [2] *L. and C.* II, 424.
[3] J. C. Frémont, *Report*, p. 22.
[4] J. Gregg, *op. cit.* E.W.T. xx, 270–1.

Captain Clark with 15 men went out and found the Indians engaged in killing buffalo. The hunters, mounted on horseback and armed with bows and arrows, encircle the herd and gradually drive them into a plain or an open place fit for the movement of horse; they then ride in among them, and singling out a buffalo, a female being preferred, go as close as possible and wound her with arrows till they think they have given the mortal stroke; when they pursue another, till the quiver is exhausted. If, which rarely happens, the wounded buffalo attacks the hunter, he evades the blow by the agility of his horse, which is trained for the combat with great dexterity. When they have killed the requisite number they collect their game, and the squaws and attendants come up from the rear and skin and dress the animals.[1]

The method of hunting by which great herds were enticed over precipices is described as follows:

On the north we passed a precipice about 120 feet high, under which lay scattered the fragments of at least 100 carcasses of buffaloes, although the water which had washed away the lower part of the hill must have carried off many of the dead. These buffaloes had been chased down the precipice in a way very common on the Missouri, by which vast herds are destroyed in a moment. The mode of hunting is to select one of the most active and fleet young men, who is disguised by a buffalo-skin round his body; the skin of the head with ears and horns be'ng fastened on his own head in such way as to deceive the buffalo. Thus dressed, he fixes himself at a convenient distance between a herd of buffalo and any of the river precipices, which sometimes extend for some miles. His companions in the meantime get in the rear and side of the herd, and at a given signal show themselves and advance towards the buffaloes. These instantly take the alarm, and finding the hunters beside them, they run toward the disguised Indian or decoy, who leads them on at full speed toward the river; when, suddenly securing himself in some crevice of the cliff which he had previously fixed on, the herd is left on the brink of the precipice. It is then in vain for the foremost buffaloes to retreat or even to stop; they are pressed on by the hindmost rank, which, seeing no danger but from the hunters, goad on those before them till the whole are precipitated, and the shore is strewn with their dead bodies. Sometimes, in this perilous seduction, the Indian himself is either trodden under foot by the rapid movements of the buffaloes, or missing his footing in the cliff is urged down the precipice by the falling herd. The Indians then select as much meat as they wish; the rest is abandoned to the wolves, and creates a most dreadful stench. The wolves which had been feasting on these carcasses were very fat, and so gentle, that one of them was killed with an espontoon.[2]

The trappers and explorers hunted the buffalo by stalking a herd and shooting the animals which they thought looked to be

[1] *L. and C.* I, 209, December 7, 1804.
[2] *L. and C.* I, 334–5, May 29, 1805.

the best. A hunter could shoot at least half a dozen before the animals would have the intelligence to move away. In the spring, when the ice was in the Missouri, hundreds of buffalo would be stranded on the moving ice and captured. Lewis and Clark describe the method of capture.

We have had few Indians at the fort for the last three or four days, as they are now busy in catching the floating buffalo. Every spring, as the river is breaking up, the surrounding plains are set on fire, and the buffalo are tempted to cross the river in search of the fresh grass which immediately succeeds the burning. On their way they are often insulated on a large cake or mass of ice, which floats down the river. The Indians now select the most favorable point for attack, and, as the buffalo approaches, dart with astonishing agility across the trembling ice, sometimes pressing lightly a cake of not more than two feet square. The animal is of course unsteady, and his footsteps are insecure on this new element, so that he can make but little resistance; and the hunter, who has given him his death-wound, paddles his icy boat to the shore and secures his prey.[1]

NUMBERS OF BUFFALO. It is difficult to realise the immense number of these animals which roamed over the region during this period. All travellers were impressed with the size of the herds. Pike estimated that he saw 3000 buffalo at one time on the Arkansas.[2] "The face of the prairie", he says, "was covered with them, on each side of the river; their numbers exceeded imagination."[3] Captain Clark believed that he saw 10,000 buffalo at one view.[4] Frémont states that "a few miles brought us into the midst of the buffalo, swarming in immense numbers over the plains, where they had left scarcely a blade of grass standing.... In the sight of such a mass of life, the traveller feels a strange emotion of grandeur".[5] Catlin witnessed the crossing of a river by one of these great herds, and describes the event in the following words:

We met immense numbers of buffaloes in the early part of our voyage, and used to land our canoe almost every hour of the day; and oftentimes all together approach the unsuspecting herds, through some deep and hidden ravine within a few rods of them, and at the word "pull trigger", each of

[1] *L. and C.* I, 249, March 29, 1805.
[2] Z. M. Pike, *Expeditions*, II, 438.
[3] *Ibid.* II, 440.
[4] *L. and C.* II, 397, June 30, 1805.
[5] J. C. Frémont, *Report*, pp. 18–19.

us bring down our victim....In one instance, near the mouth of White River, we met the most immense herd crossing the Missouri River, and from an imprudence got our boat into imminent danger amongst them, from which we were highly delighted to make our escape. It was in the midst of the "running season", and we had heard the "roaring" (as it is called) of the herd when we were several miles from them. When we came in sight, we were actually terrified at the immense numbers that were streaming down the green hills on one side of the river, and galloping up and over the bluffs on the other. The river was filled, and in parts blackened, with their heads and horns, as they were swimming about, following up their objects, and making desperate battle whilst they were swimming.[1] (Fig. 15).

Fig. 15. Buffalo crossing the Missouri.

The number of the buffalo diminished very rapidly. The destruction of the animal was carried out on such a great scale that it was believed that they were retreating before the white men at the rate of 10 miles per year. In 1807 they had receded as far as the 97th meridian.[2] Gregg says that the number of buffalo skins or robes sent out of the region was 100,000 a year.[3] Frémont wrote an interesting account of their disappearance from the regions earliest explored, and gives the average annual

[1] G. Catlin, *The North American Indians* (1845), II, 13.
[2] H. M. Chittenden, *History of the American Fur Trade* (1902), II, 816.
[3] J. Gregg, *op. cit.* E.W.T. xx, 265.

return of buffalo robes traded during the years 1830–40 as
follows:

American Fur Company	70,000 robes
Hudson's Bay Company	10,000 ,,
All other Companies, probably	10,000 ,,
Making a total of	90,000 robes [1]

These figures only include the number of buffalo killed for
their robes, and do not include the number killed for food or
other purposes. Buffalo were only killed for their robes during
the four months of November to March, during which period
it was possible to dress the skins. As the majority of animals
were killed in the summer, when they were not used for trade,
it is impossible to estimate the immense number which must
have been slaughtered annually. After the construction of the
Union Pacific Railway the buffalo were even more ruthlessly
destroyed, and it is estimated that the annual rate of slaughter
between 1870 and 1875 was about two and a half million head.
Not all the hunters had the same feelings as Pike, who said: "I
prevented the men shooting at the game, not merely because of
the scarcity of ammunition, but, as I conceived, the laws of
morality forbid it also".[2]

OTHER ANIMALS AS FOOD. Other animals were used as
food. "The flesh of the antelope", says Gregg, "is rather coarse,
and but little esteemed".[3] There is no true antelope in America,
and the prongbuck (*Antilocapra americana*), which is usually
called antelope in America, is quite distinct from the real antelope. The animal was sometimes called a "goat" by Lewis and
Clark. The prongbuck abounded in "the high prairies",[4] and
sometimes roamed far to the east. Hunters occasionally used it
as it could always be caught because of its curiosity. "This fleet
and quick-sighted animal is generally the victim of its curiosity.
When they first see the hunters they run with great velocity; if
he lies down on the ground and lifts up his arm, his hat, or his

[1] J. C. Frémont, *Report*, pp. 143–5.
[2] Z. M. Pike, *Expeditions*, II, 402.
[3] J. Gregg, *op. cit.* E.W.T. xx, 276.
[4] *Ibid.* xix, p. 205.

foot, the antelope returns on a light trot to look at the object, and sometimes goes and returns two or three times, till it approaches within reach of the rifle".[1] The bighorn or mountain sheep (*Ovis montana*) was exceedingly difficult to capture, but its flesh was deemed superior to that of the buffalo. Gregg says that it is preferable to venison.[2] The elk (*Cervus canadensis*) provided the most generally eaten meat except buffalo, while the skins of various species of deer were all valuable in the fur trade. Gregg says: "The *elk* as well as the *deer* is found somewhat abundant upon the Arkansas river, as high as the Santa Fé road, but from thence westward they are both very scarce; for these animals do not resort to the high prairie plains. Further south, however, in the prairies bordering the brushy tributaries of the Canadian and Red River, deer are exceedingly plenty— herds of hundreds are sometimes seen together; but in these southern regions there are but few elks".[3]

Even the dogs of the Indians were sometimes used as food. Lewis and Clark were compelled to eat them, because of scarcity of game. There are three entries in their journals about dogs as food. On September 26, 1804, they wrote: "Of all these luxuries, which were placed before us...we could as yet partake but sparingly of the dog".[4] On October 10, 1805, they wrote: "Being again reduced to fish and roots, we made an experiment to vary our food by purchasing a few dogs, and after having been accustomed to horse-flesh, felt no disrelish for this new dish. The Chopunish have great numbers of dogs, which they employ for domestic purposes, but never eat; and our using the flesh of that animal soon brought us into ridicule as dog-eaters".[5] Finally, on January 3, 1806, they wrote: "Having been so long accustomed to live on the flesh of dogs, the greater part of us have acquired a fondness for it, and our original aversion to it is overcome, by reflecting that while we subsisted on that food we were fatter, stronger, and in general enjoyed better health

---

[1] *L. and C.* I, 291, April 30, 1805.
[2] J. Gregg, *op. cit.* E.W.T. xx, 276.
[3] *Ibid.* xx, 274-5.
[4] *L. and C.* I, 136.
[5] *Ibid.* II, 621.

than at any period since leaving the buffalo country, eastward of the mountains".[1]

THE PRAIRIE MARMOT (*Cynomys ludovicianus*), commonly known as the prairie dog or barking squirrel, was utterly useless for purposes of trade, but was, nevertheless, described at great length by all the early travellers. Lewis and Clark were the first to write an account of the animal.[2] It lived in "towns", and was frequently accompanied by rattlesnakes and owls. The holes in the warrens were dangerous to riders, as a horse could easily have a bad fall by putting its foot into one of them. The animals were used as food, and Lewis and Clark described the flesh as "not unpleasant to the taste".[3] Gregg in describing this animal says:

This singular quadruped is but little larger than a common squirrel, its body being nearly a foot long, with a tail of three or four inches. The color ranges from brown to a dirty yellow. The flesh, though often eaten by travellers, is not esteemed savory. It was denominated "the barking squirrel", the "prairie ground squirrel", etc., by early explorers, with much more apparent propriety than the present established name. Its yelp, which resembles that of the little toy-dog, seems its only canine attribute. It rather appears to occupy a middle ground betwixt the rabbit and the squirrel—like the former in feeding and burrowing, like the latter in frisking, flirting, sitting erect, and somewhat so in its barking.[4] (Fig. 16).

THE BEAR. The chief enemies of men in the region were bears and mosquitoes. The grizzly bear (*Ursus horribilis*), or the "white bear" of the fur-traders, was the most important zoological discovery made by Lewis and Clark.[5] The animals inhabited "the timbered parts of the Rocky mountains. They are rarely found on the westerly side, and are more common below the Rocky mountains, on the plains, or on their borders, amidst copses of brush and underwood, and near the water-courses. We are unable to learn that they inhabit at all the woody

[1] *L. and C.* II, 743.
[2] *Ibid.* I, 110–11. See also Z. M. Pike, *Expeditions*, II, 430.
[3] *L. and C.* III, 861.
[4] J. Gregg, *op. cit.* E.W.T. xx, 277.
[5] *L. and C.* I and II, 288, 298, 306, 307, 309, 310, 342, 370, 381, 392 and 393 for earliest accounts.

Fig. 16. "Dog Town" or settlement of prairie dogs.

country bordering on the coast as far in the interior as the (Cascade) range of mountains".[1] This animal was the only one which could be described as dangerous. Washington Irving says that "the grizzly bear is the only really formidable quadruped of our continent".[2] Brackenridge observed that "the grizzly bear is sufficient to disprove the idle theories of Buffon or Raynal, as to the impotency of the New World in the production of animals".[3] The bear seemed to be very common in the neighbourhood of the Great Falls of the Missouri. One bear is said to have weighed "between 500 and 600 pounds at least, and measured 8 feet and $7\frac{1}{2}$ inches from the nose to the extremity of the hind feet, 5 feet $10\frac{1}{2}$ inches round the breast, 3 foot 11 inches round the neck, 1 foot 11 inches round the middle of the foreleg, and his talons, five on each foot, were $4\frac{3}{8}$ inches in length".[4] These bears were very ferocious if once aroused, and had great tenacity of life.

The wonderful power of life which these animals possess renders them dreadful; their very track in the mud or sand, which we have sometimes found 11 inches long and $7\frac{1}{4}$ wide, exclusive of the talons, is alarming; and we had rather encounter two Indians than meet a single brown bear. There is no chance of killing them by a single shot unless the ball goes through the brain, and this is very difficult on account of two large muscles which cover the side of the forehead and the sharp projection of the center of the frontal bone, which is also thick.[5]

Indians only attacked bears when in parties of about six persons, and as they were armed with inferior guns, purchased from white traders, or bows and arrows, frequently lost their lives. In the first recorded description of the animal, Lewis and Clark state that the Indians, owing to their lack of weapons, "are obliged to approach very near to the bear; as no wound except through the head or heart is mortal, they frequently fall a sacrifice if they miss their aim".[6] White traders sometimes lost their lives, and one such occasion is recorded by Jacob Fowler, who

[1] *L. and C.* III, 842.
[2] W. Irving, *Astoria*, p. 201.
[3] H. M. Brackenridge, *Views of Louisiana* (1817), p. 115.
[4] *L. and C.* I, 298, May 5, 1805.
[5] *Ibid.* I, 307, May 11, 1805.
[6] *Ibid.* I, 288, April 29, 1805.

described the event in his diary. "A gun Was fyered off and the Cry of a White Bare Was Raised. We Ware all armed in an Instent and Each man Run His own Cors to look for the desperet anemel". One, Lewis Dawson, was wounded and died in two days.[1] Lewis and Clark were compelled to keep a good watch because of bears. "The white bears have now become exceedingly troublesome; they constantly infest our camp during the night, and though they have not attacked us, as our dog which patrols all night gives us notice of their approach, yet we are obliged to sleep with our arms by our sides for fear of accident, and we cannot send one man alone to any distance, particularly if he has to pass through brushwood".[2]

The fur of the grizzly was of no great value, although traps were set to catch them. The fur of the black bear (*Ursus americanus*), on the other hand, was very valuable, and this animal was not dangerous. Lewis and Clark say that he "differs in no respect from the bear common to the United States. They chiefly inhabit timbered parts of the Rocky mountains, and likewise the borders of the great plains of the Columbia. They are sometimes found in that tract which lies between those plains and the Pacific ocean".[3] The skins of black bears were exported in large numbers to England, where they were used by the army.

Lewis and Clark frequently mentioned the mosquito as the chief enemy of their journey, Lewis said that "musquetoes, eye knats and prickley pears" were "equal to any three curses that ever poor Egypt laiboured under, except the *mahometant* yoke".[4] It would be impossible to exaggerate the inconvenience which was caused by the ravages of this pest. "And what shall I say of musquitoes?" asks de Smet.

I have suffered so much from them, that I cannot leave them unnoticed. In the heart of the prairie they do not trouble the traveller, if he keeps aloof from the shade, and walks in the burning sun. But at nightfall they light on him, and hang on him till morning, like leeches sucking his blood.

[1] *Journal of Jacob Fowler*, ed. Elliott Coues (1899), p. 41.
[2] *L. and C.* II, 393, June 28, 1805.
[3] *Ibid.* III, 842.
[4] *Ibid.* II, 436.

There is no defence against their darts, but to hide under a buffalo skin, or wrap oneself up in some stuff which they cannot pierce, and run the risk of being smothered. When green or rotten wood can be procured, they may be driven away by smoke, but in such case the traveller himself is smoked, and in spite of all he can do, his eyes are filled with tears. As soon as the smoke ceases, they return to the charge till other wood is provided and thrown on the fire, so that the traveller's sleep is frequently interrupted, which proves very annoying after the fatigue of a troublesome journey.[1]

Note. *L. and C.* III, 821–900, contains a comprehensive account of the animal life of the Pacific coast.

[1] P. J. de Smet, S.J. *op. cit.* E.W.T. XXVII, 259.

Chapter VIII

THE INDIAN INHABITANTS
OF THE REGION

The region under consideration was not devoid of human inhabitants when it was first visited by white men. Indian tribes roamed over the whole area and had established some permanent settlements.

Explorers found that assistance from the Indians was indispensable. The greatest service which the Indian rendered was that of guide. Many of these men had travelled immense distances and knew the trails and passes over the mountains. Lewis and Clark were accompanied by Indian guides for the greater part of their journey. The geographical knowledge of an Indian was always limited, but they had an extraordinary faculty for finding their way.

The assistance of the Indians was always required in all matters of transport. They supplied the explorers with canoes or with horses,[1] as they were generally ready to sell these commodities provided they kept sufficient for their own use.

Food was often obtained from the Indians, who were willing to give or sell buffalo meat, salmon, and other foods. They also helped the white man in the hunting of animals for food and for fur.

Although generally friendly to the white man, the Indian could prove to be a very dangerous foe. The white traders of Manuel Lisa were constantly harried by Indians in the neighbourhood of the Three Forks. The position of the fur-traders in that region became so intolerable, because of the ravages of the Blackfoot Indians, that trade had to be abandoned. The experiences of John Colter in 1807 are typical of the hardships which the Indians could inflict. This unfortunate man was captured by the Blackfoot Indians and compelled to run a race for his life, stark naked, over the plain "abounding in prickly pear".

[1] The Arikara supplied the Astorian expedition of 1811 with horses.

Colter was fortunate to escape but he died in 1813, at a very early age, possibly as a result of the hardships he had suffered.[1] The Arikara were another tribe who were dreaded by the whites, as they were fierce enemies and treacherous friends.

The Indian tribes can be divided into groups which correspond very closely with the physical and climatic divisions already discussed. Five distinct cultures can be recognised in the area under consideration, the cultures of the Plain, the Plateau, and the Pacific border. The Plateau and the Pacific border can be divided into northern and southern divisions (Fig. 17). The differences in culture depended very largely on differences of food supply. In the Plains buffalo meat provided the Indian with food. In the northern part of the Plateau salmon and buffalo meat which had been imported from the Plains were the chief foods of the Indians, while in the southern part of the Plateau the Indians practised agriculture, and lived on maize, beans, and squashes. In the northern Pacific border region, salmon was the principal food of the Indian, and in the southern portion of that area wild seeds formed the chief article of diet. As the southern part of the Plateau had been explored by the Spaniards before the nineteenth century, the area inhabited by the agricultural tribes of the south-west is outside the scope of this book and only brief reference will be made to the interesting culture of that region.

THE PLAINS REGION. This region contained over thirty tribal groups. All these tribes were dependent on the buffalo for subsistence. In this vast treeless area they hunted their prey and they have often been called the Buffalo Indians. Brackenridge says: "I have called the region watered by the Missouri and its tributaries, THE PARADISE OF HUNTERS".[2] They rarely practised agriculture and transported their goods

[1] For a thrilling account of Colter's adventures see W. Irving, *Astoria*, pp. 118–21. Also Bradbury, *Travels in the Interior of America* (1819), E.W.T. v, 44–7, and Chittenden, *History of the American Fur Trade*, II, 713–23.

[2] Brackenridge, *Journal of a Voyage up the River Missouri* (1816), E.W.T. VI, 152. The methods of hunting have been described in the previous chapter.

by means of horses and dogs. They clothed themselves with the skins of buffalo and deer. In the southern part of this region, the Gulf Plains, some of the Indian tribes cultivated a little maize, but they depended on the buffalo for their main supply of food. Some tribes who were established along the banks of the Missouri had more permanent settlements, practised agriculture, and used the rivers for transport.[1] The country of

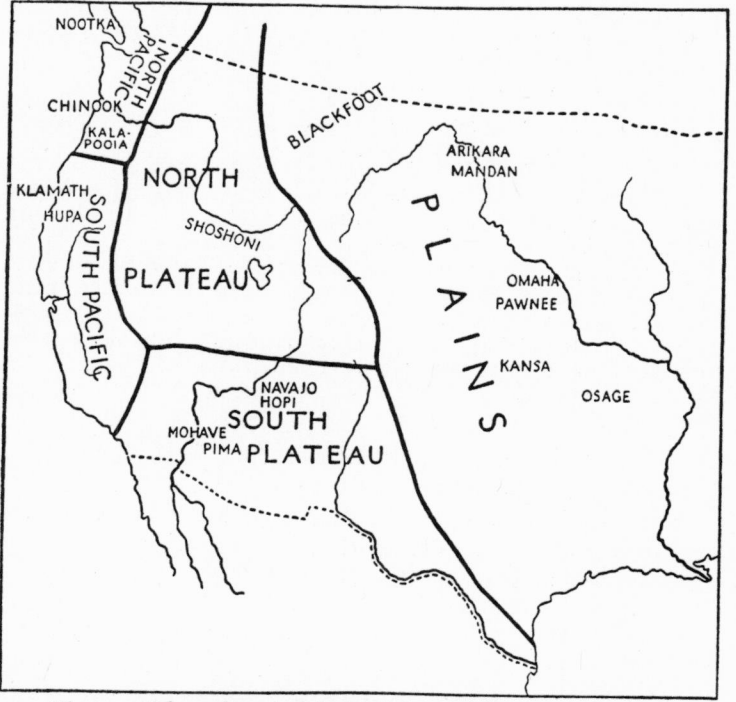

Fig 17. The cultural regions of the Indian tribes (adapted from Wissler).
The tribes marked on the map are mentioned in Chapter VIII.

these settled tribes was the area first visited by explorers. There are many early descriptions of the Mandans. At the time of

[1] These tribes include the Arikara, Kansa, Mandan, Omaha, Osage and Pawnee. The journal of Long's expedition contains the best account of the Kansa and Omaha tribes. See E.W.T. vols. XIV–XVII.

Lewis and Clark there were two villages with about two thousand inhabitants. Lewis and Clark describe the food of the Mandans in the following words:

The Mandans are very much in want of meat, and that he himself had not tasted any for several days. To this distress they are often reduced by their own improvidence, or by their unhappy situation. Their principal article of food is buffalo-meat, their corn, beans, and other grains being reserved for summer, or as a last resource against what they constantly dread, an attack from the Sioux, who drive off the game and confine them to their villages. The same fear also prevents their going out to hunt in small parties to relieve their occasional wants, so that the buffalo is generally obtained in large quantities and wasted by carelessness.[1]

Lewis and Clark again refer to the food of the inhabitants of the Missouri valley as follows:

Along the bottoms, which have a covering of high grass, we observed the sunflower blooming in great abundance. The Indians of the Missouri, more especially those who do not cultivate maize, make great use of the seed of this plant for bread, or in thickening their soup. They first parch and then pound it between two stones, until it is reduced to a fine meal. Sometimes they add a portion of water, and drink it thus diluted; at other times they add a sufficient proportion of marrow-grease to reduce it to the consistency of common dough, and eat it in that manner. This last composition we preferred to all the rest, and thought it at that time a very palatable dish.[2]

The Blackfoot Indians and the Arikara were dreaded by travellers on the northern route across the continent. The Pawnees were the foes of traders on the Santa Fé trail. The Pawnees were generally allies of the Spanish, and, as Pike observed, hostile to the Americans.

THE PLATEAU REGION. The Plateau can be divided into two regions, a northern and a southern. The northern region consists of the Columbia Plateaux and the greater part of the Interior Basin. The Indian culture of this area was not so uniform as the culture of the Plains area. The chief characteristics of the group were the extensive use of salmon, deer, roots, berries, and occasionally insects, as food. They stored dried salmon and roots for future use. They made crude canoes for

[1] *L. and C.* I, 231, February 8, 1805.
[2] *L. and C.* II, 418, July 17, 1805.

water transport. The dressing of deerskin was highly developed, but pottery was unknown. The tribal organisation was not very strong.

The life of this group was very arduous, and explorers who passed through the area experienced the same difficulties with regard to lack of food as those which the Indians had to undergo. Father de Smet says that the Shoshones "are called Snakes, because in their indigence they are reduced, like such reptiles, to burrow in the earth and live upon roots".[1]

The tribes of the Plateau were continually wandering from one place to another.

Their lives are indeed migratory [say Lewis and Clark]. From the middle of May to the beginning of September they reside on the waters of the Columbia, where they consider themselves perfectly secure from the Pawkees, who have never yet found their way to that retreat. During this time they subsist chiefly on salmon, and as that fish disappears on the approach of autumn, they are obliged to seek subsistence elsewhere. They then cross the ridge to the waters of the Missouri, down which they proceed slowly and cautiously, till they are joined near the Three Forks by other bands, either of their own nation or of the Flatheads, with whom they associate against the common enemy. Being now strong in numbers, they venture to hunt buffalo in the plains eastward of the mountains, near which they spend the winter, till the return of the salmon invites them to the Columbia. But such is their terror of the Pawkees, that as long as they can obtain the scantiest subsistence they do not leave the interior of the mountains; and as soon as they obtain a large stock of dried meat, they again retreat, thus alternately obtaining their food at the hazard of their lives, and hiding themselves to consume it. In this loose and wandering existence they suffer the extremes of want; for two-thirds of the year they are forced to live in the mountains, passing whole weeks without meat, and with nothing to eat but a few fish and roots. Nor can anything be imagined more wretched than their condition at the present time, when the salmon is fast retiring, when roots are becoming scarce, and they have not yet acquired strength to hazard an encounter with their enemies.[2]

The poverty of the Shoshones did not prevent them from being "excessively fond of the pipe, in which, however, they are not able to indulge much as they do not cultivate tobacco

[1] P. J. de Smet, S.J., *Letters and Sketches*, E.W.T. XXVII, 163. See *L. and C.* II, 543–4, August 22, 1805, for a description of the roots eaten by the Indians.
[2] *L. and C.* II, 554–6, August 26, 1805. Compare *L. and C.* II, 623, October 10, 1805, for a similar account of the Chopunnish.

themselves, and their rugged country affords them but few articles to exchange for it".[1]

Frémont wrote the following graphic description of the "root diggers":

scattered over the great region west of the Rocky mountains, and south of the Great Snake river, are numerous Indians whose subsistence is almost solely derived from roots and seeds, and such small animals as chance and great good fortune sometimes bring within their reach. They are miserably poor, armed only with bows and arrows, or clubs; and, as the country they inhabit is almost destitute of game, they have no means of obtaining better arms. In the northern part of the region just mentioned, they live generally in solitary families; and farther to the south, they are gathered together in villages. Those who live together in villages, strengthened by association, are in exclusive possession of the more genial and richer parts of the country; while the others are driven to the ruder mountains, and to the more inhospitable parts of the country.... Roots, seeds, and grass, every vegetable that affords any nourishment, and every living animal thing, insect or worm, they eat. Nearly approaching to the lower animal creation, their sole employment is to obtain food; and they are constantly occupied in a struggle to support existence.[2]

The southern portion of the Plateau was occupied by Indians who practised intensive agriculture.[3] As this region had been partly explored by the Spaniards before 1800, only a brief mention is necessary. In this area the Indians lived in settled communities or Pueblos, the inhabitants cultivating maize, beans, and squashes. The Pueblo Indians of New Mexico are well described by the explorer Pike, who observed that they had adopted many Spanish customs.

THE PACIFIC REGION. The Pacific region can be divided into two parts. The north Pacific coast[4] was an area in which salmon was the chief human food. This area was inhabited by a large Indian population when the white explorers entered it

---

[1] L. and C. II, 500, August 15, 1805.

[2] J. C. Frémont, Report, p. 142.

[3] In November 1826, J. S. Smith, when describing the Mohave Indians of this region, wrote: "they cultivate the soil, and raise corn, beans, pumpkins, watermelons and muskmelons in abundance, and also a little wheat and cotton". H. C. Dale, Ashley-Smith Explorations, p. 189.

[4] See L. and C. II, 747–93, for an account of north Pacific coast Indians.

from the east. All the streams draining into the Pacific are visited by salmon. The salmon penetrated to the headwaters of the drainage system and were used by tribes which lived far inland. The salmon ascends the river once a year and this developed seasonal habits among the Indians. The Indians would all come down to the river at the right season. Lewis and Clark, when speaking of the Indians who live on the Columbia, say:

Fish is their chief food, except roots and casual supplies of antelope, which latter, to those who have only bows and arrows, must be very scanty. This diet may be the direct or the remote cause of the chief disorder which prevails among them, as well as among the Flatheads on the Kooskooskee and Lewis' rivers. With all these Indians a bad soreness of the eyes is a very common disorder, which is suffered to ripen by neglect, till many are deprived of one of their eyes, and some have totally lost the use of both. This dreadful calamity may reasonably, we think, be imputed to the constant reflection of the sun on the waters, where they are constantly fishing in the spring, summer, and fall, and during the rest of the year on the snows of a country which affords no object to relieve the sight.[1]

Tribes on the coast engaged in fishing all the year round, but the inland people were compelled to hunt to supplement the fish. Fish was carefully preserved and the method of doing this is described by Lewis and Clark.

The manner of doing this is by first opening the fish and exposing it to the sun on scaffolds. When it is sufficiently dried it is pounded between two stones till it is pulverized, and is then placed in a basket about two feet long and one in diameter, neatly made of grass and rushes, and lined with the skin of a salmon stretched and dried for the purpose. Here the fish are pressed down as hard as possible, and the top is covered with fish-skins, which are secured by cords through the holes of the basket. These baskets are then placed in some dry situation, the corded part upward, seven being usually placed as close as they can be put together, and five on the top of these. The whole is then wrapped up in mats, and made fast by cords, over which mats are again thrown. Twelve of these baskets, each of which contains 90 to 100 pounds, form a stack, which is left exposed till it is sent

[1] *L. and C.* II, 639, October 17, 1805. On the same day Clark describes the vast quantity of salmon in the following words: "Here were great quantities of salmon drying on scaffolds; and indeed from the mouth of the river upward he saw immense numbers of dead salmon strewed along the shore or floating on the surface of the water, which is so clear that the salmon may be seen swimming in the water at the depth of 15 or 20 feet", p. 640.

to market. The fish thus preserved keep sound and sweet for several years and great quantities, they inform us, are sent to the Indians who live below the falls.[1]

The tribes of the Interior of the Columbia Basin pounded dried fish in mortars in the same way that agriculturists pounded grain.

The tribes along the coast lived in permanent dwellings while the more interior tribes were nomadic, moving "in an annual cycle according to their food habits". The Indians below the Great Falls lived in houses, which Lewis and Clark describe as "the first wooden buildings we have seen since leaving the Illinois country, are nearly equal in size, and exhibit a very singular appearance".[2] These large houses were made of cedar planks. The Indians of this area were experts in the handling of sea-going canoes, some of which had sails.[3] The tribes who inhabited the neighbourhood of the falls of the Columbia were a great source of trouble to white travellers from the time of Lewis and Clark.[4]

The southern part of the Pacific region consisted of the Californian valleys, the coastal mountains, and the Sierra Nevada. In this area wild seeds and acorns formed the principal articles of food. The raw acorns were pounded into a flour from which a kind of bread was made. Berries and fruits were only of secondary importance as a source of food. The Indians of

[1] *L. and C.* II, 659, October 22, 1805.

[2] *Ibid.* II, 666, October 24, 1805.

[3] *Ibid.* II, 770–2.

[4] Elliott Coues came to the conclusion "that there was some natural demoralizing agency at the Dalles and Cascades of the Columbia", and describes the character of the Indians, who inhabited this region, in the following words: "Certainly the tribes at these points were thievish and murderous from their first contact with white men,...till they were finally broken up in very late years. The difficulty of passing these points, where navigation was necessarily interrupted, was taken every advantage of by the wily savages, who infested these places as bandits do mountain passes, and played on the Columbia the part of the Sioux on the Missouri—that of river pirates. It seems to have been rather a local than a tribal matter— that is, no tribe could resist the temptation and opportunity that offered at the portages. Books of Columbian travel and adventure are full of such incidents, and much blood has been spilled in these places". *L. and C.* III, 959 footnote.

California used dogs for transport, and although they had no canoes, they used rafts to cross rivers. Strange as it may seem, the region of North America which enjoys a climate similar to that of Mediterranean lands did not favour human development, and Indian culture in this area was comparatively low.[1]

Washington Irving well describes the influence of differing environments on the lives of the Indians in the following words:

The effect of different modes of life upon the human frame and human character are strikingly instanced in the contrast between the hunting Indians of the prairies, and the piscatory Indians of the sea coast. The former, continually on horseback scouring the plains, gaining their food by hardy exercise, and subsisting chiefly on flesh, are generally tall, sinewy, meagre, but well-formed, and of bold and fierce deportment; the latter lounging about the river banks, or squatting and curved up in their canoes, are generally low in stature, ill-shaped, with crooked legs, thick ankles, and broad flat feet. They are inferior also in muscular power and activity, and in *game* qualities and appearance to their hard-riding brethren of the prairies.[2]

The lives of the Indians were adapted to their environment and white explorers found that it was best to copy the methods of the red man. As hunters, the white explorers with their muzzle-loading weapons were definitely inferior to the bow-using Indian. In the Plains, the white explorers lived mainly on buffalo meat, in the Plateau and the Great Basin they shared the precarious existence of the inhabitants and in the Pacific border region they had to become accustomed to a diet of fish and travel by canoe.

Note

The following books contain original descriptive accounts of Indian tribes.

Bradbury, J., *Travels in the Interior of America*, 1809–11, London, 1819. E.W.T. vol. v.

Catlin, G., *The North American Indians*, *being letters and notes on their manners, customs and conditions, written during eight years' travel*

---

[1] "Thus, notwithstanding the popular idea of modern California as an ideal habitat for modern Americans, it must be regarded as rather unfavorable to the development of primitive tribes, for while enough food could be found, the daily routine of gathering it in small lots was time-consuming in the extreme." C. Wissler, *The American Indian* (1922), p. 12.

[2] W. Irving, *Astoria*, p. 65.

amongst the wildest tribes of Indians in North America, 1832–1839, 2 vols. London, 1845.

De Smet, P. J., S.J., *Life, Letters and Travels*, 1801–1873. *Including his missionary labors and adventures among the wild tribes of North American Indians; their manners, customs, games, modes of warfare, and torture, legends, traditions*, ed. H. M. Chittenden, 4 vols. New York, 1905.

James, E., *Account of an Expedition from Pittsburgh to the Rocky Mountains performed in the years 1819–1820 under the command of Major S. H. Long*, 3 vols. London, 1823. E.W.T. XIV–XVII.

Nuttall, T., *A Journal of Travels into the Arkansa Territory during the year 1819, with occasional observations on the manners of the aborigines*, Philadelphia, 1821. E.W.T., vol. XIII. Contains notes on the Chicksaw, Cherokee and Osage Indians.

Schoolcraft, H. R., *Historical and Statistical Information respecting the Conditions and Prospects of the Indian Tribes*, 5 vols. Philadelphia, 1853.

Wied, Prince Maximilian of, *Travels in the Interior of North America*, translated by H. E. Lloyd, London, 1843. E.W.T. vols. XXII–XXV. Vol. XXV is an "Atlas" of illustrations.

PART II

THE EXPLORATION OF WESTERN AMERICA, 1800–1850

INTRODUCTION

No great physical obstacles hinder movement westward from the Mississippi until the barrier of the Rocky Mountains is reached. There is only a gradual and almost imperceptible rise towards the west, and no forests delay the rapid movement of the traveller. The direction of the natural drainage was the most important factor in the history of westward movement to the Rockies. The rivers flow in parallel courses from the west to the east before they join the Mississippi. Explorers and traders followed the courses of these rivers, because they provided a supply both of water and of fuel, the latter being obtained from the cottonwood trees, which grew along their banks.

There are many eastward flowing rivers, but the Missouri was by far the most important, as it was the only river on which navigation was always possible. The other rivers either possessed so little water that they entirely evaporated in the plains, or in some cases were only navigable for short periods of the year.

The superior navigability of the Missouri resulted in the early exploration of this river. The Missouri was already known as far as the villages of the Mandans, when Lewis and Clark pushed their way up the river in 1804. The fur-traders who followed Lewis and Clark explored the sources of the Missouri, from the source of the Big Horn in the south, to the source of the Milk River in the north. It seems natural that the earliest explorations of the west of the present United States should have been confined to the sources of the Missouri.

The explorers of the northern trans-continental route were fortunate, in that, at the point where they crossed the mountains, they came upon the waters of the Columbia River, the only river that crosses the whole of the complicated mountain region. By following the Columbia, it was possible to cross the Interior Plateaux, the Cascades, and the Coastal range and so reach the sea. Lewis and Clark discovered three passes, which led them over the Rocky Mountains from the waters of the Missouri to the waters of the Columbia. On their outward journey they used the Lemhi Pass, and on their return they used the Lewis and Clark Pass, the route most familiar to the Indians, and the Gibbon Pass. By finding these Passes, they had discovered the shortest route across the mountains themselves, "because the Rockies contract as they near Canada; this route had the longest river approach on a navigable stream, the best mountain pass, the narrowest stretch of desert on the west, and the most direct approach to the great bend of the Columbia where regular canoe navigation began".[1] Chapter IX describes the exploration of this northern trans-continental route to the Pacific.

The northern route made it necessary to undertake a great detour to the north from St Louis. The Astor expedition of 1812 attempted to make the journey shorter and more direct by crossing the Rockies further south in the neighbourhood of Union Pass. On the return journey it is possible that the expedition may have passed through what was later called South Pass. The discovery of the South Pass, which resulted in the use of a central route to the Pacific, was principally due to the expeditions of Ashley and Smith between 1822 and 1829. The exploration of the central route and the discovery of South Pass is described in chapter X.

In 1800 the region between St Louis and Santa Fé was imperfectly known. As the result of the work of Pike, a route between the American town and the Spanish settlement developed and became known as the Santa Fé trail. Santa Fé proved to be an admirable base for southern routes to California and the discovery of these routes is considered in chapter XI.

[1] E. C. Semple, *American History and its Geographic Conditions* (1903), p. 204.

The discovery of the real character of the Interior Basin and of the various passes over the Sierra Nevada to California forms the subject of chapter XII.

Different incentives urged men to undertake the work of the exploration of western America. In many cases the work of pioneer exploration was carried out by men whose sole motive was the acquisition of furs. These traders and trappers did not always keep a full or accurate account of their discoveries, and the immense geographical knowledge which they acquired was often not represented on published maps. The Government sent out scientific expeditions, such as the expeditions of Lewis and Clark, of Pike, and of Long. These expeditions were endeavours to determine the character of the land of Louisiana purchased by the United States, and were, for the most part, journeys of original exploration. Some of the work accomplished by the Government's agents, although it cannot be classified under this head, is nevertheless the first written record of the geographical facts discovered; most of Frémont's work was of this character. Lastly, there were a number of purely military expeditions, such as those connected with the campaigns of the war with Mexico, which added to the sum of geographical knowledge by constructing adequate maps of regions previously explored.

It should be made clear that the following description of the exploration of the region does not pretend to be exhaustive. The object of this part of the book has not been to compile a complete historical summary of the exploration of the region, but rather to select the more important narratives and to show the gradual development of a geographical knowledge of the area. The main criterion of selection has been, wherever possible, to give a full account of the original journeys of exploration. In some cases, however, the earliest explorers did not realise the significance of their discoveries and, in such cases, a lengthy description of the work of the men who first grasped the real geographical meaning of the discoveries of others is included. With this aim in mind it has only been necessary to include a brief mention of the military expeditions. The history of the Mormon settlement, the migration to Oregon, and the gold

rush to California have been entirely omitted as they concern the history of emigration and settlement rather than exploration. The following chapters are an attempt, not only to describe the history of the discovery of the geographical facts which have been analysed in Part I, but also to show how those facts influenced the order of events.

Chapter IX

THE DISCOVERY OF A NORTHERN TRANS-CONTINENTAL ROUTE[1]

(a) The Expedition of Lewis and Clark, 1803–1806

Thomas Jefferson had long been interested in the exploration of Louisiana. He had been concerned in the abortive expeditions of Ledyard and Michaux, and when, in 1801, he became President of the United States, he determined that the exploration of western America should be carried out. Before the purchase of Louisiana had even been suggested by Napoleon, Jefferson had drawn up a scheme of exploration. On January 18, 1803, in a confidential message to Congress, Jefferson said that "the river Missouri, and the Indians inhabiting it, are not as well known as is rendered desirable by their connection with the Mississippi, and consequently with us".[2] He proposed that an expedition be sent out to trace the Missouri to its source, and added that "an intelligent officer, with ten or twelve chosen men, fit for the enterprise, and willing to undertake it, taken from our posts, where they may be spared without inconvenience, might explore the whole line, even to the Western ocean, have conferences with the natives on subjects of commercial intercourse, get admission among them for our traders, as others are admitted, agree on convenient deposits for an interchange of articles, and return with the information acquired, in the course of two summers".[3] Congress approved this proposal and voted the money to carry it into execution.

Jefferson's private secretary, Captain Meriwether Lewis (Fig. 18), was chosen to lead the expedition, and Lieutenant

[1] The routes of the explorers described in this chapter are shown on end Map A, Fig. 32.

[2] *Annals of the Congress of the United States*, 7th Congress, 2nd Session, 1802–3, Tuesday, January 18, 1803, confidential message from the President, Washington, 1851.

[3] *Ibid.*

William Clark (Fig. 19), a brother of the famous George Rogers Clark, was to be the second in command. Lewis was sent to Philadelphia to acquire an additional knowledge of botany and astronomy from members of the Philosophical Society. Jefferson took the greatest interest in the preparations for the expedition and sent Lewis many letters of advice. In April, 1803, the formal instructions were despatched to Lewis and were signed on June 20. Lewis was ordered to "explore the Missouri river, and such principal streams of it, as, by its course and communications with the waters of the Pacific ocean, whether the Columbia, Oregon, Colorado, or any other river, may offer the most direct and practicable water communication across the continent, for the purposes of commerce".[1] Jefferson drew up elaborate orders with regard to the treatment of the Indians. Lewis was commanded to treat the Indians "in the most friendly and conciliatory manner which their own conduct will admit; allay all jealousies as to the object of your journey, satisfy them of its innocence; make them acquainted with the position, extent, character, peaceable and commercial dispositions of the United States".[2] Special notice was to be taken of "climate, as characterized by the thermometer, by the proportion of rainy, cloudy and clear days, by lightning, hail, snow, ice, by the access and recess of frost, by the winds prevailing at different seasons, the dates at which particular plants put forth or lose their flower or leaf, times of appearance of particular birds, reptiles or insects".[3] Jefferson gave Lewis full instructions as to what he was to do when he reached the Pacific. "On your arrival on that coast", says Jefferson, "endeavor to learn if there be any post within your reach frequented by the sea vessels of any nation, and to send two of your trusty people back by sea, in such way as shall appear practicable, with a copy of your notes; and should you be of opinion that the return of your party by the way they went will be imminently dangerous, then ship the whole, and return by sea, by the way either of Cape Horn or the Cape of Good Hope, as you shall be able."[4]

[1] *Writings of Thomas Jefferson*, ed. H. A. Washington, VIII, 486.
[2] *Ibid.* pp. 488–9.   [3] *Ibid.* p. 488.   [4] *Ibid.* p. 490.

Fig. 18. Meriwether Lewis.

Fig. 19. William Clark.

The news of the purchase of Louisiana reached Washington on July 1, when Lewis was still obtaining instructions from the President. The purchase of Louisiana obviously altered the whole complexion of the expedition. It was of the utmost importance that the Americans should obtain a knowledge of the territory which they had bought, and about which so little was known. Jefferson was prepared to send out several expeditions to explore the newly acquired territory and describes his object in a letter which he wrote to Lewis on November 16, 1803.

The object of your mission is single, the direct water communication from sea to sea formed by the bed of the Missouri, and perhaps the Oregon; by having Mr Clarke with you we consider the expedition as double-manned, and therefore the less liable to failure; for which reason neither of you should be exposed to risks by going off of your line. I have proposed in conversation, and it seems generally assented to, that Congress shall appropriate ten or twelve thousand dollars for exploring the principal waters of the Mississippi and Missouri. In that case, I should send a party up the Red river to its head, then to cross over to the head of the Arkansas, and come down that. A second party for the Pani [Platte] and Padouca [Kansas] rivers, and a third, perhaps, for the Morsignona [Des Moines] and St Peter's [Minnesota].[1]

Jefferson did everything in his power to assist Lewis in his task; he compiled a digest of all the information about Louisiana which existed at the time. This digest and all available maps[2] were sent to Lewis, in order that he might know what had already been accomplished in the exploration of the region.

The expedition[3] under the command of Captain Meriwether

[1] *Writings of Thomas Jefferson*, ed. H. A. Washington, IV, 516.

[2] See A. H. Abel, "A New Lewis and Clark Map", *Geographical Review* (1916) I, 329–45. A map, which was discovered in the U.S. Indian Office, is described in this article and is believed by Dr Abel to be a map sent by Jefferson to Lewis. The map contains the geographical information acquired by John Evans. See also F. J. Teggart, "Notes Supplementary to any edition of Lewis and Clark", *Annual Report of the American Historical Association for the year* 1908, I, 185–95.

[3] *Bibliographical Note on Texts.* There was very considerable delay in publishing the results of the expedition. Jefferson had published a brief message, which contains some account of the earlier part of the expedition, and certain other documents, in 1806. (Reprinted by R. Phillips, London, 1806.) The Journal of Patrick Gass, a member of the expedition, was published at Pittsburgh in 1807. The publication of the official account was delayed by the sudden death of Lewis in 1809. Clark then took up the work of writing, but finally handed over all the journals and note

Lewis and William Clark went into winter quarters at Fort Dubois, north of St Louis. Here they spent the winter of 1803–4 in training and preparation for their great adventure. On March 9, 1804, St Louis, the capital of Upper Louisiana, was handed over to the Americans by the French. Captain Lewis was present and signed the formal document of transfer. The party of forty-five men left St Louis on May 14, 1804, and embarked "on board of three boats: the first was a keel boat 55 feet long, drawing three feet of water, carrying one large square-sail and 22 oars.... This was accompanied by two perioques [periogues] or open boats, one of six and the other of seven oars".[1]

The first part of the journey took them as far as the Mandan villages and was not one of original discovery. The journal is full of accounts of descending traders.[2] At the Mandan villages were found both French and British traders.

books to one, Nicholas Biddle, who prepared the history for publication. After much difficulty and delay the task of completing the book was given to Paul Allen, who "faced, prefaced and defaced" Biddle's work. The book was eventually published in 1814 under the title: *History of the Expedition under the command of Captains Lewis and Clark to the source of the Missouri, thence across the Rocky Mountains and down the River Columbia to the Pacific Ocean. Performed during the years* 1804–5–6. Prepared for the Press by Paul Allen, Esquire. In two volumes. Published at New York, 1814. This edition is known as the Biddle edition and was used by Dr Elliott Coues in his scholarly reprint, *History of the Expedition under the Command of Lewis and Clark*, 4 vols. New York, 1893. This contains a reprint of the Biddle text with valuable introductions and copious notes. Other useful reprints of the Biddle edition are: (1) J. K. Hosmer (ed.), *History of the Expedition of Captains Lewis and Clark*, 1804–5–6, with Introduction and Index, 2 vols. Chicago, 1902, and (2) J. B. McMaster (ed.), *History of the Expedition under the Command of Captains Lewis and Clark*, 3 vols. published by D. Nutt, London, 1905. The actual journals of the expedition itself were finally published in *The Original Journals of the Lewis and Clark Expedition*, 1804–1806, ed. R. G. Thwaites, 8 vols. New York, 1904–5. This is the most exhaustive work on the subject. References in the following chapter, however, are given to the Elliott Coues edition, as this should enable a reader to refer to any Biddle edition. The dates of each entry are given, in order to facilitate reference. The abbreviation, *L. and C.* has been used to refer to Lewis and Clark, Elliott Coues' edition.

[1] *L. and C.* I, 4.

[2] References to traders are found in *L. and C.* I, pp. 15, 25, 150 (Valle), 189 (Lepage) and 191 (Gravelines). The following may be quoted and it

The country, the vegetation, and the animals were all fully described. The river valleys were said to be well wooded with walnut, hickory, ash, oak, and cottonwood, while beyond the river the prairies were devoid of trees. On August 21, 1804, the surrounding region was described in the following words: "The country through which we passed has the same uniform appearance ever since we left the Platte—rich, low grounds near the river, succeeded by undulating prairies, with timber near the waters".[1] The game in the prairies, which was always plentiful, furnished an abundant supply of food. On August 23, 1804, they killed their first buffalo. Elk, beaver tails, turkey, geese, and fish were all included in their diet. The journal contains frequent references to the trapping of beaver, which seems to have been especially abundant in this part of the river.[2]

The difficulties of navigation were very great; there were many islands and sand-bars, and the river was full of sunken timber. The journal contains many accounts of the dangers of the sand-bars and the concealed logs. The winds were frequently contrary, as on October 17, 1804, when "the wind from the northwest then became so strong that we could not move after ten o'clock until late in the afternoon, when we were forced to use the towline; we therefore made only six miles".[3]

Captain Lewis held many councils with the Indians and attempted to arbitrate in inter-tribal wars. The origin of the name of Council Bluffs arose from one of these meetings.[4] Long conferences took place with the Sioux, the Yankton,[5]

will be seen that a French trader had penetrated as far as the Black Mountains: *L. and C.* I, 15, June 5, 1804. "At eleven o'clock we met a raft made of two canoes joined together, in which two French traders were descending, from 80 leagues up the Kansas River, where they had wintered and caught great quantities of beaver, but had lost much of their game by fires from the prairies." *L. and C.* I, 150, October 2, 1804. "Mr Valle tells us that he has passed the last winter 300 leagues up the Chayenne under the Black Mountains."

[1] *L. and C.* I, 81.

[2] "This part of the river abounds in beaver" (near Council Bluffs). *L. and C.* I, 73, August 12, 1804.

[3] *L. and C.* I, 170.   [4] *L. and C.* I, 65, August 3, 1804.

[5] *Ibid.* I, 92, August 30, 1804.

the Tetons,[1] and the explorers wrote a very full description of the Sioux tribe.[2]

On October 21 the expedition reached the ruins of the nine villages of the Mandans in the neighbourhood of the present town of Bismarck. The weather became very cold and on October 26 "the wind blew very cold in the evening from the southwest. Two of the party are affected with rheumatic complaints".[3] It was decided to build winter quarters in the neighbourhood, and Fort Mandan was completed on November 20. The expedition was now 1600 miles from the mouth of the Missouri and had to undergo a very hard winter. It was noticed that on November 14 "the river rose last night half an inch, and is now filled with floating ice",[4] and that on November 29 "the wind is again from the northwest, the weather cold, and the snow which fell yesterday and last night is 13 inches in depth".[5] On December 12 the river was frozen over and on December 17 the temperature was as low as 45° below zero. The journal records many cases of frost-bite.

At Fort Mandan the Americans were visited by many British traders, who had come from Canada, and were members of the North-West Fur Company. There were also a number of French voyageurs and one, Chaboneau, who had married a Shoshone woman, was engaged as interpreter to the expedition. The woman was very useful when the explorers reached her native home, the land of the Snake nation in the Rocky Mountains.

During March the party was occupied in the construction of canoes made of cottonwood. The river broke up by the end of March and, on April 7, 1805, the main party of thirty-two persons departed in six canoes and two large periogues. Thirteen men returned home in the barge, to take back news of the expedition's progress.

The Little Missouri was passed on April 12. The interpreter Chaboneau had travelled as far as this on a previous journey and various French traders had reached Mussell Shell Creek, but beyond this point the river was completely unexplored. Game

---

[1] *L. and C.* I, 132, September 25, 1804.   [2] *Ibid.* I, 96–102.
[3] *Ibid.* I, 179.   [4] *Ibid.* I, 193.   [5] *Ibid.* I, 203.

was still abundant, and two entries show that the food was enjoyed. On April 17 "we obtained three beavers, the flesh of which is more relished by the men than any other food which we have",[1] and on April 21 "we procured four buffalo calves, which are equal in flavor to the most delicious veal".[2] On April 25 they reached the Yellowstone and one of the party ascended the river for a few miles. On May 4 the explorers remarked that "there are, as usual, vast quantities of game, extremely gentle; the male buffalo particularly will scarcely give way to us, and as we approach will merely look at us for a moment, as something new, and then quietly resume their feeding".[3] On May 9 they passed "a most extraordinary river", which they called the Bigdry River; "though as wide as the Missouri itself,—that is about half a mile,—it does not discharge a drop of water, and contains nothing but a few standing pools.... Like the dry rivers we passed before, this seemed to have discharged its waters recently, but the watermark indicated that its greatest depth had not been more than two feet".[4]

On May 26, near Windsor River, "Captain Lewis first caught a distant view of the Rock Mountains—the object of all our hopes, and the reward of all our ambition,...and as the sun shone on the snows of their summits, he obtained a clear and satisfactory view of those mountains which close on the Missouri, the passage to the Pacific".[5]

On June 3 they came to a junction of two rivers and were uncertain which river was the Missouri. "It now became an interesting question, which of these two streams is the Missouri ...on our right decision much of the fate of the expedition depends; since if, after ascending the Rocky Mountains or beyond them, we should find that the river we were following did not come near the Columbia, and be obliged to return, we should not only lose the traveling season, two months of which have already elapsed, but probably dishearten the men."[6]

On June 8 they decided that the northern stream was not the Missouri and named it Maria's River. The Mandans had assured them that, on the Missouri, there existed a series of great falls.

[1] L. and C. 1, 276.   [2] Ibid. 1, 278.   [3] Ibid. 1, 295.
[4] Ibid. 1, 302–3.   [5] Ibid. 1, 328.   [6] Ibid. 1, 343.

Lewis pushed on ahead and discovered these falls; the party were thus assured that they were following the right river. On June 13 Lewis, "seating himself on some rocks under the center of the falls, enjoyed the sublime spectacle of this stupendous object, which since the creation had been lavishing its magnificence upon the desert, unknown to civilisation".[1]

The expedition had to use a portage of 18 miles, in order to pass the falls. Lewis wrote an admirable account of the falls[2] and Clark drew a map of the falls (Fig. 20), which has been described by a modern engineer as "remarkably accurate and a monument to the faithful work of these early explorers".[3] A rough cart was constructed and used to transport the goods round the falls. Buffalo were still abundant and Captain Clark had a remarkable escape from a grizzly bear.[4]

The canoes were launched on the river above the falls and a difficult journey began. On July 13 the country is described in the following words: "The country exhibits its usual appearances; the timber being confined to the river, and the country on both sides, as far as the eye can reach, being entirely destitute of trees or brush".[5] On July 18 they passed the Dearborn River, which leads to the Lewis and Clark Pass, which they were to discover in the following year, and on July 25 they reached the three forks of the Missouri, named after three statesman, Jefferson, Madison, and Gallatin. They were eager to know whether they would find that the Missouri would lead them to the Columbia.

We are now very anxious to see the Snake Indians. After advancing for several hundred miles into this wild and mountainous country, we may soon expect that the game will abandon us. With no information of the route, we may be unable to find a passage across the mountains when we reach the head of the river,—at least, such a pass as will lead us to the Columbia. Even are we so fortunate as to find a branch of that river, the timber which we have hitherto seen in these mountains does not promise us any fit to make canoes, so that our chief dependence is on meeting some tribe from which we may procure horses. Our consolation is that this southwest branch can scarcely head with any other river than the Columbia;

[1] *L. and C.* II, 365.   [2] *Ibid.* II, 383–5.
[3] M. S. Parker, *Trans. Amer. Soc. Civil Engineers,* XXVIII, no. 1 (July 1892), 56–68.
[4] *L. and C.* II, 371.   [5] *Ibid.* II, 410–11.

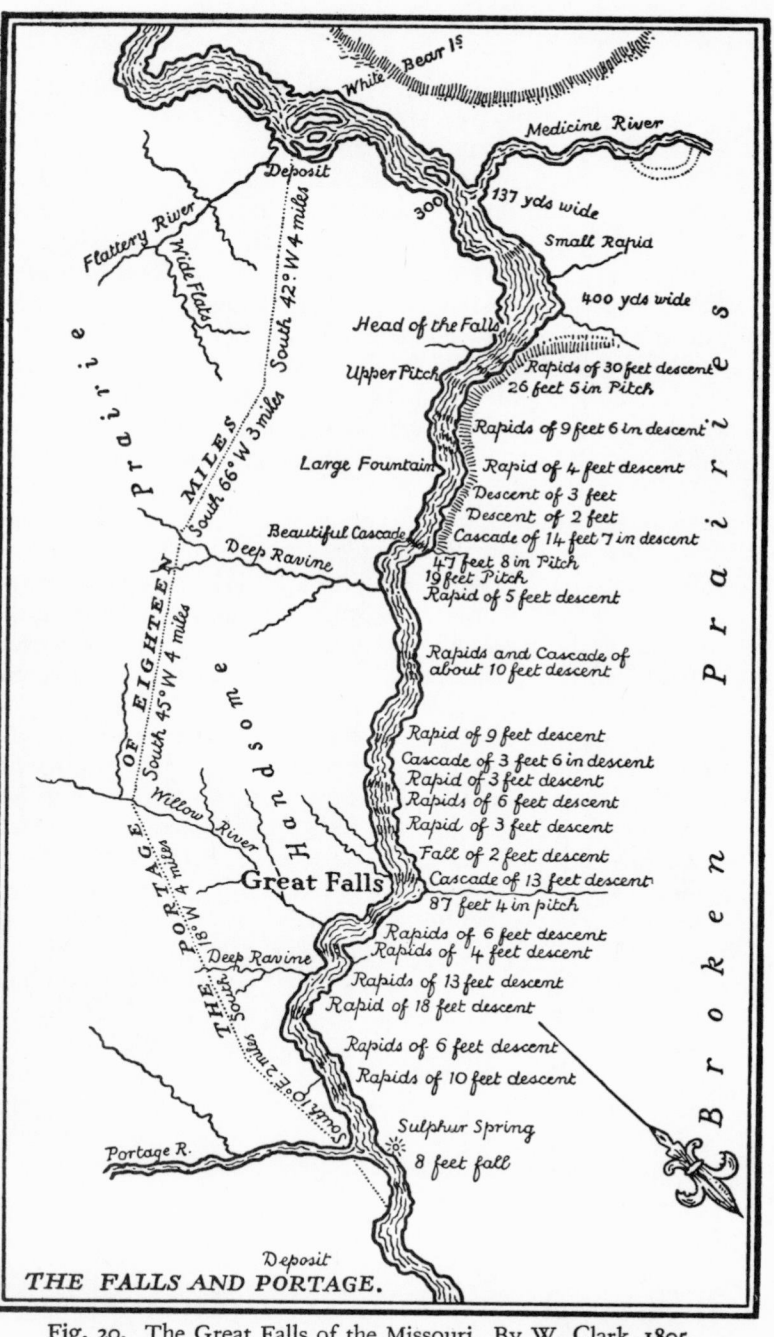

Fig. 20. The Great Falls of the Missouri. By W. Clark, 1805.

and that if any nation of Indians can live in the mountains we are able to endure as much as they can, and have even better means of procuring subsistence.[1]

They advanced up the Jefferson and on August 8 crossed the 5000 foot contour line at Beaver Head. They reached two forks of the Jefferson and as it was impossible to navigate the river further,[2] the canoes were abandoned. Dr Elliott Coues considers that "the Expedition here strikes the Rocky mountains at perhaps the very worst point that could have been found, for their journey beyond the Divide, since leaving Maria's river. They will make the Continental Pass easily enough, but at a point which has never yet been available for a through route, in consequence of the character of the country on the Pacific side".[3]

Lewis pushed along the southern fork of the Jefferson River (Trail Creek) and followed the river to its source in Lemhi Pass. He crossed the divide and on August 12 found a stream flowing towards the west (Lemhi Creek). The party encountered members of the Indian tribe called Shoshones, who lived on the far side of the pass and possessed large numbers of horses. Captain Lewis was entertained by an Indian, who provided him with salmon. "This was the first salmon he had seen, and perfectly satisfied him that he was now on the waters of the Pacific".[4] The party were informed of the difficulty of attempting to continue their trans-continental journey by means of the Lemhi River. "The chief informed him that this stream discharged at the distance of half a day's march, into another (Salmon river) of twice its size, coming from the southwest; but added, on further inquiry, that there was scarcely more timber below the junction of the rivers than in this neighborhood and that the river was rocky, rapid, and so closely confined between high mountains that it was impossible to pass down it either by land or water to the great lake (Pacific Ocean)."[5] There was also no timber for the construction of canoes and hardly sufficient for fuel. Nevertheless, Clark made an attempt

[1] *L. and C.* II, 445.
[2] *Ibid.* II, 514. On pp. 514–18 a general description of the course of the whole River Missouri is given.
[3] *L. and C.* II, 472–3, footnote.
[4] *Ibid.* II, 493.   [5] *Ibid.* II, 493.

to follow the route, but he confirmed in striking language the account given by the Indians.[1] Clark gave the name of Lewis to the river now called Salmon River, but after going 70 miles and back, he was compelled to return.

The expedition had now to face the hardest part of the journey. They were compelled to make a long detour to the north, nearly two degrees of latitude, before they were able to continue their westward march to the Columbia. The Indians had little to eat except berries, roots, and salmon and the party were short of food during their stay with the Shoshones. The weather was exceedingly cold and on August 21 it was recorded that a frost occurred so that "Ink freezes in the pen".[2] The whole party crossed the Lemhi Pass on August 26. Dr Elliott Coues points out that this is the only place where both Lewis and Clark crossed the continental divide. The pass deserves the name of Lewis and Clark Pass much more than the pass which actually bears both their names.[3]

On September 4 the expedition crossed the Bitter Root Mountains by the Nez Perces Pass, to a branch of the Bitter Root River, which they named Clark River. They advanced north along the valley, and on September 13 crossed the Bitter Root Mountains once more, this time by the Lo Lo Pass. They reached the southern fork of the Clearwater River (Kooskooskee) and were now in the Columbia Basin. Snow fell on several days, but they realised that they must push forward and leave the mountains before winter came on. On September 16 the snow was 6 or 8 inches deep. The road was very bad going and there was little food, "for there is no living creature in these mountains, except a few small pheasants, a small species of gray squirrel...even these are difficult to shoot".[4] Clark marched on ahead and on September 20 he "descended the last of the Rocky mountains and reached the level country. A beautiful open plain, partially supplied with pine, now presented itself".[5] The horses were left in charge of Twisted Hair, a chief of the Chopunnish. By October 7 canoes had been constructed at the

[1] *L. and C.* II, 531–2.
[3] *Ibid.* II, 551, footnote.
[5] *Ibid.* II, 603.

[2] *Ibid.* II, 541.
[4] *Ibid.* II, 600.

junction of the north and south forks of the Kooskooskee, and on October 10 the expedition reached the junction of the Snake and the Kooskooskee. The party had now been four months in the mountains and found navigation more satisfactory than travelling by land, but was still short of food and fuel. The Columbia was reached on October 16, and Clark ascended the river for a few miles. On October 19 they saw the mountain called Mount St Helens in the west. On October 23 they portaged round the great falls of the Columbia, and on October 25 they were in camp near the site of the modern town of Dalles. Below the falls they found Indians, who had had previous contact with whites. On entering one of their houses they saw "a British musket, a cutlass, and several brass tea kettles".[1] On November 1 they portaged round the Cascade Falls and on November 2 they reached tidal water.

As soon as the expedition had passed the Cascade Mountains, they realised that they had entered a different type of country— a forested region. On November 2 they recorded that "the river widens to nearly a mile in extent; the low grounds become wider, and they as well as the mountains on each side are covered with pine, spruce-pine, cottonwood, a species of ash, and some alder. After being so long accustomed to the dreary nakedness of the country above, the change is as grateful to the eye as it is useful in supplying us with fuel".[2] The climate of the region which they had now entered was entirely different from the climate of the mountains. They were now in a land of fogs and rain. On November 3 and on November 7, they were detained by fog. They missed the Willamette River, but saw the Cowlitz, and late on November 7 they saw the ocean. The canoes experienced rough weather in the estuary. Continual rain and storms kept them in a precarious position on the north side of the river. On December 8 a site on the south side of the river was chosen for a fort, and Fort Clatsop was completed by December 24. Dr Elliott Coues describes their situation as follows: "In the dismal semi-aquatic life to which the party is about to be condemned, living in almost continuous rain for four months, in miserable sheds, like muskrats in their holes,

---

[1] *L. and C.* ii, 673.   [2] *Ibid.* ii, 688.

they will have nothing to do but shoot elk for a living, make salt to season their meat, and dicker with the natives".[1]

The contrast in climate between the camp at Fort Mandan with its hard cold winter and the continual rain of Fort Clatsop is very striking. From the meteorological register[2] compiled by the expedition it appears that rain was recorded on 66 days out of the 89 days spent at Fort Clatsop. On many days it rained "without intermission". There was continuous rain during the construction of the fort and rain brought with it its normal companion in England, "influenza and bad cold".[3] The climate is described as "obviously much milder than above the first range of mountains, for the Indians are thinly clad, and say they have little snow; indeed, since our arrival, the weather has been very warm, sometimes disagreeably so".[4] There are many references to the dense vegetation of this region and the Cascades. On November 11 "a hunter was dispatched in hopes of finding some fresh meat; but the hills were so steep, and so covered with undergrowth and fallen timber, that he could not penetrate them, and he was forced to return".[5]

The Indians of the region were also very different from the Indians whom they had encountered on the prairies and in the mountains. They lived in houses,[6] were expert with canoes, and subsisted largely on fish and wappatoo roots. They appear to have been great thieves,[7] much demoralised by the white traders with whom they had come in contact. The explorers hunted elk for food in addition to the usual food of the Indians. During the visit, the Indians obtained a whale that had been washed ashore.[8]

While they were confined in their huts, the two explorers compiled careful accounts of the Indian tribes and the flora and fauna of the region.[9] Clark also completed a map of the region through which they had passed; from this map they drew the

[1] *L. and C.* II, 720, footnote.
[2] *Ibid.* III, 1264, Appendix IV.
[3] *Ibid.* II, 792.
[4] *Ibid.* II, 720, November 24, 1805.
[5] *Ibid.* II, 705.
[6] *Ibid.* II, 666–7.
[7] *Ibid.* II, 693.
[8] *Ibid.* II, 745.
[9] *Ibid.* III, 821–901.

following remarkable conclusions with regard to a trans-continental route:

The inference deduced...is, that the best and most practicable route across the continent is by way of the Missouri to the entrance of Dearborn's river, or near that point; thence to Flathead (Clark's) river at the entrance of Traveler's-rest creek; thence up this creek to its forks; whence you pursue a range of mountains which divides the waters of the two forks of this creek, and which range, still pursuing its westerly course, divides the waters of two main forks of the Kooskooskee river to their junction; thence you descend this river by water to the S.E. branch of the Columbia, thence down this S.E. branch to the Columbia, and down this last to the Pacific Ocean.[1]

Some of the men occupied the winter in making over 300 pairs of moccasins for purposes of trade.

Lewis and Clark became alarmed as to the means of subsistence at Fort Clatsop, as the elk were migrating to the hills, and the fort was evacuated on March 23, 1806. They ascended the river in canoes and on their return Clark explored the Multnomah (Willamette) River. Clark formed an exaggerated idea concerning the basin of the river. He says that the river and its tributaries "water the vast extent of country between the western mountains and those of the seacoast, as far, perhaps, as the waters of the Gulf of California".[2] He described the Willamette country as "the only desirable situation for a settlement on the western side of the Rocky mountains, and being naturally fertile, would, if properly cultivated, afford subsistence for 40,000 or 50,000 souls".[3] The Cascade Mountains were observed and Mounts Rainier, St Helens, Hood, and Jefferson were sighted.

The journal of the return contains more elaborate accounts of the two great series of falls of the Cascades[4] and of the Dalles,[5] 50 miles further up. At the Dalles they sold their canoes in exchange for horses and proceeded by land on the north side of the river. They crossed the Columbia on April 29, and encamped near the mouth of the Walla-Walla River and found that the Walla-Walla tribe of Indians were one of the kindest tribes that

---

[1] L. and C. II, 802.
[2] Ibid. III, 925, April 3, 1806.
[3] Ibid. III, 930, April 4, 1806.
[4] Ibid. III, 945.
[5] Ibid. III, 954-5.

they had encountered. The expedition now proceeded straight across country to the mouth of the Kooskooskee River, arriving on May 4, and by this short cut saved a considerable amount of time. The expedition then proceeded along the northern side of the Kooskooskee (Clearwater River), having obtained horses as payment for medical treatment. On May 7, "from the plain we observed that the spurs of the Rocky mountains are still perfectly covered with snow, which the Indians inform us is so deep that we shall not be able to pass before the next full moon—that is, the 1st of June".[1] Falls of snow are recorded on May 9 and 10, on the latter occasion as much as 8 inches.[2] The horses left with the chief, Twisted Hair, in the previous season were recovered, and a camp was made, called Camp Chopunnish, to await the melting of the snows. On June 10 the expedition left the camp and proceeded to cross the Bitter Root Mountains by the same route and pass (Lo Lo Pass), as in the previous season. "The route was through thick woods and over high hills, intersected by deep ravines and obstructed by fallen timber. We found much difficulty also in following the road, the greater part of it being covered with snow, which lies in great masses eight or ten feet deep".[3] On June 11 the snow was "12 to 15 feet in depth, even on the south side of the mountain, with the fullest exposure to the sun".[4] Only after two attempts were the party able to cross the ridge.

Traveler's-rest Creek was reached on June 29, and the expedition was now divided into two parties. Lewis with nine men was to cross the divide by the usual Indian route, a direct crossing to the Missouri, and to explore Maria's River. Clark with the rest of the party was to follow a route to the Jefferson and the Missouri and explore the upper waters of the Yellowstone. This admirable plan was entirely successful.

Lewis left Clark on July 3 and travelled east along the course of the Blackfoot River, eventually reaching the divide and crossing by the pass afterwards called Lewis and Clark Pass.[5] The region was described as abundantly supplied with beaver

---

[1] *L. and C.* III, 995. [2] *Ibid.* III, 1000.
[3] *Ibid.* III, 1044, June 16, 1806.
[4] *Ibid.* III, 1046. [5] *Ibid.* III, 1077, July 7, 1806.

and deer. The land of the buffalo was soon reached and the
party were then free from all danger of starvation. On July 11
"there could not have been fewer than 10,000 buffalo within a
circuit of two miles".[1] Lewis, with three men, now proceeded
directly north to Maria's River, where he met a party of Minne-
tarees, and in an unfortunate encounter two Indians were killed.
Lewis hastened to return to the Missouri to escape the vengeance
of the Indians, and his whole party were united with Clark on
August 12. Parties of American traders were met[2] at the mouth
of the Yellowstone, a fact which shows how quickly the region
explored by Lewis and Clark was utilised by traders.

Clark and his party followed up the Bitter Root valley and
then struck directly across to the head of Wisdom River, thus
shortening the outward route. The divide was crossed on July 6
by a pass now known as Gibbon's Pass[3] (sometimes misprinted
Gibson's Pass), or more properly as Clark's Pass.[4] This crossing
was found to be an excellent route. "We had now crossed the
whole distance from Traveler's-rest creek to the head of Jefferson river, which seems to form the best and shortest route over
the mountains, during the whole distance of 164 miles. It is, in
fact, a very excellent road, which by cutting a few trees might
be rendered a good route for wagons, with the exception of
about four miles over one of the mountains, which would
require some leveling".[5] At the three forks the party divided.
Sergeant Ordway and nine men descended the Missouri in six
canoes, while Clark and ten men proceeded to the Yellowstone
by land with fifty horses. They followed the line subsequently
taken by the railway route, Gallatin City, Bozeman to Livingston. They crossed the divide between the Gallatin and the
Yellowstone by the Bozeman Pass. On July 24 the party embarked in canoes on the Yellowstone[6] and reached the Missouri

---

[1] *L. and C.* III, 1081.   [2] *Ibid.* III, 1116.

[3] General J. Gibbon fought a battle here on August 9, 1877.

[4] Elliott Coues gives a full description of the passes used by Lewis and
Clark in *L. and C.* II, 580–1, footnote and III, 1122–3, footnote.

[5] *L. and C.* III, 1127–8, July 8, 1806.

[6] The lower course of the Yellowstone with its southern tributaries was
explored by Larocque a month before Clark. L. J. Burpee (ed.), "Journal
de Larocque" in *Publications des Archives Canadiennes*, no. 3 (1911), p. 30.

on August 3. The Big Horn tributary of the Yellowstone,[1] and the Yellowstone itself,[2] were fully described.

The party reunited on August 12, and the descent of the Missouri to St Louis, where they arrived on September 23, 1806, was accomplished without difficulty. John Colter, one of the party, was discharged on August 15, and made his famous journey in the Yellowstone Park region in the following year. Many efforts were made to promote peace between the various Indian tribes, Mandans, Ricaras, and Chayennes.[3] The party noticed the rapid advance and great increase of settlement along the banks of the Missouri as they neared St Louis.

The two explorers did not reach Washington until February of 1807. Captain Clark was made a general of the militia of Louisiana and became Indian agent for Louisiana. In 1813 he was appointed as Governor of Missouri Territory. He subsequently became Superintendent of Indian Affairs and Surveyor-General of the States of Illinois and Missouri and of the Territory of Arkansas, and died in September, 1838.

Captain Lewis was made Governor of Louisiana and took up his residence at St Louis. In September of 1809 it became necessary for him to return to Washington. Before he completed his journey, his life came to a sudden end. It has been generally believed that Lewis was overcome by depression and took his own life, but there are some grounds for the assertion that he was murdered. Jefferson contributed a life of Captain Lewis to the history of the expedition, which appeared in 1814. In this life Jefferson paid the great explorer a striking tribute and described his character in the following words:

Of courage undaunted, possessing a firmness and perseverance of purpose which nothing but impossibilities could divert from its direction, careful as a father of those committed to his charge, yet steady in the maintenance of order and discipline, intimate with the Indian character, customs and principles. Habituated to the hunting life, guarded by exact observation of the vegetables and animals of his own country, against losing time in the description of objects already possessed, honest, disinterested, liberal,

[1] *L. and C.* III, 1153.
[2] *Ibid.* III, 1167–9.
[3] Lewis contributed a useful essay on Indian policy for the government. This essay is reprinted in *L. and C.* III, 1215–44.

of sound understanding, and a fidelity to truth so scrupulous that whatever he should report would be as certain as if seen by ourselves.[1]

Results of the Expedition. The results of this expedition were indeed immense. Lewis and Clark were the first to discover the great width of the continent. They found that the continent was much wider than they supposed before they started. Lewis drew a map at Fort Mandan before they went on their journey. A comparison of this map actually compiled at the end of the journey shows the great extent of their discoveries. They actually passed through six of the physical regions described in chapter II of this book, and thus made a much greater addition to geographical knowledge than any of their successors. The discoveries of Lewis and Clark have been summed up by Professor H. C. Dale in the following words:

The Columbia, instead of being merely a Pacific coast stream, was found to drain a vast interior valley or series of valleys between the Cordilleras and the Coast Range. Instead of one mountain system lying between the headwaters of the Missouri and the Pacific, they found two, separated from each other by four hundred miles and more of intervening valleys. They discovered the whole interior drainage of the Columbia with its two main arteries, fittingly named for the discoverers themselves, and their network of tributaries. The Missouri they found to head in the northwest and not in the southwest. The upper waters, though not the source, and many of the higher tributaries, with those of its great affluent, the Yellowstone, they were the first white men to cross. The network of ridges that characterizes the Rocky Mountain System along the forty-fifth parallel, they also sighted for the first time.[2]

The results of the expedition are important not only from the point of view of the discovery of surface relief and drainage, but also from all the other aspects of geographical knowledge. These explorers were the first to observe the differences in climate which exist in this area. They made a remarkable contrast between the climate of Fort Mandan on the prairies and of Fort Clatsop on the Pacific. They discussed the different rainfall *régimes* of three distinct regions. They described the summer

[1] *Writings of Thomas Jefferson*, ed. H. A. Washington, VIII, 484.
[2] H. C. Dale, *Ashley-Smith Explorations*, pp. 25–6. Professor Dale's claim, on behalf of Lewis and Clark, that they discovered "the whole interior drainage of the Columbia", should be estimated in the light of the subsequent exploration of the fur-traders detailed below.

rains of the Plains, the comparative aridity of the Plateau, and the torrential rainfall of the Pacific coast.

With regard to vegetation, an admirable account is given of the timbers of the Pacific coast, and of the coniferous forests of the interior mountains.

The zoological discoveries of the explorers are especially remarkable. The ten animals whose names follow were first described by Lewis and Clark. 1, the grizzly bear (*Ursus horribilis*); 2, the black-tailed fallow deer (*Cariacus columbianus*); 3, the mule deer (*Cariacus macrotis*); 4, the tiger cat or lynx of the Columbia (*Lynx rufus fasciatus*); 5, the mountain goat or sheep (*Haplocerus montanus*); 6, the barking squirrel or prairie dog (*Cynomys ludovicianus*); 7, the sewellel (*Haplodon rufus*) (this small animal was used by the natives of the Columbia for robes) 8, the cock of the plains or sage grouse (*Centrocercus urophasianus*); 9, the steelhead salmon trout (*Salmo gairdneri*); and 10, various types of snails. In addition to these discoveries the journal gives valuable accounts of the habits of other animals.

The descriptions of Indian tribes are full and elaborate. The contrasts between the three different types of Indians are clearly brought out. The Indians who live on buffalo are contrasted with those who live on fish and those who live on roots.

The fur-traders completed the map of the Columbia Basin by discovering the courses of the two forks of the Lewis and the Clark Rivers. The work of the two pioneer explorers concerning land relief and drainage was completed by these fur-traders, but the fur-traders did not draw up elaborate scientific journals. The expedition of Lewis and Clark must be praised for its discoveries in the fields of climate, vegetation, zoology, and anthropology.

The work of these two great men has too often been neglected in general works on the history of exploration. There is no doubt that they deserve a place beside the great explorers of the world, and may justly be compared with Livingstone and Stanley in Africa and with Hedin and Stein in central Asia.

(b) The Fur-Traders, 1806–1811

After Lewis and Clark returned, the Government abandoned exploration of the region, but their work was continued by the traders who soon followed in their trails. Only six months after the return of the official expedition, Manuel Lisa, who had made some attempts to increase the fur trade during the Spanish *régime*, sent a party of men up the Missouri River. Lisa determined to erect forts at convenient points on the upper river, as bases of the trade. Lisa's first expedition of 1807 erected a fort at the mouth of the Big Horn. From this fort, John Colter, who had been one of the party under Lewis and Clark, was sent out in the winter of 1807–8 to confer with the Crow Indians and induce them to bring in furs to Lisa's fort. The actual route and discoveries of this journey have been much disputed.[1]

From Lisa's fort, in 1808, other fur-traders explored much of the country between the Yellowstone and Missouri and pushed their way up streams whose mouths only had been noticed by Lewis and Clark. Later in 1808 Lisa's company was enlarged by the inclusion of various other traders and named the Missouri Fur Company. This new company established a fort at the Three Forks. This fort was in the heart of the country of the Blackfoot Indians and, owing to the hostility of this fierce tribe, was very soon evacuated.

In 1810, Andrew Henry, after the abandonment of the fort, pushed his way up the Madison River and crossed the continental divide. He discovered the river now called Henry River, which is the northern branch of the Snake, and built a fort in the unexplored country. During the winter he discovered several of the headwater streams of the Snake or Lewis fork of

[1] For two opposite points of view see H. M. Chittenden, *History of the American Fur Trade*, II, 715, and H. C. Dale, *Ashley-Smith Explorations*, p. 28. See also H. M. Chittenden, *The Yellowstone National Park* (1895), and Stallo Vinton, *John Colter, Discoverer of Yellowstone Park* (1926). Colter's route appears on Lewis and Clark's map of 1814 and is there described as "Colter's route in 1807". Chittenden's interpretation of this map is shown on Map A at the end of this book. The route is also indicated on Fig. 27.

the Columbia. The small Henry Lake is named after this fur-trader.[1]

Henry's expedition was not a financial success, as only forty packs of beaver were secured, and trading in this region was abandoned. The hostility of the Indians was found to be too great and the Missouri Fur Company declined in importance and, after 1823, moved its main operations to the Great Salt Lake region. The Company had also to face the competition of the Pacific Fur Company of Astor. The geographical achievements of the latter Company will be more appropriately considered in the chapter on the central route to the Pacific. The expedition of the Astorians added considerably to the geographical knowledge of the southern basin of the Columbia, that is the Snake or Lewis Basin.

A certain amount of geographical exploration was accomplished by British traders of the North-West and Hudson's Bay Companies, working from the north. The expeditions of these traders, although important, can only be briefly mentioned. Their work filled in the gaps which had been left by the Lewis and Clark expedition.

The most remarkable of these British explorers was David Thompson.[2] He worked his way up the Saskatchewan River, crossed the Rockies in 1806, and discovered the upper waters of the Columbia. In 1809 he crossed the present international

[1] "The route taken by Lewis and Clarke across the mountains, was, perhaps, the very worst that could have been selected. Mr Henry, a member of the Missouri company, and his hunters, have discovered several passes. . . . Mr Henry wintered in a delightful country, on a beautiful navigable stream."

H. M. Brackenridge, *Views of Louisiana*, p. 162, Baltimore, 1817. See also pp. 143–5.

[2] See Elliott Coues, *New Light on the Early History of the Greater North-west*, 3 vols. This book contains the journals of Alexander Henry (of the North-West Company) and of David Thompson. See J. B. Tyrrell, "David Thompson, A Great Geographer", *Geographical Journal* XXXVII (1911), 49–58, and J. B. Tyrrell (ed.), *David Thompson's Narrative of his Explorations in Western America*, 1784–1812, Toronto, The Champlain Society, 1916. Mr J. N. L. Baker considers that Thompson "was one of the greatest explorers of all time, and is probably the greatest of all those who opened up the New World". J. N. L. Baker, *A History of Geographical Discovery and Exploration* (1931), pp. 368–9.

boundary, and in 1811 he descended the Columbia and followed that river to the sea. Thompson had discovered the main direction of Clark's fork as Henry and the Astorians discovered the direction of Lewis' fork.

The exploration of the detailed drainage of the two forks of the Columbia was thus completed by fur-traders, British and American. The work of Lewis and Clark was finished, and the possibilities of a northern trans-continental route were known. The journals of the fur-traders do not give such a wealth of geographic information as the journals of the successful explorers Lewis and Clark. For this reason, and for the reason that they ended a work which had already been begun, only a brief account of their journeys is necessary in this book.

Chapter X

THE DISCOVERY OF A CENTRAL TRANS-CONTINENTAL ROUTE[1]

(a) Astoria, 1810–1813

John Jacob Astor, a fur-trader of Montreal, was one of the first to realise the importance of the great trans-continental route discovered by Lewis and Clark. Astor settled in New York and endeavoured to obtain a monopoly of the fur trade in the United States. In 1808 he founded the American Fur Company and in 1810 the Pacific Fur Company.

Astor determined to establish his headquarters near the mouth of the Columbia. From this place expeditions were to penetrate the interior in all directions, and return with furs. Supplies were to be sent out to the fur-trading centre by sea from New York. The supply ships were then to sell the furs in China and return home with eastern goods. Astor also decided to establish a line of posts across the continent, along the whole length of Lewis and Clark's route.

With these objects in view, two expeditions were prepared, one to travel by sea, the other by land. The *Tonquin*, a ship of 250 tons, under Captain Thorn carried the maritime expedition. The ship left New York in September, 1810, and arrived in the Columbia on May 25, 1811. The journey was enlivened by the constant quarrels which that iron disciplinarian, Captain Thorn, carried on with the traders. While some of the party remained on the Columbia to establish a fort, which they named Astoria, the ship proceeded to Nootka Sound. When the *Tonquin* arrived at Nootka, a large number of Indians came on board, apparently for trade, and treacherously seized the ship. On the following day an explosion of the magazine completely destroyed the *Tonquin* and all who were on board at the time.

---

[1] The routes of explorers described in this chapter are shown on end Map B, Fig. 33.

Astor's expedition to the Columbia by sea had ended in complete disaster.[1]

The overland expedition is of greater importance in the history of exploration. The party was organised by William P. Hunt in Montreal in June, 1810, but did not leave St Louis until March, 1811. Hunt had quarrelled with Manuel Lisa during the winter, and when Hunt started on his journey, Lisa pursued him, but the quarrel was settled by the time both parties reached the Arikara villages on June 12, 1811.[2] Hunt was accompanied by three of Andrew Henry's men (see chapter IX, pp. 124–5). Hunt decided that it would be folly to go any further up the Missouri, because of the danger of the Blackfoot Indians. He therefore abandoned Lewis and Clark's route and attempted to cross the mountains a good deal further south than the crossings made by the earlier explorers. Horses were purchased from the Arikara and the party of sixty-four persons set out westward across the plains. The expedition traversed a country that was virtually unexplored between the Missouri and

[1] *A Note on Books.* The firsthand accounts of the expedition to Astoria are contained in

(1) G. Franchère, *Narrative of a Voyage to the Northwest Coast, 1811–1814*, New York, 1854. Reprinted in E.W.T., ed. R. G. Thwaites, vol. VI.

(2) Alexander Ross, *Adventures of the First Settlers on the Oregon*, London, 1849. Reprinted in E.W.T., ed. R. G. Thwaites, vol. VII.

(3) Ross Cox, *Adventures on the Columbia River*, London, 1831.

The following two books contain accounts of part of the expedition:

(1) John Bradbury, *Travels in the Interior of America*, London, 1819. Reprinted in E.W.T., ed. R. G. Thwaites, vol. V. Bradbury accompanied the Astorians as far as the villages of the Arikara.

(2) H. M. Brackenridge, *Journal of a Voyage up the River Missouri in 1811*, Baltimore, 1816. Reprinted in E.W.T., ed. R. G. Thwaites, vol. VI. Brackenridge travelled with Manuel Lisa in pursuit of the Astorians.

An admirable secondary account of the expedition is to be found in Washington Irving's *Astoria; or, Enterprise Beyond the Rocky Mountains*, London, 1839. This book is brilliantly written and has been rightly described by Chittenden as a classic. H. H. Bancroft, in his *History of the Northwest Coast*, vol. II, accuses Irving of plagiarism and of invention in his treatment of the subject. These charges cannot be upheld as the accuracy of Irving's statements can be verified by the above firsthand accounts.

[2] The journey to the Arikara villages is fully described by Bradbury and Brackenridge, E.W.T. vols. V and VI. See list of books above.

the Big Horn. They passed to the north of the Black Hills, "an extensive chain, lying about a hundred miles east of the Rocky mountains, and stretching in a north-east direction from the south fork of the Nebraska, or Platte river, to the great north bend of the Missouri.... The wild recesses of these hills are retreats and lurking places for broken and predatory tribes".[1] On August 17, Hunt saw the Big Horn Mountains and a fortnight later he crossed them. He was guided across the mountains by Crow Indians, reached the Big Horn River and then marched towards the north-west up the valley of the Wind River. "This river gives its name to a whole range of mountains consisting of three parallel chains, eighty miles in length and about twenty or twenty-five broad. One of its peaks is probably fifteen thousand feet above the level of the sea, being one of the highest of the Rocky Sierra. These mountains give rise, not merely to the Wind or Big Horn river, but to several branches of the Yellowstone and the Missouri on the east, and of the Columbia and Colorado on the west; thus dividing the sources of these mighty streams."[2] For five days the party journeyed up the valley of the Wind River[3] and crossed the Wind River Mountains by Union Pass on September 16; on the next day they encamped on the Spanish or Green River. From the top of the pass they saw the Three Tetons. They now crossed the divide between the Green River and the Snake, and reached the latter river on September 26. Hunt now decided to construct canoes and navigate the river; fifteen canoes were made and the expedition proceeded downstream until they were wrecked at Caldron Linn. An exploring party which was sent in advance reported that further navigation was impossible. "For nearly forty miles that they had explored, the river foamed and roared along through a deep and narrow channel, from twenty to thirty yards wide, which it had worn in the course of ages, through the heart of a barren country. The precipices on each side were often two or three hundred feet high."[4] They now

[1] W. Irving, *Astoria*, p. 197.
[2] *Ibid.* p. 217.
[3] "The country in general was destitute of trees." *Ibid.* p. 217.
[4] *Ibid.* p. 236.

realised that it had been folly to leave their horses and take to canoes.

The third part of the journey from Caldron Linn to Astoria was made on foot. For a part of the way the expedition was divided into five parties. As all the parties more or less followed the direction of the Snake River, it is unnecessary to describe their movements in detail. Hunt with the main party followed the right bank of the Snake, while Crooks followed the left bank. They were afraid to leave the river because "in abandoning the river, they would have to launch forth upon vast trackless plains destitute of all means of subsistence, where they might perish of hunger and thirst. A dreary desert of sand and gravel extends from Snake river almost to the Columbia".[1] Hunt proceeded down the river and crossed the Snake near the junction of that river and the Weiser tributary. Hunt followed an Indian trail across the Blue Mountains and down the Umatilla, reaching the Columbia River near the mouth of the Walla-Walla, and finally arrived at Astoria on February 15, 1812. The latter part of the route was almost identical with the later Oregon trail.

The whole length of the Snake or Lewis fork of the Columbia had now been explored, the upper part by Henry, between 1810 and 1811, and the lower part by the Astorians. The Astorians had also discovered the difficult Union Pass and they were the first Americans to visit Green River.

On June 29, 1812, a party under the leadership of Robert Stuart was sent back overland to St Louis with reports for Astor. The party followed the same route as taken on the outward journey as far as Caldron Linn, where they arrived on August 29. On August 20 they met four men who had been detached from the westward expedition in the previous year. It seems quite possible that these four men visited Bear River and Great Salt Lake and were therefore the first men to penetrate the Interior Basin from the north. Stuart now turned south-east and probably reached Bear River. Instead of continuing east, the expedition seems to have lost all sense of direction and marched north until they were on the Snake River once more.

[1] W. Irving, *Astoria*, p. 242.

They crossed the Tetons and after following the Green River for a short distance they pursued a south-easterly course along the base of the Wind River Mountains. They appear to have just missed South Pass,[1] and on October 26 they reached the Sweetwater. Winter quarters were established on the Platte and canoes were constructed. Navigation on the Platte was impossible and the canoes were abandoned. "On the 8th of March they launched forth in their canoes, but soon found that the river had not depth sufficient even for such slender barks. It expanded into a wide, but extremely shallow stream, with many sand bars, and occasionally various channels. They got one of their canoes a few miles down it, with extreme difficulty, sometimes wading and dragging it over the shoals."[2] Stuart and his party reached St Louis on April 30, 1813, after a journey of some ten months. Chittenden did not exaggerate, when he concluded that "the two Astorian expeditions, therefore, are entitled to the credit of having practically opened up the Oregon Trail from the Missouri river at the mouth of the Kansas to the mouth of the Columbia river".[3]

Meanwhile war had broken out between Great Britain and the United States, and on December 13, 1813, Astoria was handed over to the British and renamed Fort George.[4]

(b) British Fur-Traders from the North, 1816–1829.

The work of David Thompson, a British fur-trader who entered the region from the north, has already been briefly described. After the cession of Astoria to the British North-West Company, a whole series of expeditions extended British influence far south into the region traversed by the Astorians.

In 1816 the Company decided to extend operations "on the south and west towards California and the mountains em-

[1] See *infra*, pp. 140–1 for a discussion of this question.
[2] W. Irving, *Astoria*, p. 361.
[3] H. M. Chittenden, *History of the American Fur Trade*, I, 214.
[4] See Elliott Coues, *New Light on the Early History of the Greater North-west*, New York, 1897. Contains the Journal of Alexander Henry, who spent the winter of 1813–14 at Fort George.

bracing a new and unexplored tract of country".[1] The leaders
of these expeditions were Donald M'Kenzie, Alexander Ross,
Peter Skene Ogden, and John Work. The first of these expeditions was led by M'Kenzie into the Snake River valley, and
did not add to the geographical knowledge of that region
already obtained by the Astorians. M'Kenzie's expedition of
1819 travelled up Bear River as far as Bear Lake and therefore
journeyed further south into the Interior Basin than any other
white men before them. The expeditions of 1820–21 and of
1823 were in regions already well known. In 1821 the North-
West and the Hudson's Bay Companies were merged in one
company and in 1824 Alexander Ross left Flathead House, a
station of the Hudson's Bay Company, on an eastward journey.
He followed Lewis and Clark's route as far as the Lemhi River
and proceeded to explore all the upper tributaries of the Salmon
River (a tributary of the Snake).

The next five expeditions were made under the command of
Peter Skene Ogden, another servant of the North-West Company.[2] Little is known of his first expedition in 1824–5, but in
1825–6 he travelled up the Deschutes tributary of the Columbia
and crossed to the sources of John Day's River, a region which
had not been previously explored. He then pushed up the
valley of the Snake as far as the Portneuf, returning to Fort
Vancouver with a great quantity of furs.

Ogden again travelled up the valley of the Deschutes in
1826–7, and a section of his party visited Malhéur and Harney
Lakes. Ogden then travelled towards the Klamath and reached
the headwaters of that river. He discovered the Klamath River
lake and possibly the Pitt River. He realised that these waters
flowed into the Pacific directly, and were not tributaries of the
Columbia. He saw Mount Shasta and retained its Indian name.
After wintering among the Shasta Indians, Ogden returned
eastward across the south of the modern State of Oregon,
finally reaching Fort Vancouver by way of the Snake.

---

[1] A. Ross, *Fur Hunters of the Far West*, I, 73 (1855). This book contains
accounts of the British expeditions.

[2] See T. C. Elliott (ed.), "The Peter Skene Ogden Journals, 1825–
1829", *Oregon Hist. Soc. Quarterly*, vols. X and XI, Portland, 1909–10.

The expedition of 1827–8 did not visit any unexplored regions and wintered in the valley of Portneuf, but the expedition of 1828–9 had very important results. In December, 1828, Ogden was guided by Snake Indians to the neighbourhood of Salt Lake and explored the northern side of the lake. He described it as a "barren country destitute of everything". He then travelled west from the Salt Lake and discovered the river now called the Humboldt. The river should properly be called Ogden's or Mary's River. "One of Mr Ogden's party took a woman for his wife from among the Indians found on this river, to whom the name of Mary was given. From this circumstance the stream came to be called Mary's river. It is also called Ogden's river after its discoverer."[1] Ogden returned to Fort Nez Percé in the summer of 1829. Ogden's discoveries were used by Arrowsmith, the London cartographer, as a basis for the maps which he drew for the Hudson's Bay Company.

John Work,[2] who had entered the Hudson's Bay Company in 1814, carried out a considerable amount of exploration during the years 1831–2. In June, 1825, he made a journey from Fort Vancouver to trade with the Flathead Indians. In July, 1826, he traded in the valley of Clark's fork. He spent the following years in the Columbia region, and in the spring of 1831 was appointed chief-trader, and succeeded Ogden in charge of "the Snake River brigade". In April–July, 1831, he travelled up the Snake valley to the Great Salt Lake and back. In August of the same year, he left Fort Vancouver and proceeded up the Columbia to Walla-Walla. He then used the Lo Lo Pass across the Rocky Mountains into the country of the Blackfoot Indians and returned to Fort Vancouver in July, 1832.

(c) The Rocky Mountains Fur Company, 1822–1836.

In 1821 General W. H. Ashley formed a new trading company, called the Rocky Mountains Fur Company. He persuaded many courageous trappers to join him, including among others

[1] G. K. Warren, *Memoir to accompany the Map of the Territory of the United States* (1859), p. 36.
[2] W. S. Lewis and P. C. Phillips, *The Journal of John Work* (1923).

Jedediah S. Smith, Andrew Henry, the Sublettes, and James Bridger. This Company made substantial additions to geographical knowledge in the course of the search for fur. Unfortunately, the Journals of the Company, which exist to-day, are very meagre, as Smith's Journals, which would have been the most valuable, were destroyed. The Journals of Ashley on his expedition of 1824–5, and those of H. G. Rogers, who was a member of Smith's company 1826–8, have been edited in a very scholarly book by Professor H. C. Dale.[1] These Journals, however, do not contain a great amount of descriptive geographical information, and can therefore bear no comparison with the journals of Lewis and Clark. It is only possible to give a bald account of the routes of these traders illustrated by a map (see end Map B).

The earlier expeditions were unfortunate. In 1822, Henry's expedition up the Missouri was robbed of all its horses by the Assiniboines, but a post was established at the mouth of the Yellowstone. In 1823, Henry moved on to the Great Falls and in a skirmish with the Blackfoot Indians, four of his trappers were killed. Ashley himself came up the river to assist Henry, with the intention of purchasing horses from the Arikara tribe and pursuing a westward route across the Plains, as the Astorians had done in 1812. While negotiations for the sale of horses were proceeding, Ashley was attacked and fourteen of his men were killed. Henry managed to return to Ashley and they both retired a safe distance down the river. Colonel Leavenworth subsequently led a punitive military expedition against the Arikara, which need not be described in this book.[2]

In August, 1823, Henry was again on the Yellowstone, but his horses were stolen, two of his men were killed, and he was obliged to abandon his post. Henry despatched a party under Provot which followed the valley of the Big Horn. This party is believed, by some writers, to have discovered the South Pass, but it seems more probable that a party under Thomas Fitz-

[1] H. C. Dale, *The Ashley-Smith Explorations and the Discovery of a Central Route to the Pacific*, 1822–1829 (1918).

[2] See H. M. Chittenden, *op. cit.* vol. II, part III, chap. III, The Aricara Campaign of 1823.

patrick discovered the pass in the spring of 1824. He led his men up the valley of the Big Horn to Wind River and across the pass to the Big Sandy and the Green River. Fitzpatrick obtained quantities of beaver, but after constructing skin boats on the Sweetwater, was wrecked and lost the greater number of his furs. Ashley now decided to abandon the country of the upper Missouri and transfer his operations to the Green River and utilise the South Pass. Ashley also changed his methods of trade. He abandoned the system of establishing permanent posts and replaced it by arranging an annual *rendez-vous*. Large numbers of separate parties were sent out to collect furs and bring them to some pre-arranged meeting-place. Under the old system furs had been obtained by the whites from the Indians, who bartered them at the permanent posts. Henceforward the white traders themselves became the trappers.[1]

By discovering South Pass, the Rocky Mountains Fur Company had found an easy route across the Rockies to streams which abounded in beaver. The route formed a great contrast to the northern routes. "The only known way to the Columbia", says Dale, "was by the northern passes, discovered and used by Lewis and Clark, and after them, by the Missouri Fur Company in its palmier days. But the northern passes were scarcely ways; they were rather obstacles."[2]

During the winter of 1824 a party of Ashley's men under Bridger were trapping on Bear River and its tributaries. James Bridger followed the river to its outlet in Great Salt Lake and found that the lake was salt. "The fact of the water being salt induced the belief that it was an arm of the Pacific ocean; but, in the spring of 1826, four men went in *skin* boats around it to discover if any streams containing beaver were to be found emptying into it, but returned with indifferent success."[3]

[1] The classic account of the fur trade is Washington Irving, *The Adventures of Captain Bonneville, U.S.A., in the Rocky Mountains and the Far West* (1837). See chap. xx, p. 111, (1850 ed.), for a brilliant account of the Green River *rendez-vous*. [2] H. C. Dale, *op. cit.* p. 109.

[3] G. K. Warren, *Memoir*, p. 35, in a letter from Robert Campbell to G. K. Warren, dated April 4, 1857. The respective claims of Ogden and Provot to be considered as the discoverers of Great Salt Lake are discussed by H. C. Dale, *op. cit.* pp. 46 ff., 103 ff.

Bridger can, therefore, be regarded as the discoverer of the lake.

In the winter of 1824, Ashley himself set out on an expedition. The route is approximately indicated on end Map B. He left Council Bluffs and ascended the Platte River until he reached the mountains. He probably crossed the mountains some miles to the south of the South Pass by what is called Bridger's Pass which is in the neighbourhood of the route used by the modern Union Pacific Railway. He described the "dividing ridge" as "almost entirely destitute of vegetation except wild sage with which the earth is so bountifully spread that it proved a considerable impediment in our progress".[1] On April 21, 1825, Ashley embarked on a bull-boat and navigated the Sandy River and continued down the Green River. He said that the "navigation became difficult and dangerous, the river being remarkably crooked with more or less rapids every mile, caused by rocks which had fallen from the sides of the mountain".[2] He learnt from Indians "that the river which I had descended, and which I supposed to be the Rio Colorado of the West, continued its course as far as they had any knowledge of it, southwest through a mountainous country".[3] He followed the course of the river for a considerable distance on foot and then returned towards the west by way of the valleys of the Uinta and Duchesne Rivers. He crossed the Uinta Mountains[4] near Bald Peak. Ashley did not visit Sevier Lake or the Great Salt Lake on this expedition. He returned by following the old trail through South Pass to the Sweetwater and completed his journey by navigating the Big Horn and the Yellowstone. "The Yellowstone", says Ashley, "is a beautiful river to navigate. It has rapids extending from above Powder river about fifty miles, but I found about four feet of water over the most."[5] Ashley arrived at Council Bluffs in September, 1825, with about one

[1] H. C. Dale, op. cit. p. 133. Ashley's Journal.
[2] H. C. Dale, op. cit. p. 142. Ashley's Journal, May 3, 1825.
[3] Ibid. p. 151.
[4] "This range of mountains is in many places fertile and closely timbered with pine, cedar, quaking-asp and a dwarfish growth of oak." H. C. Dale, op. cit. p. 152. Ashley's Journal.
[5] Ibid. p. 161. Ashley's Journal.

hundred packs of beaver.[1] In the following spring, he visited the Great Salt Lake and returned to St Louis by a land journey along the banks of the Platte. He had sold his business to the other partners and returned, having made a fortune of eighty thousand dollars from furs.[2] Ashley was the first to cross the Plains along the line of the Platte in winter (December, 1824), the first to use Bridger's Pass and the first to navigate the Green River.

Jedediah S. Smith was now the leading man in the Company, and his explorations continued Ashley's work. Smith's Journals have been lost, but portions of the journals of one of his companions, Rogers by name, have survived.

On August 22, 1826,[3] Smith left Great Salt Lake with fifteen men, "for the purpose of exploring the country S.W. which was entirely unknown to me".[4] He made his way to Utah Lake and then across the Sevier valley to the Virgin River, a river which was named after Thomas Virgin, who was with Smith in this neighbourhood, in 1827. He descended the Virgin to the Colorado. Smith crossed to the eastern bank of the Colorado and on recrossing the river he followed a westerly course across the barren wastes of southern California. He followed the valley of the Mohave and described the Mohave desert in the following words: "I crossed a Salt plain about 20 miles long and 8 wide; on the surface was a crust of beautiful white salt, quite thin. Under this surface there is a layer of salt from a half to one and a half inches in depth; between this and the upper layer there is about four inches of yellowish sand".[5] Smith must have entered California by the Cajon Pass and arrived at the mission of San Gabriel (Los Angeles) on November 27, 1826. He proceeded to San Diego and returned by sea to San Pedro (the port of Los Angeles). Smith travelled north-west, crossed the Tehachapi Pass into the San Joaquin valley and then journeyed through California for 300 miles, at a distance which he estimated to be 150 miles from the coast, and was actually

[1] A "pack" of beaver contained sixty skins and weighed 100 pounds.
[2] H. C. Dale, *op. cit.* p. 169.
[3] For route see Map B, and for an account of the journey see letter of Smith to General Clark reprinted in *ibid.* pp. 186–94.
[4] *Ibid.* pp. 186–7. Smith's letter.
[5] *Ibid.* p. 190. Smith's letter.

about 100. He spent the winter in trapping and collected a good number of furs. He now attempted to cross the Sierra Nevada. "I found the snow so deep on Mount Joseph", says Smith, "that I could not cross my horses, five of which starved to death; I was compelled therefore to return to the valley which I had left and there, leaving my party, I started with two men, seven horses and two mules, which I loaded with hay for the horses and provisions for ourselves, and started on the 20th of May (1827), and succeeded in crossing it in eight days, having lost only two horses and one mule. I found the snow on the top of this mountain from 4 to 8 feet deep, but it was so consolidated by the heat of the sun that my horses only sunk from half a foot to one foot deep."[1] He probably crossed the Sierra Nevada by the Stanislaus valley and passed to the south of Mount Stanislaus by the same route as that followed by Bidwell in 1841 (see chapter XII). After travelling twenty days he reached the southern shore of the Great Salt Lake. He described the region which he had crossed as a "country completely barren and destitute of game. We frequently travelled without water sometimes for two days over sandy deserts, where there was no sign of vegetation and when we found water in some of the rocky hills, we most generally found some Indians who appeared the most miserable of the human race having nothing to subsist on (nor any clothing) except grass seed, grass-hoppers, etc.".[2] Smith reached the *rendez-vous* at the southern end of the lake, where he met his partners Jackson and Sublette. On July 13, Smith and seventeen men left Bear Lake on a journey to California, with the object of rejoining the men who had been left behind on the previous expedition. Smith followed the route of the previous year and was attacked by the Mohave Indians. Ten men were killed and all Smith's papers and property were lost. After undergoing many hardships, Smith reached the Spanish settlement of San Gabriel (Los Angeles). On arrival in California, Smith was involved in prolonged bickerings with the Mexicans, who eventually put him into prison at Monterey. In November, 1827, he was

---

[1] H. C. Dale, *op. cit.* pp. 192–3. Smith's letter.
[2] *Ibid.* p. 193.

released and ordered to leave Mexican territory. Smith followed the valley of the Sacramento and wintered in the valley of the tributary afterwards called the American River. In April, 1828, Smith's party followed an Indian trail up Shasta River over Siskyou Pass and then to the Umpqua and the coast. Smith found his way to the Willamette valley and wintered at Fort Vancouver. In March, 1829, he ascended the Columbia and followed the British fur-traders' route to their fort among the Flatheads and thence south to the Snake, finally rejoining his partners in August, 1829, at the Tetons.

Dale compares the work of Lewis and Clark with the work of Smith. "Lewis and Clark in reaching the Pacific, discovered and utilised the northern passes; Ashley and Smith in reaching Great Salt Lake utilised the southern passes.... Lewis and Clark were able to follow the course of large rivers almost the entire distance from St Louis to the mouth of the Columbia; Ashley and Smith, crossing from one complicated drainage area to another, were obliged to traverse a series of lofty mountain barriers as well as vast stretches of difficult and trying desert."[1] Smith's contributions to cartography were very great. Albert Gallatin, in drawing his map of 1836 (see *infra*, pp. 198–201), was under a great obligation to Smith. Smith has not left behind journals as valuable as those of Lewis and Clark, but there is no doubt that if his journals had not been destroyed they would have been of very great value, as Smith was the most scientific of the fur-traders.

The subsequent operations of the Rocky Mountains Fur Company between the years 1829 and 1834 were confined to the Green River district and no new regions were explored. In 1836 the Company was wound up. Chittenden estimates that the Company must have sent one thousand packs of beaver to St Louis, worth about 500 dollars a pack, and that the Company lost about one hundred lives during its career.

The Rocky Mountains Fur Company had opened up the region in the heart of the continent in the neighbourhood of South Pass. They had explored the Green River and the Colo-

[1] H. C. Dale, *op. cit.* p. 116.

rado; the Great Salt Lake, the Utah and the Sevier Lakes. The men of the Company were the first to cross the mountains and deserts of the Interior Basin. As Lewis and Clark had discovered a northern trans-continental route, so they had discovered a central route. Smith discovered two passes over the Sierra Nevada and showed that they were practicable even in winter, and he was the first to travel by land up the Pacific coast from California to the Columbia. Nevertheless the greatest achievement of the Company was the discovery of the Great Gap or South Pass, because this discovery was the necessary preliminary of all the others.

(d) The Discovery of South Pass [1]

The discovery of the South Pass, or the Great Gap of the Rocky Mountains, was one of the most important events in American history, but it seems to be impossible to determine who was the first white man to use the pass. It has been suggested that John Colter crossed South Pass in the winter of 1807–8 and that "Colter's river of General Wm. Clark's map, published in 1814, is really the Big Sandy".[2] Brackenridge, writing in 1813, had heard from Henry, the fur-trader, that passes over the Rocky Mountains existed to the south of those discovered by Lewis and Clark. "These passes", he says, "are considerably south of the source of Jefferson river", and "even in their present state, less difficult than those of the Alleghany mountains".[3] This general statement does not necessarily imply a knowledge of the existence of South Pass.

The expedition of the returning Astorians left the Columbia in June, 1812, and in October they crossed the Rockies very near what is now called South Pass, but it seems probable that they did not use the pass itself. Dr Elliott Coues, the authority on this question, finally concluded that the Astorians followed

[1] Section (d) of this chapter, on The Discovery of South Pass, is reprinted with slight modifications from an article entitled "South Pass: A Study in the Historical Geography of the United States", which appeared in *Scottish Geographical Magazine* (May 1929), XLV, 144–54.

[2] W. J. Ghent, *The Road to Oregon* (1929), p. 17. Ghent quotes the authority of John G. White and gives detailed references.

[3] H. M. Brackenridge, *Views of Louisiana*, p. 163, Baltimore, 1817.

a course "very near South Pass—perhaps within twelve or fifteen miles of it—when they wandered off the Indian trail which would have brought them through this pass, and kept about south-east till they had headed the Sweetwater entirely. They then struck east, south of that river and finally fell on it lower down".[1] Mr Ghent believes that "they crossed the range somewhere north of the southern wall of the pass, Table Mountain", but he is positive "that they did not journey along the Indian trail, which subsequently became the trappers and the emigrants roadway".[2]

It is quite certain that the pass was discovered by members of General W. H. Ashley's Rocky Mountains Fur Company, either in the autumn of 1823 or in the spring of 1824. Étienne Provot and Thomas Fitzpatrick have both been credited with the discovery of South Pass. Étienne Provot (sometimes spelt Provost), a free trapper who worked for Ashley, after whom a river which enters the eastern side of Utah Lake has been named, has been traditionally described as the discoverer of the pass.[3] Provot is said to have accomplished the feat in the autumn of 1823. Professor Dale[4] brings weighty arguments to bear against Provot's claim to be the original discoverer, and concludes that "until more positive evidence is brought forward in support of Provot's claim, the distinction of having discovered the South Pass may rest with Thomas Fitzpatrick, provided, of course, that the returning Astorians missed the actual pass itself". Fitzpatrick had learnt from the Crows of the existence of a pass across the Rockies. In the spring of 1824 he led his men down the Big Horn to Wind River and so across the mountains to the Big Sandy, and returned through South Pass.[5] The year 1824 marks the effective discovery of the pass.

[1] Elliott Coues, *Forty Years a Fur Trader, The Personal Narrative of C. Larpenteur, 1833–1872* (1899), 1, 28. See also H. C. Dale, "Did the returning Astorians use the South Pass?" *Oregon Hist. Soc. Quarterly*, vol. XVII, Portland, 1916.

[2] W. J. Ghent, *op. cit.* p. 17.   [3] H. M. Chittenden, *op. cit.* 1, 271.

[4] H. C. Dale, *op. cit.* pp. 93–95.

[5] See W. J. Ghent, *op. cit.* p. 16, who also concludes that the Fitzpatrick party was the first through the pass and included J. Smith as one of its members.

Captain Bonneville, in 1832, was the first to take wagons through South Pass to Green River, although Ashley had taken a wheeled cannon by this route in 1826. Frémont in 1842–3, Stansbury in 1848, and Hayden, King, and Wheeler after 1872, surveyed and mapped the route through the pass.

Lewis and Clark, on their famous expedition in 1804–6, discovered several passes across the Rocky Mountains. South Pass received its name to distinguish it from the northern passes discovered by Lewis and Clark. Chittenden[1] says that the name South Pass was applied to two other passes south of the northern passes, before South Pass proper was discovered. The pass sometimes received the name of the Great Gap. Farnham[2] says: "Grand River is a branch of the Colorado. It rises far in the east among the precipitous heights of the eastern range of the Rocky Mountains, about midway from the Great Gap and the Kenyon of the south fork of the Platte". It became the most celebrated pass in the Rocky Mountains, for it was the easiest crossing of the divide between the waters of the Atlantic and the Pacific. South Pass is 950 miles distant from Independence and 1070 miles from Fort Vancouver, and was therefore approximately the half-way station of the Oregon trail. The traveller to Oregon felt that he was well on his way when he reached this point. "Here, then, we hailed Oregon", said Palmer[3] on reaching the pass.

South Pass is situated in lat. 42° 26′ at the south of the Wind River Mountains. Farnham[4] describes its relation to them as follows: "The Wind River Mountains are a spur which shoots from the great northern chain, commonly called the Rocky Mountains, in lat. 42° and odd minutes north; and running in a south-easterly direction into the Great Prairie Wilderness, forms the northern wall of the Great Gap or Great Southern Pass".

---

[1] H. M. Chittenden, *op. cit.* 1, 475–6.

[2] Thomas J. Farnham, *Travels in the Great Western Prairies, the Anahuac and Rocky Mountains, and in the Oregon Territory*, London, 1843, E.W.T. xxviii, 223.

[3] Joel Palmer, *Journal of Travels over the Rocky Mountains to the mouth of the Columbia River made during the years 1845 and 1846*, Cincinnati, 1847, E.W.T. xxx, 71.

[4] T. J. Farnham, *op. cit.* E.W.T. xxviii, 305.

The pass lies in the physical region known as the Wyoming Basin, which extends between the Northern and the Southern Rocky Mountains. A gap is clearly indicated on the contoured map forming Fig. 21 at the southern end of the Wind River Mountains. The ascent to this gap was so gradual that Frémont in 1843 had considerable difficulty in ascertaining the highest point of the divide, although the actual height of the summit of the pass is 7489 feet. Chittenden[1] describes it as "situated in an open valley of gentle slopes in either direction, with little to mark it as a crossing of the main chain of the Rocky mountains". The pass is about twenty miles broad.[2] This great breadth resulted in the fact that as early as 1843 there was more than one emigrant road through the pass. The pass, therefore, cannot be described in any sense as a defile or mountain gorge.

The position of South Pass in relation to the natural drainage of North America is unique. The pass leads from the Sweetwater branch of the North Platte westward to the Big Sandy branch of the Green River. It is therefore situated at the head of the waters of some of the greatest rivers of the continent. The headwaters of the North Platte and the Big Horn rise very near South Pass. On the Pacific side the headwaters of the Snake and the Green Rivers are not far distant from the pass. For this reason South Pass possessed immense strategic advantages. Frémont[3] speaks of it as "that great gate in the ridge of the Rocky mountains called the South Pass, and on the lofty peak of the mountain which overlooks it, deemed the highest peak in the ridge and from the opposite sides of which four great rivers take their rise, and flow to the Pacific or the Mississippi". The pass could be reached by means of the Platte River. The Platte was unnavigable and the earlier explorers pushed their way up the navigable Missouri and neglected the Platte. The Platte did provide sufficient water and food for horses, and when the horse supplanted the boat as the mode of transport the route to the west along the Platte became important. On the Pacific side the pass led to the Snake River, the best route to Oregon. The pass also led to Bear River, Salt Lake, and so to the Humboldt

[1] H. M. Chittenden, *op. cit.* II, 727.
[2] Frémont, *Report*, p. 128.   [3] *Ibid.* p. 106.

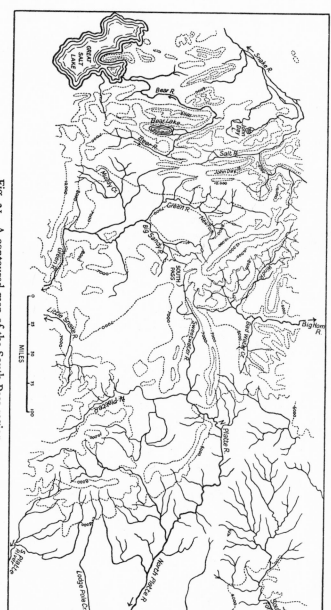

Fig. 21. A contoured map of the South Pass region.

River, the most direct route across the Great Basin to California. South Pass, because of its position with regard to the waterways, was bound to control the communications of the continent. The importance of the Platte as the main line of travel to the pass is emphasised by Farnham [1] in the following words:

The Platte, therefore, when considered in relation to our intercourse with the habitable countries on the Western Ocean, assumes an unequal importance among the streams of the Great Prairie Wilderness! But for it, it would be impossible for man or beast to travel those arid plains, destitute alike, of wood, water, and grass, save what of each is found along its course. Upon the head waters of its North Fork, too, is the only way or opening in the Rocky mountains at all practicable for a carriage road through them. That traversed by Lewis and Clark, is covered with perpetual snow; that near the debouchure of the South Fork of the river is over high and nearly impassable precipices; that travelled by myself farther south, is, and ever will be, impassable for wheel carriages. But the Great Gap, nearly on a right line between the mouth of the Missouri and Fort Hall on Clark's River—the point where the trails to California and Oregon diverge—seems designed by nature as the great gateway between the nations on the Atlantic and Pacific seas.

The Great Gap was not blocked by snow as often as the other passes over the Rockies. This was another considerable factor in the importance of the pass. "This range" (the Rocky Mountains), says Farnham,[2] "is generally covered with perpetual snows; and for this and other causes is generally impassable for man or beast. There are, however, several gaps through which the Indians and others cross to the Great Prairie Wilderness.... The most important of all is situated between Wind river cluster and Long's mountains." On Fig. 11 the South Pass region is shown as an area which has fewer days with snow-cover than the regions immediately to the north and south of it. It must not be imagined that there is no snowfall in the pass. Palmer[3] describes a journey through the pass in May, 1846, in the following words: "On the 25th we traveled to the Little Sandy. On the 26th we arrived at the *South Pass*, and encamped on Sweet Water. Here we saw a few buffalo. The ride from Little Sandy to Sweet Water was extremely unpleasant on ac-

[1] T. J. Farnham, *op. cit.* E.W.T. xxviii, 114.
[2] *Ibid.* xxix, 29–30.
[3] Joel Palmer, *op. cit.* E.W.T. xxx, 247.

count of the wind and snow. We were sometimes compelled to walk, in order to keep warm". Frémont's entry for August 7, 1842,[1] is typical of the weather experienced when crossing the pass in summer.

As we rose from the bed of the creek, the *snow* line of the mountains stretched grandly before us, the white peaks glittering in the sun. They had been hidden in the dark weather of the last few days, and it had been *snowing* on them, while it *rained* in the plains. We crossed a ridge, and again struck the Sweet Water—here a beautiful, swift stream with a more open valley, timbered with beech and cottonwood.... The afternoon was cloudy, with squalls of rain; but the weather became fine at sunset, when we again camped on the Sweet Water, within a few miles of the South Pass.

The pass consists of a wide belt of open country that is almost entirely free from timber. The mountains to the north and to the south were obstructed by forests. By using the pass, it was possible to make a journey from the grasslands of the prairies and the plains direct to the comparative desert of the Interior Basin without passing through a forest. The absence of trees was a great advantage to rapid transport. The route followed by Lewis and Clark over the northern Rockies compelled them to make a difficult journey through forests. The journey was arduous not only because of the hindrance of the vegetation but also because the trees held up the snow. Fig. 14 shows that the passage through South Pass was a passage between two areas of forest, the forests of the northern and southern Rocky Mountains. Palmer[2] gives a good description of the vegetation of the pass in the following words:

July 18, 1845.... The appearance of the country is extremely barren. We passed several rivulets where small parties may obtain grazing for their stock. The day has been quite cold. The Wind River Mountains are on our right, about twenty miles distant. They presented a most grand appearance. Huge masses of ice and snow piled up peak upon peak, with large bodies of timber covering portions of the mountains. We viewed the southern termination of this range; but they extend to the north further than the eye can penetrate. The country between us and the mountains is rolling, and much of it is apparently barren. Hard frost.—July 19. This morning we ascended the bank on the south side of the Sweet Water. Six

[1] J. C. Frémont, *Report*, p. 59.
[2] Joel Palmer, *op. cit.* E.W.T. XXX, 70–2.

miles brought us again to the creek, where is good grass in the bottom and willow for fuel. We crossed, went up the bottom two miles, and crossed back and left the Sweet Water. *This day we passed over the dividing ridge which separates the waters flowing into the Atlantic from those which find their way into the Pacific Ocean. We had reached the summit of the Rocky Mountains.* Six miles brought us to a spring, the waters of which run into Green river, or the great Colorado of the west.—Here, then, we hailed Oregon. Here we found a bottom covered with good grass.... Ten miles more brought us to Little Sandy, which we reached at one o'clock in the night, having traveled thirty-one miles. The road was over a barren plain of light sand and was very dusty. From the spring to Little Sandy there is no vegetation but the wild sage, and it had a withered appearance. The night was cold, freezing quite hard....—July 20th. This day we traveled about thirteen miles to Big Sandy. The road was over a level sandy plain, covered with wild sage.

In 1840 the pass was approximately the western limit of the range of the buffalo (American bison), and was therefore of great importance from the point of view of food supply. Palmer[1] says: "The buffalo seldom range beyond the South Pass, and never west of Green river", and also, when he had crossed the pass, he says, "We are now out of the range of the buffalo, and although not often mentioned, we have seen thousands of these huge animals".[2] Frémont on his return journey to the east through the pass expresses the delight he experienced because he was once more in the land of the buffalo. On August 19, 1842, Frémont[3] writes: "At 10 o'clock, we stood exactly on the divide in the pass, where the wagon road crosses, and, descending immediately upon the Sweet Water, halted to take a meridian observation of the sun. In the course of the afternoon we saw buffalo again, and at our evening halt on the Sweet Water the roasted ribs again made their appearance around the fires; and, with them, good humor, and laughter, and song were restored to the camp". Thus, when the traveller had passed through the Great Gap from the east he was no longer able to enjoy what had been his staple food on the plains.

Lewis and Clark experienced considerable difficulty in crossing the northern passes because of the hostility of the Indians

[1] Joel Palmer, *op. cit.* E.W.T. xxx, 260.
[2] *Ibid.* xxx, 72.
[3] J. C. Frémont, *Report*, p. 71.

in that neighbourhood. The trappers who followed in the paths of these explorers suffered very considerably at the hands of the warlike Blackfoot Indians. This tribe inflicted heavy losses on the traders sent out by Manuel Lisa. The Indians who frequented the neighbourhood of South Pass were comparatively friendly. The Crows were frequently the allies of the white traders against the Blackfoot Indians, while the Snakes were not of a very warlike disposition.

Frémont wrote two admirable accounts of his journey through the South Pass, and as his descriptions illustrate many of the points already discussed, they are quoted at length:

August 8th, 1842. About six miles from our encampment brought us to the summit. The ascent had been so gradual, that, with all the intimate knowledge possessed by Carson, who had made this country his home for seventeen years, we were obliged to watch very closely to find the place at which we had reached the culminating point. This was between two low hills, rising on either hand fifty or sixty feet. When I looked back at them, from the foot of the immediate slope on the western plain, their summits appeared to be about one hundred and twenty feet above. From the impression on my mind at this time, and subsequently on our return, I should compare the elevation which we surmounted immediately at the Pass, to the ascent of the Capitol hill from the avenue, at Washington. It is difficult for me to fix positively the breadth of this pass. From the broken ground where it commences, at the foot of the Wind river chain, the view to the southeast is over a champaign country, broken, at the distance of nineteen miles, by the Table rock; which, with the other isolated hills in its vicinity, seems to stand on a comparative plain. This I judged to be its termination, the ridge recovering its rugged character with the Table rock. It will be seen that it in no manner resembles the places to which the term is commonly applied—nothing of the gorge-like character and winding ascents of the Allegheny passes in America: nothing of the Great St Bernard and Simplon Passes in Europe. Approaching it from the mouth of the Sweet Water, a sandy plain, one hundred and twenty miles long, conducts, by a gradual and regular ascent, to the summit, about seven thousand feet above the sea; and the traveller, without being reminded of any change by toilsome ascents, suddenly finds himself on the waters which flow to the Pacific ocean. By the route we had travelled, the distance from Fort Laramie is three hundred and twenty miles, or nine hundred and fifty from the mouth of the Kansas.

Continuing our march, we reached, in eight miles from the pass, the Little Sandy, one of the tributaries of the Colorado, or Green river of the Gulf of California.[1]

[1] J. C. Frémont, *Report*, p. 60.

August 13th, 1843. Leaving this encampment, (our last on the waters which flow towards the rising sun), we took our way along the upland, towards the dividing ridge which separates the Atlantic from the Pacific waters, and crossed it by a road some miles further south than the one we had followed on our return in 1842. We crossed very near the table mountain, at the southern extremity of the South Pass, which is near twenty miles in width, and already traversed by several different roads. Selecting as well as I could, in the scarcely distinguishable ascent, what might be considered the dividing ridge in this remarkable depression in the mountain, I took a barometrical observation, which gave 7490 feet for the elevation above the Gulf of Mexico. You will remember that, in my report of 1842, I estimated the elevation of this pass at about 7000 feet; a correct observation with a good barometer enables me now to give it with more precision. Its importance, as the great gate through which commerce and travelling may hereafter pass between the valley of the Mississippi and the north Pacific, justifies a precise notice of its locality and distance from leading points in addition to this statement of its elevation. As stated in the report of 1842, its latitude at the point where we crossed is 42° 24′ 32″, its longitude 109° 26′ 00″; its distance from the mouth of the Kansas, by the common travelling route, 962 miles; from the mouth of the Great Platte, along the valley of that river, according to our survey of 1842, 882 miles; and its distance from St Louis about 400 miles more by the Kansas, and about 700 by the Great Platte route; these additions being steamboat conveyance in both instances. From this pass to the mouth of the Oregon is about 1400 miles by the common travelling route: so that, under a general point of view, it may be assumed to be about half way between the Mississippi and the Pacific ocean, on the common travelling route. Following a hollow of slight and easy descent, in which was very soon formed a little tributary to the Gulf of California, (for the waters which flow west from the South Pass go to this gulf), we made our usual halt four miles from the pass, in latitude by observation 42° 19′ 53″. Entering here the valley of Green river—the great Colorado of the West—and inclining very much to the southward along the streams which form the Sandy river, the road led for several days over dry and level uninteresting plains; to which a low scrubby growth of artemisia gave a uniform dull grayish colour.[1]

South Pass had every natural advantage as an avenue of communication. It could be reached by an easy gradient, and was conveniently situated with regard to water routes. A traveller could cross the pass unhindered by snow, forests, or Indians. Although the pass is not a striking natural feature on the ground or on the map, it was undoubtedly the most practicable pass over the Rocky Mountains. Two of the great movements of the

[1] J. C. Frémont, *Report*, p. 128-9.

American people towards the West crossed the South Pass.[1] The first emigrants followed the Oregon trail through South Pass to the Columbia. By the year 1845, eight thousand Americans had settled in the Columbia region, and the Oregon boundary dispute with Great Britain was settled in 1846. The trail to California also passed through South Pass, branched off from the Oregon trail at Bear River and, following the Humboldt, crossed the Sierra Nevada by the Truckee Pass. After 1844, the year in which the Truckee Pass was discovered, Americans began to migrate to California by the South Pass route. The Mormons used South Pass on their way to the Salt Lake. In 1849 and the following years, seekers after Californian gold poured through the Great Gap. It is said that many of the pioneers to Oregon and California carried Frémont's report and map, which was often their only guide.[2] In the words of Professor Turner,[3] "What Cumberland Gap was in the advance of settlement across the Alleghenies, South Pass was in the movement across the Rocky Mountains; through it passed the later Oregon and Californian trails to the Pacific coast". From 1824 to 1860 the South Pass route was the most important route to the West. The daily overland mail to Salt Lake City used South Pass, but in 1860 the Pony Express followed the route of Bridger's Pass, south of South Pass.[4] In and after 1868 the Union Pacific Railway was constructed along the more direct route of Bridger's Pass, as the South Pass was too far north. Many wagons are said to have crossed the pass as late as 1893–5,[5] but with the construction of the railway the great days of South Pass were ended.

[1] See E. C. Semple, *American History and its Geographic Conditions* (1903), chap. XI, and S. Dunbar, *A History of Travel in America* (1915), chap. LIII.

[2] Frederick L. Paxson, *The History of the American Frontier, 1763–1893*, p. 338.

[3] F. J. Turner, *The Rise of the New West*, p. 189. Vol. XIV of *The History of the American Nation*.

[4] See L. R. Hafen, *The Overland Mail*, 1849–1868 (1926), for a full account of the Pony Express. W. J. Ghent, *op. cit.* p. 203, says "the month of July 1862 marks the permanent abandonment as a mail and stage line of the long stretch of the Oregon trail from Julesburg by way of Fort Laramie and South Pass to Fort Bridger".   [5] W. J. Ghent, *op. cit.* p. 247.

Chapter XI

THE DISCOVERY OF SOUTHERN TRANS-CONTINENTAL ROUTES[1]

(a) *The Exploration of the Western Tributaries of the Mississippi, South of St Louis, 1803–1806*

After the annexation of Louisiana by the United States, several expeditions were sent out to explore the right bank tributaries of the Mississippi, south of St Louis. The American Government was eager to survey the newly acquired territory, and shortly after the purchase, Congress commissioned Dr John Sibley to ascend the Red River, while William Dunbar, with George Hunter, were sent up the principal tributary of the Red River, namely the Washita. The exploration of the Red River was of special interest to the Government, as they wished to determine the exact boundary between Louisiana and the Spanish dominions. Four expeditions under Sibley (1803), Sparks (1806), Pike (1806), and Long (1820) endeavoured to determine the course and sources of this river, which was supposed to be the southern boundary of Louisiana.

Sibley set out in March, 1803, and sent in his report in April, 1805. He pushed his way up the Red River as far as the modern site of Shreveport. He described the country, with its fertile alluvial soil, as one of the richest he had ever seen. Sibley only travelled 80 miles above Natchitoches, but he obtained information about the upper river from two Frenchmen, Francis Grappe and M. Brevel. He learnt that the Red River, like many of the tributaries of the Mississippi, was not navigable. Sibley also reported that the Indians had no boats, partly because there was no timber available and partly because the stream, rising to a torrent with spring and autumn floods, made canoes an un-

[1] The routes of explorers described in this chapter are shown on end Map A, Fig. 32.

certain means of transport.[1] The Indians had a good supply of horses, and, mounted on them, hunted the buffalo. Sibley compiled an account of the "Indian Tribes in Louisiana, south of the Arkansa River, and between the Mississippi and River Grand".[2]

Dunbar and Hunter set out in October, 1804, and travelled to the north, following the course of the Washita River as far as Hot Springs. They saw the hills which divide the waters of the Washita from those of the Arkansas. A French trader informed them that the Platte rose in the mountains, near the source of the Arkansas and the Red Rivers. They returned in January, 1805, with a very favourable report of the country.[3] This report was among the documents laid before the Senate by President Jefferson, in 1806, when he informed them of the progress of Lewis and Clark. Dunbar's expedition is notable for observations made concerning the Indian tribes and the animal life of the region. Dunbar wrote the following interesting account of the animals of the western prairies:

The great western prairies, besides the herd of wild cattle (bison, commonly called buffaloe), are also stocked with vast numbers of wild goat (not resembling the domestic goat), extremely swift footed. As the description given of this goat is not perfect, it may, from its swiftness, prove to be the antelope, or it possibly may be a goat which has escaped from the Spanish settlements of New Mexico. A Canadian, who had been much with the Indians to the westward, speaks of a wool-bearing animal larger than a sheep, the wool much mixed with hair, which he had seen in large flocks. He pretends also to have seen a unicorn, the single horn of which, he says, rises out of the forehead and curls back, conveying the idea of the fossil cornu ammonis. This man says he has travelled beyond the great dividing ridge so far as to have seen a large river flowing to the westward.[4]

[1] M. Brevel "told me that the Indians there knew nothing of the use of perogues; for, instead of there being for hundreds of miles a tree large enough for a canoe, one could scarcely be found large enough to make a fowl trough". J. Sibley, *An Account of the Red River*, in R. Phillips, *Collection of Modern and Contemporary Voyages and Travels* (1807), VI, 71.

[2] R. Phillips, *op. cit.* VI, 40–53.

[3] *Observations of William Dunbar and Dr Hunter, made on the Washita River in Oct. 1804–Jan. 1805.* Laid before the Senate by the President of the United States in February, 1806. Reprinted in R. Phillips, *op. cit.* VI, 74–116. See also Isaac J. Cox, "The Exploration of the Louisiana Frontier, 1803–1806," *Annual Report of the American Historical Association for the Year* 1904, pp. 149–74.

[4] *Observations of William Dunbar and Dr Hunter*, R. Phillips, *op. cit.* VI, 108–109. Elliott Coues, in his edition of the Lewis and Clark Expedi-

In 1806 a larger expedition ascended the Red River, under the command of Captain Sparks, with Thomas Freeman as surveyor. This expedition reached a point 635 miles above the mouth of the river, but was compelled to return owing to the opposition of the Spaniards. The western country was described as "level, rich and almost continuous prairies, where range immense herds of buffalo, upon which the Indians almost entirely subsist, moving their camps as these animals migrate with the season from north to south and back again".[1]

The three expeditions described above are of little importance when compared with Lieut. Z. M. Pike's expedition of 1806–7. This expedition, also, was sent out to determine the course of the Red River, and the results achieved by this journey deserve special consideration.

(b) The Expedition of Pike, 1806–1807

In the years 1805 and 1806, Lieutenant Zebulon Montgomery Pike (Fig. 22) led an expedition which explored the source of the Mississippi River, and after the successful accomplishment of this work he was despatched by the Government with orders to explore the sources of the Red River.[2] Pike left St Louis on July 15, 1806, with twenty men, and ascended the Missouri by boat. On July 28, the expedition ascended the Osage River, and having arrived at the Osage villages, abandoned its boats

tion, comments on this account of animal life in the following words: "Here in a few lines of one paragraph are unequivocally noticed four of the most remarkable ruminants of Western North America. 1. The buffalo, *Bison americanus*. 2. The antelope, *Antilocapra americana*. 3. The Rocky Mountain goat, *Haplocerus montanus*, possibly the actual basis of the 'woolly horse' legends of the West. 4. The Rocky Mountain sheep, *Ovis montana*, which, though not a 'unicorn', has horns quite like the cornu Ammonis, and in fact is a near relative of the Barbary sheep". *L. and C.* I, 35.

[1] E. James, *Account of an Expedition to the Rocky Mountains under the command of Major S. H. Long*, E.W.T. vols. XIV–XVII. See XVII, 66–76, for an account of the expedition of Sparks and Freeman.

[2] *The Expeditions of Zebulon M. Pike*, 3 vols. ed. Elliott Coues (1895). Vol. I contains the account of the Mississippi voyage of 1805–6 and vol. II describes the Arkansas Journey and Mexican Tour (hereafter cited as Z. M. Pike, *Expeditions*).

and purchased horses from the Indians. On September 6, Pike crossed the divide between the Osage River and the Arkansas, and described the scene in the following words: "The prospect from the dividing range to the east and southeast is sublime. The prairie rising and falling in regular swells, as far as the sight can extend, produces a very beautiful appearance".[1] He was hindered by a considerable amount of rain. He proceeded west, and having crossed Grand River, marched north across the Smoky Hill Fork of the Kansas River, and finally encamped on the banks of the Republican River. This river was named the Republican because the settlement of the Pawnee nation or Republic was established on its banks. Pike was surprised to learn that a large body of Spanish troops, under Malgares, had recently visited the Pawnee settlements. The Spaniards had received definite instructions to intercept the American explorer. Pike now marched south, until, on October 24, he reached the Arkansas, near a bend of the river called Pawnee Fork. On October 28, the party separated into two divisions: Lieutenant Wilkinson with four men descended the Arkansas River, while Pike continued his route to the mountains of Colorado.

Wilkinson attempted to descend the river in canoes, but found that navigation was impossible, owing to shallows and the formation of ice. He was compelled to march along the river bank. On November 8 he says that he saw more than 9000 head of buffalo. Farther down the river his renewed attempts to navigate the river were attended by considerable difficulty. "On the 6th (December) the ice began to drift, and I immediately pushed off with it; but as my evil stars would have it, my boats again grounded. Being in the middle of the river, my only alternative was to get out and drag them along for several miles, when we halted to warm our benumbed feet and hands. The next day several large cakes of ice had blocked up the river, and we had to cut our way through them with axes; the boats as usual grounded, and the men, bare-legged and bare-footed, were obliged to leap into the water. This happened so frequently that two more of them got badly frosted".[2]

[1] Z. M. Pike, *Expeditions*, II, 397.
[2] *Ibid.* II, 555.

Fig. 22. Zebulon Montgomery Pike.

Fig. 23. John Charles Frémont.

Shortly after this incident, Wilkinson passed the Cimarron River and finally reached the Mississippi on January 9, 1807.[1]

Pike, with sixteen men, continued along the Arkansas, as far as the site of the modern city of Pueblo (Colorado). During this part of the journey he made frequent entries in his diary concerning the immense numbers of buffalo, deer, elk, and wild horses. Pike estimated that he could see 3000 buffalo at one time. On November 15 the party were cheered because they sighted the "Mexican mountains" (Rocky Mountains). On November 24 they put up a breastwork as a fortification against the Indians. A party set out to climb the dominating peak, which they called the Grand Peak, and is now known as Pike's Peak. Although they carried insufficient food and had no blankets, they reached a height of 9000 feet. The height of the peak was estimated to be 18,581 feet (in reality 14,147).[2] "The condition of my soldiers, who had only light overalls on, no stockings, and were in every way ill provided to endure the inclemency of the region... determined us to return",[3] and the party made its way back to the breastwork.

The months of December and January were spent in a search for the source of the Red River. The condition of the expedition in mid-winter in the mountains was indeed desperate. On December 1 the snow was one foot deep, and on December 3 Pike wrote: "I wore myself cotton overalls, for I had not calculated on being out in that inclement season of the year". The guns burst with cold, and the hardships of the men were well nigh intolerable. The actual route of the journey northwards is uncertain, as Pike's account is somewhat vague. He probably discovered the sources of the South Platte and the Arkansas. The river which Pike marks as the Yellowstone on his map was obviously not the Yellowstone. Some writers have believed that Pike actually crossed the divide between the Pacific and the Atlantic and that his Yellowstone was the source of the

[1] See Wilkinson's report on the Arkansas, Z. M. Pike, *Expeditions*, II, 539–61.

[2] James, of Long's expedition of 1820, was the first to reach the summit of the mountain.

[3] Z. M. Pike, *Expeditions*, II, 458.

Grand River branch of the Colorado.[1] Dr Elliott Coues, after a detailed study of the region, considered that this theory was highly improbable. At the head of the Arkansas River the party was plentifully supplied with buffalo as food. The buffalo did not always migrate to the Plains in winter; otherwise Pike and his party must surely have perished. The party returned and built a block-house near the site of the modern town of Cañon City, on January 9, 1807. On January 17 the feet of nine men were frozen, and if Pike had not been so lucky as to kill a stray buffalo, his party would have died of starvation. He was compelled to leave behind two men with frozen feet. Despite great sufferings, Pike marched southward and crossed what he called the "Great White Mountains" (Sangre de Cristo Mountains) by a pass believed to be the Sand Hill Pass. He found himself on the banks of a stream flowing south, which he imagined to be the Red River and which was in reality the Rio Grande del Norte. Here, on Spanish territory, on February 5, he built a stockade. On February 26 Pike was visited by a large body of mounted cavalry, who informed him that he was in Spanish territory, and insisted on taking him and his party to Santa Fé. The following conversation took place between Pike and the Spanish commander:

"What!" said Pike, "Is not this the Red River?"

"No, Sir! The Rio del Norte."[2]

Pike was taken to Santa Fé, and was then escorted to El Paso and Chihuahua.[3] The governor ordered that the Americans be deported by way of Texas. Pike returned to the United States by way of Texas and arrived at Natchitoches, on the Red River, on July 1, 1807.

It has been suggested that Pike wandered into Mexican territory with the deliberate object of being captured and then to report his observations of the country to the Government. Pike wrote

[1] G. K. Warren held this opinion. See G. K. Warren, *Memoir to accompany the Map of the Territory of the United States*, p. 21.

[2] Z. M. Pike, *Expeditions*, II, 509.

[3] The Spanish authorities at Chihuahua deprived Pike of his papers. The originals of some of these papers have been discovered in the City of Mexico, and are discussed by H. E. Bolton in *The American Historical Review*, XIII (1908), 798–827, "Papers of Zebulon M. Pike, 1806–1807".

a long account of New Mexico,[1] and described the geographical
knowledge of the Spaniards. Pike's account proves that the
Spaniards had a good idea of the course of the Gila River. The
rivers of Texas, the San Antonio, the Colorado, the Brazos,
were all well known. Pike described the Texas plains with their
immense herds of wild horses.[2] When discussing the drainage
of the Rocky Mountains, Pike said that the Spaniards had a
vague knowledge of the existence of a great inland lake, Lake
Timpanogos, and of a river, the River Buenaventura, flowing
into the lake. Pike doubted the existence of this lake, but the
lake corresponds to the Great Salt Lake or Utah Lake.[3] Pike
estimated the population of Santa Fé as 4500 and the population
of New Mexico as 30,000, and stated that the only prosperous
city was El Paso. Pike's accounts of New Mexico were eagerly
read in the United States, and were of great importance in
fostering the Santa Fé[4] trade and American immigration into
New Mexico.

Pike's work is well summarised by his biographer Whiting
in the following words:

At the time Captain Pike explored those regions of our wide-spread interior, almost nothing authentic was known of them. More satisfactory
information of the headwaters of the Mississippi than was in the possession
of the public was highly desirable, and his narratives relating to them were
read with interest. But his accounts of the Mexican territories were looked
for with much more interest, and when they came out were received with
avidity. The jealous policy of Spain had surrounded her provinces with
guards and restraints, that rendered them almost inaccessible. Their conditions and prospects were veiled from all foreign observation; and at the
time Captain Pike obtained, through an unintentional aberration from his
prescribed route, access to them, unusual attention was turned upon the
Mexican country by the events of Burr's conspiracy. This extraordinary
transaction had awakened an intense curiosity respecting a region which
was known to abound with gold, and which precious metal was supposed
to have been its ultimate object. The trial of Colonel Burr was beginning,

[1] Z. M. Pike, *Expeditions*, II, 718–806. Observations on New Spain.
[2] *Ibid.* II, 781.
[3] *Ibid.* II, 728–37.
[4] "The Santa Fé trade attracted very little notice, however, until the
return of Captain Pike, whose exciting descriptions of the new El Dorado
spread like wildfire through the western country." J. Gregg, *Commerce of
the Prairies*, E.W.T. XIX, 175.

or in progress, when Captain Pike returned, and was known to have visited the El Dorado, on which this individual was said to have fixed an eye of cupidity and ambition. Scarcely anything had been heard of Mexico since the conquest of Cortes, excepting vague reports of the unbounded wealth that flowed from its mines into the public and private coffers of Spain. It is not strange, then, that Captain Pike's tour through some of its provinces should have been regarded as a rare and most opportune work. His statements were of course founded on hasty and imperfect observations, it being obvious from his journal, that, from the time he left Santa Fé, until he reached the United States, he was under a surveillance, and could only take notes by stealth. He could neither survey attentively what passed beneath his eye, nor inquire about that which he did not see, without exciting suspicion and provoking a rebuke. Still, with an acute eye, and a retentive memory, he appears to have gathered up many new and interesting facts, that were well received at the time.[1]

Pike himself believed that he had discovered the best possible route across the continent. In his suggested route he exaggerated the importance of the Colorado. The tributaries of that river, rather than the river itself, were eventually the most important lines of communication in the south. He says:

By the route of the Arkansaw and the Rio Colorado of California, I am confident in asserting, if my information from Spanish gentlemen of information is correct, there can be established the best communication, on this side of the Isthmus of Darien, between the Atlantic and Pacific Oceans; as, admitting the utmost, the land carriage would not be more than 200 miles, and the route may be made quite as eligible as our public highways over the Alleghany Mountains. The Rio Colorado is to the great Gulph of California what the Mississippi is to the Gulph of Mexico, and is navigable for ships of considerable burden, to opposite the upper parts of the province of Senora.[2]

It is reasonable to assert that Pike's exploratory work resulted in the establishment of the Santa Fé trail from St Louis to Santa Fé, and that Santa Fé proved to be the best southern base for the routes to the Pacific, namely the Spanish trail and the Gila trail.

(c) The Expedition of Long and Bell, 1819–1820

The expedition usually associated with the name of Major Long was known as the Yellowstone expedition. This expedition was

[1] H. Whiting, A Life of Z. M. Pike (1845), Jared Sparks Library of American Biography, xv, 282.
[2] Z. M. Pike, Expeditions, II, 522–3.

sent out by the Government with orders to proceed up the Missouri River as far as the mouth of the Yellowstone. The expedition was partly military and partly scientific in character, but its objects were largely political. The Government desired to protect the fur trade from the Indians, and by exercising some control over the Indian tribes they hoped that British influence with these tribes would be diminished.[1] The expedition gave rise to immense expectations, and a contemporary writer went so far as to assert that the expedition would open a "safe and easy communication to China, which would give such a spur to commercial enterprise that ten years shall not pass away before we shall have the rich productions of that country transported from Canton to the Columbia".[2]

The military expedition under Colonel Atkinson proceeded up the River Missouri in steamboats—the first experiment in steam navigation on that river. The expedition was badly managed, and the soldiers got no farther than Council Bluffs, where they spent the winter of 1819–20. A very large number of men died of scurvy, and the military expedition was an abject failure.

The scientific section of the expedition was commanded by Major Stephen H. Long and had orders to explore the region between the Missouri and the Rockies. Major Long and his party left Pittsburgh in April, 1819, also on a small steamboat. They descended the Ohio, reached St Louis in June and went into winter quarters at Fort Lisa (near the junction of the Platte and the Missouri). Major Long returned to Washington for the winter.

As the expedition had accomplished so little in the first year, the Government gave very little financial support in 1820. The object in this year was "to go to the source of the River Platte and thence by way of the Arkansas and Red Rivers to the Mississippi".

On June 6, 1820, Long and his party left their winter camp,

---

[1] See E. James, *op. cit.* E.W.T. vols. XIV–XVII. See H. M. Chittenden, *The History of the American Fur Trade*, II, 562–87, for a good secondary account of the expedition.

[2] H. M. Chittenden, *op. cit.* p. 565.

and journeyed to the west along the north bank of the Platte[1] as far as the junction of the two forks of that river. On June 30 they first sighted the Rockies. They then pushed their way towards a mountain, which is now called Long's Peak, and which they first mistook for Pike's Peak. Both forks of the Platte were crossed and the expedition continued its journey along the banks of the South Platte to the mountains. They now explored the mountainous region between the South Platte and the Arkansas River. During their course to the south, Dr James and two men ascended the peak described by Pike and named it James' Peak.[2] One of the party, Swift by name, determined the height of the peak as 8500 feet above his observation point, which he considered to be 3000 feet above sea-level. It seems certain that Dr James was the first white man to ascend the mountain.

The expedition turned south and reached the Arkansas River. One party followed the river up to the gorge where it leaves the mountains and returned. On July 24 the expedition was divided into two parties. Captain Bell was ordered to explore the Arkansas, and Major Long with Dr James decided to continue southwards and attempt to find the source of the Red River and then to follow its course. The entire course of the Arkansas had already been examined by Pike, so Bell's expedition on the north bank of that river was of little value as a contribution to geographical knowledge.

Major Long and his party continued south, crossed several sources of the Cimarron River, until, on July 30, they came on a valley which they believed to be the Red River or a tributary. They followed this valley for four days, until the river joined the main stream of the Canadian, which they imagined was the Red River. On September 10 they reached the Arkansas, and discovered that their course had been along the Canadian and not along the Red River. From this point the reunited expedition continued its homeward journey.

The geographical results of this much advertised expedition

[1] E.W.T. xv (being vol. ii of Long's Expedition), 230–86, contains a full account of the Platte.
[2] E.W.T. xvi (being vol. iii of Long's Expedition), 11–27.

were comparatively small. It must be admitted that the expedition of 1820 was badly equipped, but it did not achieve very much. Its main objective, the discovery of the sources of the Platte and the Red Rivers, was not accomplished. The only valuable discovery was the course of the Canadian River, which later became a very important part of the route to New Mexico. The expedition made a careless itinerary and many important features were entirely missed. Bell did not notice the Cimarron tributary of the Arkansas.

Major Long gave a most unfavourable account of this western country. "In regard to this extensive section of the country", says Long, "I do not hesitate in giving the opinion, that it is almost wholly unfit for cultivation, and of course uninhabitable by a people depending upon agriculture for their subsistence. Although tracts of fertile land considerably extensive are occasionally to be met with, yet the scarcity of wood and water, almost uniformly prevalent, will prove an insuperable obstacle in the way of settling the country".[1]

Although the expedition did not make any important additions to geographical knowledge, the scientific results of the journey were considerable. "The work", says R. G. Thwaites, "was done in the spirit of modern scientific investigation."[2] The large collections of insects, plants, minerals, shells, skins of animals, and landscape sketches provided the material for "a general description of the country traversed by the exploring expedition",[3] which was of great value, as the region was at that time so little known. The accounts of the valley of the Platte were especially valuable, although the river was already well known by trappers. By far the most important contributions of the expedition to knowledge were the accounts of the life and customs of the Indians. R. G. Thwaites is of the opinion that "as an authoritative source of knowledge of the sociology of the Kansa and Omaha tribes, the *Account* has no rival".[4]

[1] E.W.T. xvii (being vol. iii of Long's Expedition), 147.
[2] E.W.T. xiv (being vol. i of Long's Expedition), 24.
[3] E.W.T. xvii (being vol. iv of Long's Expedition), 94–183.
[4] E.W.T. xiv (being vol. i of Long's Expedition), 25.

(d) The Santa Fé Trail

In 1802 an American named James Pursley (or Purcell) left St Louis and, after many wanderings, reached Santa Fé, in June, 1805. He was probably the first American to accomplish this journey, but very little knowledge can be obtained concerning him or his route.[1] In 1804 an American merchant sent a French creole called La Lande up the Platte River. This man reached Santa Fé, settled there and made a considerable fortune in that town. Pike's expedition in 1806, however, was the first detailed account of a journey between the American settlements and Santa Fé. His accounts of New Mexico were widely read throughout the whole of the West.

The possibilities for a trade between the American settlements and Santa Fé were now realised. The economic motives for the growth of this trade have been well summarised by Chittenden in the following words: "It was clear that the Missouri river near the mouth of the Kansas was much nearer to Santa Fé than was Vera Cruz, whence all imported fabrics reached that inland town. Inasmuch as there was continuous navigation from American and foreign ports to St Louis and even to the mouth of the Kansas, nearly three hundred miles farther west, it was an obvious proposition that traders from the Missouri could import goods to Santa Fé more cheaply than the Mexicans themselves by way of Vera Cruz".[2] New Mexico had obtained all its supplies from Vera Cruz at exorbitant rates. "Common calicoes, and even bleached and brown domestic goods", says Gregg, "sold as high as two and three dollars per vara (or Spanish yard of thirty-three inches)".[3] The Americans were able to sell the same goods at much cheaper rates.

In 1812 a trading expedition, under McKnight, left for Santa Fé, but the early trade met with considerable opposition from Spanish officials. McKnight was imprisoned for six years. It was not until 1821, when New Mexico became independent of Spain, that the trade really flourished. In that year a trading

[1] Z. M. Pike, *Expeditions*, II, 756–8.
[2] H. M. Chittenden, *op. cit.* II, 516.
[3] J. Gregg, *op. cit.* E.W.T. XIX, 177–8

expedition, under the command of Hugh Glenn, left Fort Smith, a post on the Arkansas river, for Santa Fé. The second in command, Jacob Fowler, kept an interesting diary of the journey.[1] The expedition followed the course of the Arkansas as far as the site of modern Pueblo. Here Glenn left the main party and proceeded to Santa Fé. Having obtained permission to trade and trap, the whole expedition was allowed to cross over the Sangre de Cristo Pass into the Rio Grande valley. In 1822, they returned home by a direct route across the Cimarron desert and experienced considerable hardships owing to lack of water. In May, 1822, the first considerable expedition left St Louis, and in 1824 eighty traders introduced wagons instead of pack-horses. The goods taken to Santa Fé included silks, hardware, velvet, calicoes, and cotton goods, while the goods brought on the return journey consisted of horses, mules, furs from the Colorado mountains, and, most important of all, gold and silver. This trade continued until 1843, when it was prohibited by the Mexican authorities.

At first, St Louis was the base both for the Santa Fé trade and for the Indian trade up the Missouri to the northern routes across the mountains. The River Missouri is the natural westward extension of the Ohio route from the east of the United States. St Louis, situated near the junction of the Missouri and the Mississippi, had become a considerable trading centre[2] in the early days of the French occupation. It was not only the natural terminus of the Ohio route from the east, but also the starting point of the main trails to the west.

The Missouri flows due east from Kansas City to St Louis (Fig. 24). At Kansas City the river takes a great bend to the north, and several towns grew up near this elbow, at points where traffic for the Santa Fé trail left the steamboat and was transferred to wagons.[3] St Louis was the earliest base, but with the development of steamboats, the traffic removed to Franklin,

---

[1] Elliott Coues (ed.), *The Journal of Jacob Fowler*, 1821–1822 (1899).
[2] For an account of early St Louis, see W. Irving, *Astoria*, pp. 106–7.
[3] See J. Gregg, *op. cit.* E.W.T. XIX, 188–9, for the history of these towns. Also see F. W. Emerson, "A Geographical Interpretation of Missouri". *Geographical Journal*, XLI (1913), 141.

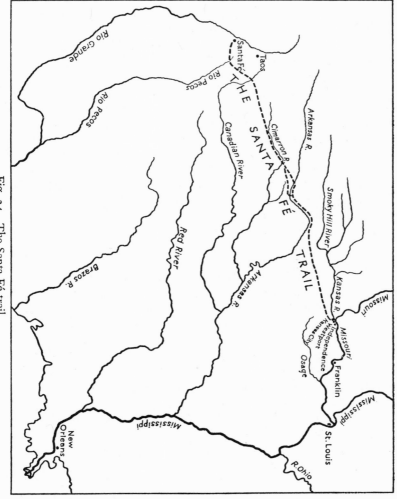

Fig. 24. The Santa Fé trail.

205 miles above the mouth of the Missouri. In 1831 Franklin was abandoned owing to river erosion and floods, and goods were taken as far as Independence. As the landing at Independence was often under water, the trade was finally transferred to a site which was safe from floods, and had the additional advantage of being the farthest point to which boats could be taken. Westport and Kansas City then became the places where mode of transport changed. From Independence the trail crossed to the great bend of the Arkansas and then led to the Cimarron River. The crossing of the desert between the Arkansas and the Cimarron was the most dreaded part of the route (Fig. 24). The trail then passed to the headwaters of the Canadian and the Pecos Rivers and crossed the Apache Cañon to Santa Fé, 775 miles from Independence.

Although this book is not primarily concerned with the history of trade, but with exploration, it has seemed best to give this summary account of the Santa Fé trail. Santa Fé became the base for two southern routes across the continent, the Gila trail and the Spanish trail, and the history of the exploration of these routes can be treated more intelligibly after a brief account of the Santa Fé trail.[1]

(e) The Routes from Santa Fé to California

The two southern routes to California from Santa Fé, known as the Gila trail and the Spanish trail, were discovered as the

---

[1] For the Santa Fé trail see J. Gregg, *op. cit.* E.W.T. vol. XIX–XX, and J. O. Pattie, *The Personal Narrative of, during an expedition from St Louis*, E.W.T. vol. XVIII. Gregg's work is a classic and has been described as "indispensable for a knowledge of the American past". J. C. Brown undertook a survey from Fort Osage to Taos in 1825–6–7. This survey produced the first accurate map of the route of the Santa Fé trail. Later accounts of the route to Santa Fé are: (1) G. W. Kendall, *Narrative of the Texan Santa Fé Expedition*, 1841 (2 vols. 1844). Kendall travelled with a military expedition from Austin (Texas) to Santa Fé. It is probable that this was the first expedition to visit the sources of the Red River. (2) A. Wizlizenus, *Memoir of a Tour to Northern Mexico, connected with Colonel Doniphan's Expedition in 1846 and 1847* (1848). Dr Wizlizenus left St Louis in 1846 and followed the Santa Fé road by the Cimarron route to Santa Fé. He then continued his journey down the Rio Grande to Chihuahua. He joined Colonel Doniphan's expedition in the war with Mexico and marched with him to Monterey.

result of the activities of the Patties and William Wolfskill respectively.

Santa Fé has an admirable position for making a journey to the two westward flowing rivers, the Colorado in the north and the Gila in the south. Santa Fé is situated in the Rio Grande Basin but access to the valleys of the Colorado and the Gila is comparatively easy. Southern California was reached from Santa Fé by means of two westward extensions of the old Santa Fé trail.

The watershed between the Rio Grande and the Gila is only three or four thousand feet higher than the Rio Grande, and the distance from the Rio Grande to the source of the Gila is only about fifty miles. Thus a trail was made across the mountains to the Gila which flows directly west. The route along the banks of this river was soon continued as far as the Californian coast, crossing the mountains by Warner's Pass (3780 feet) to San Diego. As has been described in chapter x, Smith's expedition of 1826, the first expedition to reach California by land, followed a more northerly route from the Great Salt Lake to San Diego. The route along the Gila was much shorter and the first surveys for a trans-continental railway were made along this river.

The discovery of the practicability of the Gila route was largely accomplished by the Patties.[1] J. O. Pattie, with his father Sylvester Pattie, arrived at Santa Fé in 1824. They obtained permission to trap for beaver on the Gila River and, from November, 1824 to April, 1825, they hunted in the upper valley of that river. On a second journey, commenced in January, 1826, the younger Pattie descended the Gila River to its junction with the Colorado. The expedition now ascended the banks of the Colorado.

On the 28th (March), we reached a point of the river where the mountains shut in so close upon its shores, that we were compelled to climb a mountain, and travel along the acclivity, the river still in sight, and at an immense depth beneath us.—Through this whole distance, which we judged to be, as the river meanders, 100 leagues, we had snow from a foot to eighteen inches deep. The river bluffs on the opposite shore, were never more than a mile from us. It is perhaps, this very long and formidable range of

[1] *The Personal Narrative of James O. Pattie* (1831), E.W.T. vol. xviii.

mountains, which has caused, that this country of Red river, has not been more explored, at least by the American people...on April 10th, we arrived where the river emerges from these horrid mountains, which so cage it up as to deprive all human beings of the ability to descend its banks, and make use of its waters.[1]

The cañons of the Colorado had been visited by de Cardenas in 1540 but Thwaites believed that Pattie was "the first known American to traverse its banks".[2] It was not until 1869 that Major J. W. Powell descended the gorge in a rowing boat.[3] From the Colorado, Pattie pushed north to South Pass, to the Big Horn and the Yellowstone, returning across the plains to Santa Fé, which he reached in November, 1826. He then made a journey into northern Mexico. In the following year, the Patties lost all their savings by the embezzlement of a Spanish servant. They were compelled once more to undertake a trapping expedition, and in September, 1827, father and son set out with a company of thirty trappers to work on the Colorado. The junction of the Colorado and Gila Rivers was reached on December 1, and floating down the river on rafts, they reached tidal water on January 18, 1828. They then returned against the current, and, having buried their furs, crossed the Colorado desert to San Diego, where they arrived on March 27, and were immediately imprisoned by the Spanish Governor. The sufferings of the Patties in the crossing of the desert were intense.[4] The lakes only contained salt water and the party nearly perished from thirst. The discovery of the Gila trail was, therefore, the work of the Patties.

A northern tributary of the Colorado, the San Juan River, formed part of a northern route from Santa Fé to California. From Santa Fé, the trappers followed the valley of the Chama, until they reached the upper waters of the San Juan. From this river they penetrated to all the upper tributaries of the Colorado, the Grand, Green, and Gunnison Rivers.

[1] E.W.T. XVIII, 137-8.

[2] Ibid. p. 137.

[3] J. W. Powell, The Exploration of the Colorado River of the West (1875). See L. R. Freeman, The Colorado River (1923); "The Colorado", National Geographic Magazine, XLV (1924), 471-548.

[4] E.W.T. XVIII, 205-22.

William Wolfskill,[1] in 1830, fitted out a party to trap in California. He had trapped for eight years in the district round Santa Fé. He left Taos in September, 1830, crossed the Grand and Green Rivers and the Wasatch Mountains to the Sevier River. He followed the Sevier River and then passed to the south-west along the Virgin. He then crossed the Mohave desert and reached Cajon Pass (4560 feet) and proceeded to Los Angeles, where he arrived in February, 1831. This route soon became known as the Spanish trail. The trail followed the Chama and Dolores valleys to the Grand and crossed the cañon of the Green River at a point where the railway now crosses. The trade along this route was quite considerable during the period 1830–40. Frémont followed this route in 1844, and describes the difficulties of the crossing of the Mohave desert.[2]

Thus these two routes, the Gila trail and the Spanish trail, were the best routes from Santa Fé to California and are associated with the names of the Patties and Wolfskill. Although these routes were not as important as the Oregon trail in the history of the westward movement, they were used by large numbers of emigrants, especially in 1849.

Bieber[3] says that "9000 forty-niners, constituting an important element in the early American settlement of California, reached the gold mines by way of the southwestern trails". Bieber describes the routes in the following words: "The main depot for supplies was Santa Fé, where a number of argonauts bought articles at high prices from merchants who trafficked over the old Santa Fé trail.... Most of the emigrants from Arkansas passed the vicinity of Santa Fé between May and August, and reached the gold mines of California in about seven or eight months.... One of the most popular trails was the old Spanish trail from Santa Fé to Salt Lake City", where it joined the California trail. Bieber finally shows that the Gila trail was the most important.

[1] H. H. Bancroft, *History of California*, III, 386, contains a useful list of authorities.

[2] J. C. Frémont, *Report*, pp. 245, 261.

[3] R. P. Bieber, "The South-Western Trails to California in 1849", *Mississippi Valley Historical Review*, vol. XII (December, 1925). Reprinted in *New Mexico Historical Review*, I (1926), 92–4.

More extensively traveled than the routes to the northwest were the trails to the southwest along the Gila river.[1] By far the most popular of these was the wagon road made by Lieutenant Colonel Philip St George Cooke and his Mormon Battalion between November, 1846 and January, 1847.... Kearny's trail was used by a considerable number of emigrants. Well known to the fur traders ever since the early part of the nineteenth century, it had been followed by Kit Carson when he guided General Stephen W. Kearny and his "Army of the West" from New Mexico to California between October and December, 1846. It left the Rio Grande a short distance north of the point where Cooke's road began, and proceeded west along the Gila River to the Pima Indian villages, where it was joined by Cooke's road and continued to California.[2]

The southern trans-continental routes were discovered as a result of the work of many explorers and traders. The Santa Fé trail was made known largely as the result of Pike's journey and writings, while Long's expedition obtained fuller information of the region to be crossed. The final sections of the trail across this part of the United States were the Spanish and the Gila trails, which were found to be practicable routes by the Patties and Wolfskill. Nevertheless this route never assumed the importance of the central route in the history of trans-continental migration.

[1] These trails were used in the war with Mexico in 1846–7. Major W. H. Emory conducted a reconnaissance from Santa Fé to San Diego by way of the Gila and the Colorado desert. Colonel Cooke's route was south of the route used by Emory. See W. H. Emory, *Notes of a Military Reconnaissance from Fort Leavenworth in Missouri, to San Diego, in California, made in 1846–47* (1848).

[2] R. P. Bieber, *op. cit.* For a map of the southern emigrant routes to California see K. Coman, *Economic Beginnings of the Far West*, II, 230.

Chapter XII

THE DISCOVERY OF THE GREAT BASIN
AND THE ROUTES OVER THE
SIERRA NEVADA, 1832–1853[1]

The Great Basin was first visited by Spaniards coming in from
the south. In 1776 Fathers Escalante and Dominguez travelled
from Santa Fé as far as Utah Lake and then returned by way of
the Sevier River, crossing the Colorado by one of the few
possible crossings of the Cañon. English traders penetrated the
Basin from the north, in particular Peter Skene Ogden, who, in
1825, discovered the river called Mary's, Ogden's, or the Humboldt. American fur-traders reached the Basin from the east.
One of these traders, James Bridger, discovered the Great Salt
Lake in 1824. The expeditions of Ashley and Smith, previously
described in chapter x, accomplished a great deal of exploration
within the basin itself. Although all this work had been carried
out by missionaries and fur-traders, no real knowledge of the
distinctive geographical features of the area had been obtained,
and many people believed that a great river, the Buenaventura,
flowed westward from the Rockies to the Pacific. Bonneville,
a fur-trader, threw some light on the darkness of the geographical knowledge of this region, but it was Frémont, a
Government explorer, who first described the real physical
nature of the area.

Captain B. L. E. Bonneville conducted an expedition to the
Rocky Mountains in the years 1832–5, when the fur trade was
enjoying its greatest prosperity. Bonneville's principal object
was trade, and exploration was only a secondary consideration.
Bonneville's work is described by Washington Irving in a book
which is also the best available picture of the fur trade.[2]

1 The routes of explorers described in this chapter are shown on end
Map C, Fig. 34.
2 Washington Irving, *The Adventures of Captain Bonneville, U.S.A.,
in the Rocky Mountains and the Far West. Digested from his Journal
and illustrated from various other sources.* Philadelphia, 1837, London,

In May, 1832, Captain Bonneville left Fort Osage, and followed the Platte to the Sweetwater and thence up that river over the South Pass. He then proceeded to the north-west and established a depot near the mouth of the Horse Creek of the Green River. This post was called Fort Bonneville, but other trappers called it Fort Nonsense, because it was not suitable as a permanent fort; the winter climate was too severe. From this region Bonneville made a series of expeditions in pursuit of furs, but none of them were made in unexplored regions. In 1833 Bonneville decided to make a thorough exploration of Salt Lake. "To have this lake properly explored, and all its secrets revealed, was the grand scheme of the Captain for the present year; and while it was one in which his imagination evidently took a leading part, he believed it would be attended with great profit, for the numerous beaver streams with which the lake must be fringed".[1]

Joseph Walker commanded the expedition of forty men. The party was unable to proceed over the plain to the west of the lake, and marched in a north-westerly direction until they came upon Ogden's River, or the Humboldt. "They continued down Ogden's River, until they ascertained that it lost itself in a great swampy lake, to which there was no apparent discharge. They then returned directly westward, across the great chain of Californian mountains, intervening between these interior plains and the shores of the Pacific. For three and twenty days they were entangled among these mountains, the peaks and ridges of which are in many places covered with perpetual snow."[2] They probably passed Carson Lake, Walker Lake and River, and then, after crossing the Sierra Nevada to the Merced tributary of the San Joaquin, proceeded to Monterey. Chittenden believes that it is possible that they saw the Yosemite, when they crossed the Sierra Nevada.[3] After leaving Monterey they marched south and crossed the Sierra Nevada by the Walker

1850. Bonneville placed all his manuscript at the disposal of Washington Irving, who made it into a book, "interwoven with facts and details gathered from various sources."

[1] W. Irving, *op. cit.* (1850 ed.), p. 116.
[2] W. Irving, *op. cit.* p. 214.
[3] H. M. Chittenden, *The History of the American Fur Trade*, 1, 417.

Pass. From this pass they turned north and kept close to the eastern foothills of the Sierra Nevada. They crossed the Basin by following the course of the Humboldt, but they did not visit the Great Salt Lake. They made their way north to the Snake and so reached the Bear River.[1] This expedition was a failure from the financial point of view, and was a great disappointment to Bonneville. From a geographical point of view it showed that the River Humboldt was the best course to follow in a journey across the basin. Two passes across the Sierra Nevada were discovered. The accounts of the expedition were too slight to be of real scientific value.

During the period occupied by the Walker expedition to California, Bonneville himself made an expedition, but no new discoveries were made. This expedition visited the headwaters of the Big Horn River and, after many wanderings, established winter quarters on the Portneuf river. Captain Bonneville claims that the result of his own expeditions of 1833 was that "the headwaters of Snake river, of the Columbia, Muscle Shell, and Yellowstone; headwaters of the Missouri and Sweetwater, of the Platte, and those of the Colorado of the West, were brought together in one view, as reported in my journal; before this these heads of rivers were scattered far and wide".[2] In the winter of 1833 Bonneville crossed the Blue Mountains and made a visit to Fort Walla-Walla; in 1835 he again visited the Columbia. In 1835 he returned to civilisation, travelling by way of the Platte River.

The most important result of Bonneville's expedition was the publication of two maps. One of these maps shows the sources of the Missouri, Yellowstone, Snake, Green, Wind, and Sweetwater Rivers. The other map included the whole area westward of the Great Salt Lake to the Pacific. Gallatin's map of 1836 showed most of the features drawn by Bonneville, so even in cartography Bonneville does not deserve the high place which he has usually been given. A fuller discussion of these maps is given in chapter XIII.

[1] W. Irving, op. cit. pp. 220–1.
[2] In a letter dated August 24, 1857, from Col. B. L. E. Bonneville to Lieut. G. K. Warren. G. K. Warren, Memoir to accompany the Map of the Territory of the United States, pp. 33–4.

Bonneville's expedition had shown that the Humboldt was a good guide across the desert. After Walker's return from his expedition various trapping parties used this route. The accounts of California that reached Missouri spoke of it as a land of promise, and between the years 1840 and 1846 parties of emigrants pushed their way across the Great Basin and crossed the Sierra Nevada. This movement resulted in the discovery of numerous passes across the Sierra Nevada. In 1841 a party of emigrants, under Bidwell and Bartleson, crossed the Basin by following the line of Ogden's (Humboldt) River. They reached Walker River by October and crossed the Sierra Nevada by the high Sonora Pass, 10,115 feet in altitude.[1] Belden, one of the party, wrote the following account of the crossing: " We worked our way into the mountains with a great deal of difficulty and hardship. The way was very rough, and one day in winding round the side of the mountain we lost four of our animals, who missed their footing and rolled down the mountain. We finally reached the summit with great labor and difficulty ".[2]

In 1843 Joseph B. Chiles, who had been with Bidwell, led a party along the Oregon trail to Fort Hall. At Fort Hall the party divided. Chiles continued the journey to Fort Boisé and thence by the Malheur and Pitt Rivers crossed to the Sacramento. The majority of the expedition were led by Joseph Walker down Ogden's (Humboldt) River and then south to Walker Lake and across Walker Pass. The journey from Ogden Sinks to the Walker Pass lasted sixty days.

In 1844 Murphy and Elisha Stevens conducted a party of fifty emigrants along Ogden's River to the Sinks. From here they crossed 40 miles of desert, the Truckee desert, to the Truckee River. This journey resulted in the discovery of the lowest pass across the mountains, the Truckee Pass, leading from the Truckee River to Bear River.[3]

There were six main routes across the Sierra (Fig. 34). In the north was the route discovered by Chiles, along the Pitt River, later known as Beckwith's route. To the south of this was

[1] H. H. Bancroft, *History of California*, iv, 269.
[2] H. H. Bancroft, *History of Nevada*, p. 55.
[3] H. H. Bancroft, *History of California*, iv, 445–8.

another route called Lassen's road. These routes were about 300 miles longer than the Truckee but the descents were easy. The Sonora and Walker Passes, discovered respectively by Bidwell (1841) and Walker (1833), were dangerous and soon fell into disuse as routes for emigrating parties. The two most important passes were the two central passes, which were the nearest to the Humboldt, the most direct line across the Great Basin. The Truckee Pass lay to the north of Lake Tahoe, and to the south of it was Carson Pass, discovered by Frémont and Carson in 1843.[1] The Truckee Pass was the best and was used by the main body of emigrants in the Gold Rush to California. The route by way of the Truckee and the Bear was the California trail along which Joseph Walker led parties of gold seekers in 1849.[2]

John Charles Frémont was the man who really revealed the geographical character of the region, west of the Rockies (Fig. 23). Frémont, who was born in 1813, entered the navy as a teacher of mathematics in 1833. He subsequently took part in several Government surveys. He was a member of a party which surveyed a projected railroad between Charleston and Cincinnati in 1837–8 and also assisted I. N. Nicollet in his great survey of the country between the Mississippi and the Missouri in 1838. His promotion was assured as the result of his marriage to a daughter of Senator T. H. Benton. Benton was an enthusiastic believer in the natural destiny of the United States to expand to the Pacific, and used his considerable influence to help his son-

[1] J. C. Frémont, *Report*, p. 226, refers to the crossings of the Sierra Nevada in the following words: Indians "pointed out to us where they had crossed; but then, they said, it was summer time; but now it would be impossible. I believe that this was a party led by Mr Chiles, one of the only two men whom I know to have passed through the California mountains from the interior of the Basin—Walker being the other; and both were engaged upwards of twenty days, in the summer time, in getting over".

[2] It is said that the Truckee River was named after Frémont's Indian guide. See Bulletin 612, U.S. Geol. Survey, *Guidebook of the Western United States*, Part B, The Overland Route, W. T. Lee, W. Stone, and others (1916) pp. 185, 189. Bancroft states that the River was named in 1844 after "an Indian guide to whom the name Truckee had been given on account of his resemblance to a Frenchman so called". H. H. Bancroft, *History of California*, IV, 446–7.

in-law to obtain the command of the western scientific expeditions.

The expeditions of Frémont, between the years 1842 and 1853 explained the real nature of the Great Basin and discovered the best routes across the Sierra Nevada to California. Frémont's first expedition in 1842 is not connected with either of these two discoveries, but it will be convenient to describe this expedition because his remaining journeys were intended to complete the work of the first. "His purpose", says his biographer Smucker, "was to ascertain the most desirable and feasible point in the line of emigrant travel across the mountains, in order that greater facilities might be afforded for the safe and speedy termination of the toils and dangers of the westward-bound pilgrim." [1] The first expedition lasted for four months in 1842 and made a survey of the route along the Platte to the South Pass. The western side of the Wind River Mountains was surveyed and an ascent of the highest peak was accomplished.

Frémont's First Expedition. The expedition left St Louis in May, 1842, and consisted of twenty-one men, including Charles Preuss as topographer and Kit Carson as guide. Frémont left the mouth of the Kansas River on June 10 and followed a few days behind a party of sixty-four emigrants.[2] He took a northward course to the Platte and reached that river near the present site of Fort Kearney. When he reached the forks of the Platte he divided his men into two parties. Preuss and one party went up the north fork to Fort Laramie. Frémont continued up the south fork to St Vrain, which he reached on July 10, and the two parties rejoined at Laramie on July 14. Immense herds of buffalo were seen; Frémont estimates that he saw eleven thousand near the junction of the two forks.[3] He gives an interesting account of the possibility of navigating the Platte. On July 9 he writes: "From the mouth of the South fork I had

[1] Samuel M. Smucker, A.M., *The Life of Colonel J. C. Frémont* (1856), p. 16. See *Journal of the Royal Geographical Society*, XIV (1844), 299–302, for an analysis of the results of Frémont's first expedition.

[2] J. C. Frémont, *Report*, p. 12.

[3] *Ibid.* p. 23.

found it (the river) occasionally broken up by small islands; and at the time of our journey, which was at a season of the year when the waters were at a favourable stage, it was not navigable for anything drawing six inches water. The current was very swift—the bed of the stream a coarse gravel".[1] Frémont realised the strategic importance of Fort Laramie and urged that a military fort should be established there.[2] On July 31 he reached the Sweetwater and on August 8 crossed the South Pass.[3] The party then proceeded in a north-westerly direction along the western foot of the Wind River Mountains, in lat. 43° N. A party ascended one of the highest peaks and reached the summit on August 15. "The barometer stood at 18·293, the attached thermometer at 44°; giving for the elevation of this summit 13,570 feet above the Gulf of Mexico.... From the description given by Mackenzie of the mountains, where he crossed them, with that of a French officer still farther to the north, and Colonel Long's measurements to the south, joined to the opinion of the oldest traders of the country, it is presumed that this is the highest peak of the Rocky mountains."[4] This peak was afterwards named Frémont Peak, and the height is now given as 13,790 feet. Long's Peak, Pike's Peak, and Sierra Blanca are actually all higher than Frémont Peak. He descended the mountain and reached the cache at nightfall. "Here was not the inn which awaits the tired traveller on his return from Mont Blanc, or the orange groves of South America with their refreshing juices and soft fragrant air; but we found our little *cache* of dried meat and coffee undisturbed."[5] He returned to the North Platte and attempted to navigate the river in an "India-rubber boat...twenty feet long and five broad". After passing through several rapids the boat was upset, but no lives were lost. Several other attempts to navigate the river in bull-boats proved unsuccessful, but a survey of the Platte was carried out, and the expedition returned to St Louis on October 17.

[1] J. C. Frémont, *Report*, p. 31.
[2] *Ibid.* p. 48.
[3] *Ibid.* p. 60. See *supra*, p. 148, for Frémont's account of this crossing.
[4] *Ibid.* p. 70.   [5] *Ibid.* p. 71.

Frémont's Second Expedition, 1843–4. The object of Frémont's second expedition was to explore the country between the South Pass and the mouth of the Columbia, and to make a survey of the Oregon trail. In 1841 a naval expedition, under the command of Charles Wilkes, had surveyed the Columbia region as far as Walla-Walla and had compiled an accurate map of the north-west.[1] Frémont was instructed to connect the area which he had explored in 1842 with the area explored by Wilkes, and thus make a complete survey of the region through which ran the Oregon trail. It seems probable that Frémont also intended to visit California and to return home by a different route from that taken on the outward journey. The party, consisting of thirty-nine men, left Kansas City on May 29, 1843, and reached St Vrain's Fort on July 4. The expedition then travelled southward to Pike's Peak but returned to St Vrain, before continuing their journey across the Laramie plains. The South Pass was reached on August 15, and it is from this point that the interesting part of the journey began.

Frémont crossed from the Muddy Fork of the Green River to the Bear River, thus entering the Great Basin. He was eager to make a survey of the Great Salt Lake and determined to follow the Bear River, "the principal tributary to the Great Salt lake",[2] until he reached the lake itself. From Frémont we learn that, "hitherto this lake had been seen only by trappers who were wandering through the country in search of new beaver streams, caring very little for geography; its islands had never been visited; and none were to be found who had entirely made the circuit of its shores; and no instrumental observations or geographical survey of any description, had ever been made any where in the neighboring region. It was generally supposed that it had no visible outlet".[3] Frémont constructed a useful map of the Bear valley, the emigrant road to the lower Columbia River, and followed his way down the river until he reached the lake on September 6. "I am doubtful", says Frémont, "if the

[1] Captain Charles Wilkes, *Narrative of the United States Exploring Expedition*, 1838–42 (5 vols. 1845).
[2] J. C. Frémont, *Report*, p. 132.
[3] *Ibid.*

followers of Balboa felt more enthusiasm when, from the heights of the Andes, they saw for the first time the great Western ocean."[1] A rough sketch survey was made of the lake. A party paddled out to one of the smaller islands in a boat. "The water continued to deepen as we advanced; the lake becoming almost transparently clear, of an extremely beautiful bright-green color; and the spray, which was thrown into the boat and over our clothes, was directly converted into a crust of common salt."[2] The highest point on the island was 800 feet above the level of the lake and was a useful place from which to undertake a survey. The base for this expedition was Weber's fork, one of the eastern tributaries of the lake. The party made their way by the Bear River and then by a more direct route than the usual route of the Portneuf to Fort Hall. Frémont gives a glowing account of the value of the Bear River. "The bottoms of this river, (Bear), and some of the creeks which I saw, form a natural resting and recruiting station for travellers, now, and in all time to come. The bottoms are extensive; water excellent; timber sufficient; the soil good and well adapted to the grains and grasses suited to such an elevated region....The beasts of the Indians were fat upon it [bunch grass]; our own found it a good subsistence; and its quality will sustain any amount of cattle, and make this truly a bucolic region."[3]

Fort Hall was reached on September 18, and the party then proceeded by the usual route along the southern bank of the Snake River. The journey was extremely monotonous. "The sage bushes, which covered the river plain so far as the eye could reach, and, with their uniform tint of dark gray, gave to the country a gloomy and sombre appearance. All the day the course of the river has been between walls of the black volcanic

[1] J. C. Frémont, *Report*, p. 151. The mountains from which Balboa first saw the Pacific were not the Andes. Frémont's statement seems to be an echo of Humboldt's belief in the continuity of the Rockies and Andes. I am indebted to Mr J. N. L. Baker for this suggestion.

[2] *Ibid.* pp. 153–4.

[3] *Ibid.* p. 160. "As a result of Frémont's description of the Great Salt Lake and the valley, Brigham Young determined four years later to lead the Mormons into this far-off region to set up the state of Deseret." A. Nevins, *Frémont, the West's Greatest Adventurer* (1928), I, 157.

rock, a dark line of the escarpment on the opposite side pointing out its course." [1] In many places travel was difficult, and, as the Astorians had found, "the road was occasionally extremely rocky, with hard volcanic fragments, and our travelling very slow". [2] Fort Boisé was reached on October 8, and on the 13th the expedition left the valley of the Snake River "to which the absence of timber, and the scarcity of water, give the appearance of a desert". [3] The region which he now entered was a marked contrast to the region which he had just left. All the higher parts of the mountains were covered with dense forest. The Blue Mountains, according to Frémont, received their name "from the dark-blue appearance given to them by the pines". [4] On October 20 Frémont writes that "we were obliged to cut a way through a dense body of timber, from which we emerged on an open mountain side". [5] Frémont used the valley of the Walla-Walla River and reached Fort Walla-Walla on October 25. He estimated that he had now travelled 1000 miles from South Pass, or 2000 miles from Kansas. The whole party reached the Dalles on November 4. Frémont pushed on to Fort Vancouver, and afterwards returned and rejoined the expedition on November 18. The first part of the journey was completed and an accurate survey had been made of the usual emigrant route to Oregon.

Of much greater importance in the history of exploration was the homeward journey, which "contemplated a new route, and a great circuit to the south and southeast, and the exploration of the Great Basin between the Rocky mountains and the *Sierra Nevada*". [6] Three "landmarks" were marked on the existing maps. The first of these was Tlamath or Klamath Lake, the second was a lake called Mary's Lake, supposed to lie southeast of Klamath Lake. The third geographical feature, which the map-makers recorded, was the Buenaventura River. This river was supposed to flow from the Rocky Mountains to the Pacific. The existence of such a river would disprove the idea of a Great Basin. [7] On November 25 he commenced his journey up

[1] J. C. Frémont, *Report*, p. 167. [2] *Ibid.* p. 170.
[3] *Ibid.* p. 175. [4] *Ibid.* p. 178. [5] *Ibid.* pp. 180–1.
[6] *Ibid.* p. 196. [7] *Ibid.* p. 196.

the valley of the Deschutes or Fall River. "The country is now far more interesting to a traveller than the route along the Snake and Columbia rivers. To our right we had always the mountains, from the midst of whose dark pine forests the isolated snowy peaks were looking out like giants."[1] Snow is frequently recorded along the route. On December 13 the way "was sometimes obstructed by fallen trees, and the snow was four to twelve inches deep".[2] Lake Summer and Lake Abert were discovered. Frémont gives a good description of what he could see of the Great Basin to the east, "looking forward to the east, scarce a tree was to be seen...the face of the country exhibited only rocks and grass, and presented a region in which the artemisia became the principal wood....Broadly marked by the boundary of the mountain wall, and immediately below us, were the first waters of that Great Interior Basin which has the Wahsatch and Bear river mountains for its eastern and the Sierra Nevada for its western rim; and the edge of which we had entered upwards of three months before, at the Great Salt lake".[3] Of Lake Abert, which was reached on December 20, Frémont says, "the white efflorescences which lined the shore like a bank of snow, and the disagreeable odour which filled the air...informed us too plainly that the water belonged to one of those fetid salt lakes which are common in this region".[4]

The expedition continued its southward march, but failed to discover either Mary's Lake or the Buenaventura River. The country was exceedingly difficult to traverse, "the grasses being frequently of a very unwholesome character, and the hoofs of our animals were so worn and cut by the rocks, that many of them were lame, and could scarcely be got along".[5] Dense fogs covered the country and the situation of the expedition became a dangerous one. He crossed the muddy bed of another lake which he called Mud Lake, and on January 10 he reached the lake to which he gave the name of Pyramid Lake. Frémont gives the following account of the lake and its position. "The elevation of this lake above the sea is 4890 feet, being nearly

[1] J. C. Frémont, *Report*, p. 199.   [2] *Ibid.* p. 206.
[3] *Ibid.* pp. 207–8.   [4] *Ibid.* p. 209.
[5] *Ibid.* p. 213.

Fig. 25. Crossing the Sierra Nevada.

700 feet higher than the Great Salt lake, from which it lies nearly west, and distant about eight degrees of longitude...It is the nearest lake to the western rim, as the Great Salt lake is to the eastern rim, of the Great Basin which lies between the base of the Rocky mountains and the Sierra Nevada; and the extent and character of which, its whole circumference and contents, it is so desirable to know."[1] Every day he expected to see the Buenaventura River. The hunter of the party, Kit Carson, was eagerly searching for signs of beaver, as he maintained that they would be found only on waters that flowed to the Pacific. On January 18, as the condition of the horses was so bad, and it was impossible to find the Buenaventura, Frémont decided to cross the Sierra Nevada into the valley of the Sacramento by the most practicable pass he could find. In places the snow was a great hindrance to movement. The mountains had been crossed by other explorers in summer but this was the first crossing made in the winter. The hardships were very great and on February 5 "the night had been too cold to sleep".[2] The average depth of the snow was 5 feet, "but we passed over places where it was 20 feet deep, as shown by the trees"[3] (Fig. 25).

The pass lay on the south side of Lake Tahoe and the summit was reached on February 19. The elevation was estimated by Frémont as 9338 feet, and the distance as 1000 miles from the Dalles. The pass "was 2000 feet higher than the South Pass in the Rocky mountains, and several peaks in view rose several thousand feet still higher. Thus at the extremity of the continent, and near the coast, the phenomenon was seen of a range of mountains still higher than the great Rocky mountains themselves. This extraordinary fact accounts for the Great Basin, and shows that there must be a system of small lakes and rivers here scattered over a flat country, and which the extended and lofty range of the Sierra Nevada prevents from escaping to the Pacific ocean".[4] The descent on the western side of the Sierra Nevada was made difficult by the snow. On February 21 he was able to see the Sacramento and the bay of San Francisco in the distance. The weather began to be different from the weather experienced

[1] J. C. Frémont, *Report*, pp. 217–18.   [2] *Ibid.* p. 231.
[3] *Ibid.* p. 232.   [4] *Ibid.* p. 235.

on the eastern side of the mountains. "We have the deep-blue sky and sunny climate of Smyrna and Palermo, which a little map before me shows are in the same latitude."[1] Frémont followed down the valley of the Rio de los Americanos and, on March 6, he reached Nueva Helvetia, the fort of Captain Sutter, situated two miles from the junction of the Rio de los Americanos and the Sacramento. Frémont's plan was to continue southwards along the valley of the San Joaquin and cross the Sierra Nevada by the pass previously discovered by Joseph Walker. He then intended to join the Spanish trail, proceed north-east until he reached Utah Lake, and then cross the Rocky Mountains and reach the head of the Arkansas.

Sutter's Fort was left on March 24, and the southward journey was continued in the great valley of California. On April 13 he made his way up into the Sierra Nevada and on April 14 crossed the mountains. Frémont gives the following description of the pass: "As we reached the summit of this beautiful pass, and obtained a view into the eastern country, we saw at once that here was the place to take leave of all such pleasant scenes as those around us. The distant mountains were now bald rocks again; and below the land had any color but green".[2] The latitude of the pass was 35° 17' 12" N. and the longitude was 118° 35' 03" W.[3] Frémont had, by this journey in California, made some very important geographical discoveries. He had proved that the Sierra Nevada was a continuation of the Cascade range in Oregon, "between which and the ocean there is still another and a lower range, parallel to the former and to the coast, and which may be called the Coast Range".[4] Frémont had also proved that no such river as the Buenaventura existed. This river had frequently been indicated on the maps as taking its rise in the Rocky Mountains and crossing the Sierra Nevada. Frémont thus sums up his results:

There is no opening from the bay of San Francisco into the interior of the continent. The two rivers which flow into it are comparatively short, and

---

[1] J. C. Frémont, *Report*, p. 237.   [2] *Ibid.* p. 255.

[3] This pass, according to Bancroft and Warren, was the Tehachapi Pass (sometimes spelt Tah-ee-cha-pah), but it is possible that Walker Pass was used.

[4] J. C. Frémont, *Report*, p. 255.

not perpendicular to the coast, but lateral to it, and having their heads towards Oregon and southern California. They open lines of communicaton north and south and not eastwardly; and this want of interior communication from the San Francisco bay, now fully ascertained, gives great additional value to the Columbia, which stands alone as the only great river on the Pacific slope of our continent which leads from the ocean to the Rocky mountains, and opens a line of communication from the sea to the valley of the Mississippi.[1]

Frémont had revealed the real nature of the physical features of California.

On April 18 he reached the Spanish trail and proceeded along the banks of the Mohave River. He found that the trail was a very difficult road, "the roughest and rockiest road we had ever seen in the country, and which nearly destroyed our band of fine mules and horses".[2] He traversed a region of desert, "the most sterile and repulsive that we had yet seen. Its prominent features were dark *sierras*, naked and dry; on the plains a few straggling shrubs—among them, cactus of several varieties".[3] The heat was severe, and the party suffered from great thirst while travelling over the sands of the high country. On May 6 he reached the Virgin River, a tributary of the Colorado. At this point the mountains "began to be wooded with cedar and pine, and clusters of trees gave shelter to birds—a new and welcome sight".[4] After passing the desert, on May 13, he reached the Wasatch Mountains, and on May 16 he left the Spanish trail which crosses the Wasatch Mountains and continues west to Santa Fé. He reached Sevier River on May 23, and Utah Lake on May 24. Frémont described it as a fresh-water lake, which is correct, and also stated that it was connected with the Great Salt Lake. Frémont now crossed the divide to Uinta River, and on June 6 obtained a view of the Colorado River, reaching the Elk Head or Bear River on June 10. He now entered the region of the Rocky Mountains once more and crossed from the Pacific to the Atlantic divide by means of what is now called Muddy Pass, two degrees south of the South Pass, into the Platte drainage basin. In the mountains the face of the country changed: "not only the river bottoms, but the hills,

[1] J. C. Frémont, *Report*, p. 256.   [2] *Ibid*. p. 259.
[3] *Ibid*. p. 264.   [4] *Ibid*. p. 269.

were covered with grass".[1] The pass used on this occasion was 8000 feet in height. He now turned south and followed the North Platte to its source, thus making a survey of the region called New Park. Frémont re-crossed the divide and surveyed the upper waters of the Colorado in the Old Park and finally the headwaters of the Arkansas in the South Park. Thus a rapid survey was made of the relative position of the headwaters of the Colorado, the Platte, and the Arkansas. Bent's Fort was reached on July 1, after which the expedition crossed to the Smoky Hill Fork, finally arriving at St Louis on August 6. The homeward journey from Lake Utah is only briefly described by Frémont.

The discovery of the real nature of the Great Basin of interior drainage is the most important result of the expedition. It seems remarkable that the existence of the Basin should not have been realised until so late a date, but physical features explain the delay. The divides between the Basin and the Columbia on the north, and between the Basin and the Colorado on the south-east and south, are very low and ill-defined. The divide on the west consists of the elevated Sierra Nevada and is therefore clearly defined. If the Basin had been first approached from San Francisco, there is no doubt that the nature of the Basin would have been earlier understood.

It seems probable that Frémont was the inventor of the term "Great Basin".[2] He describes his meaning in the following words: "The Great Basin—a term which I apply to the intermediate region between the Rocky mountains and the next range, containing many lakes, with their own system of rivers and creeks, (of which the Great Salt is the principal), and which have no connection with the ocean, or the great rivers which flow into it. This Great Basin is yet to be adequately explored".[3] Again he says: "Interior basins with their own systems of lakes and rivers, and often sterile, are common enough in Asia; people still living in the elementary state of families, living in

[1] J. C. Frémont, *Report*, p. 281.
[2] For important reference to the Great Basin see J. C. Frémont, *Report*, pp. 170, 175, 207–8, 275–7. The last reference contains a good summary of Frémont's views.
[3] J. C. Frémont, *Report*, p. 175.

deserts, with no other occupation than the mere animal search for food, may still be seen in that ancient quarter of the globe; but in America such things are new and strange, unknown and unsuspected, and discredited when related".[1] The fur-traders, especially Joseph Walker, had believed in a Great Basin, but Frémont must have the credit for first making a comparatively accurate map of its extent. He drew a map on the scale of 1:3,000,000 in illustration of his report and he inserts the following description of the basin on his map: "The Great Basin: diameter 11° of latitude, 10° of longitude: elevation above the sea between 4 and 5000 feet: surrounded by lofty mountains: contents almost unknown, but believed to be filled with rivers and lakes which have no communication with the sea, deserts and oases which have never been explored, and savage tribes, which no traveller has seen or described". On his third expedition Frémont revealed something of the character of the Basin itself.

Frémont's Third Expedition.[2] The nominal object of Frémont's third expedition was to survey the mountains west of the Rockies, the Sierra Nevada, and the Cascades with a view to discovering the best passes from the Great Basin to California. The diplomatic relations between Mexico and the United States were at this time, very strained, and it seems probable that Frémont had received secret instructions from the Government, in case war should break out. The preparations were unusually warlike for a scientific expedition. In the summer of 1845 Frémont collected a force of sixty men which arrived at Bent's Fort in August. He ascended the Arkansas to its source, proceeded north-west to Utah Lake and spent the last week of October in exploring the Great Salt Lake, including Antelope Island.

He left the southern shore of the Great Salt Lake, and struck north-west to Pilot Peak, crossing two ranges of hills. When the expedition reached the River Ogden, a river which Frémont

[1] J. C. Frémont, *Report*, p. 277.
[2] Frémont never published a full account of this expedition. See G. K. Warren, *Memoir*, pp. 49–51, and H. H. Bancroft, *History of California*, IV, 581 ff. The results of the expedition were briefly summarised in J. C. Frémont's *Geographical Memoir*, which was published in 1848.

renamed the Humboldt, it was divided into two parties. Frémont, with ten men (including Carson), set out on a direct
route for Walker Lake. He travelled south-west from Franklin
Lake, crossed three distinct mountain ranges, before arriving at
the meeting-place of Walker Lake on November 24. Frémont
was surprised to find that the mountains of the Basin were well
wooded and that the area was not quite as barren as had been
imagined. He had certainly discovered one of the most practicable routes across what is now the State of Nevada.

The main party, led by Walker and Kern, followed the
emigrant trail down the Humboldt to the Carson Sinks, where
the river ended, and then, turning southward, rejoined Frémont
on November 27, at Walker Lake. The two parties then separated
once more, having agreed to meet on the western side of
the Sierra Nevada on the Tulare Lake. The main party under
Walker and Kern resumed their march to the south on December 8, and followed Owen's River (named after a member of
the expedition) down to Owen's Lake. They crossed the Sierra
by the Walker Pass (discovered in 1834), and passed down the
southern branch of the Kern River (named after one of the
leaders of the party).

Frémont himself, with fifteen men, had left Walker River on
November 29, and reached the Salmon Trout or Truckee
River on December 1. He crossed the Sierra by the Truckee
Pass (lat. 39° 17′);[1] a pass which is 55 miles north of the pass
which he had used in January, 1844. Frémont descended the
northern fork of the American River and reached Sutter's
Fort on December 10. Frémont then hurried to the south to
rejoin Walker's party. On December 22 he reached King's
River or Tulare Lake River, but he was unable to find Walker,
who was awaiting him on Kern River. Frémont finally gave up

---

[1] "*December* 4, 1845.—Descent from the pass, at the head of Salmon
Trout river, latitude 39° 17′, elevation 7,200 feet. At 3 in the afternoon
the temperature at 46°, at sunset 34°, at sunrise next morning 22°; the sky
perfectly clear; no snow in the pass, but much on the mountain tops. Here
the present emigrant road now crosses.... *December* 6.—The route was
over good, travelling ground, through open pine forest on a broad,
leading ridge, affording an excellent road". J. C. Frémont, *Geog. Memo.*
pp. 28–9.

the search and went to Monterey, where he found Walker, who had marched to that town when his provisions had been exhausted. The expedition was reunited in the middle of February, 1846. Frémont made preparations for his return and, when only 30 miles from Monterey, was ordered to leave the country. After a considerable delay, the expedition marched north to Sutter's Fort, which they left on March 24. He then followed the Sacramento River to Lassen's Fort and explored the upper Klamath Lake. The purely scientific work of the expedition was suddenly ended, because on May 6 Frémont received a message from Lieut. Gillespie and immediately marched south. The explorers now took part in the political and military events which resulted in the annexation of California by the United States. Frémont, having become involved in a quarrel with his own superior officers, was arrested by Kearny and had to undergo a court-martial, but the details of these proceedings do not require a discussion in a history of exploration.[1]

In his *Geographical Memoir*[2] Frémont gives a summary account of the geographical results of his third expedition. Frémont divides America west of the Great Salt Lake into three regions, the Sierra Nevada, the Great Basin, and the Maritime region west of the Sierra Nevada. Frémont emphasises the importance of the Sierra Nevada as a divide between the two other regions. This range, says Frémont, "divides California into two parts, and exercises a decided influence on the climate, soil, and productions of each. Stretching along the coast, and at the general distance of 150 miles from it, this great mountain wall receives the warm winds, charged with vapor, which sweep across the Pacific ocean, precipitates their accumulated moisture in fertilizing rains and snows upon its western flank, and leaves cold and dry winds to pass on to the east. Hence the characteristic differences of the two regions—mildness, fertility, and a superb vegetable kingdom on one side, comparative barrenness and cold on the other".[3]

[1] See A. Nevins, *op. cit.* chaps. XXII, XXIII, for an unbiassed account of the case.

[2] *Geographical Memoir upon Upper California, in illustration of his Map of Oregon and California* (1848).

[3] J. C. Frémont, *Geog. Memo.* pp. 6–7.

The most important part of the *Memoir* is the account of the
Great Basin, which Frémont had crossed on the third expedition.[1] The reasons which led Frémont to assume the theoretical
existence of the Basin have been described. The existence of the
Basin, says Frémont, "which was advanced as a theory after the
second expedition, is now established as a geographical fact".[2]
Frémont's general description of the Basin is worth quoting
in full.

Partly arid, and sparsely inhabited, the general character of the GREAT
BASIN is that of desert, but with great exceptions, there being many parts
of it very fit for the residence of a civilized people; and of these parts, the
Mormons have lately established themselves in one of the largest and best.
Mountain is the predominating structure of the interior of the Basin, with
plains between—the mountains wooded and watered, the plains arid and
sterile. The interior mountains conform to the law which governs the
course of the Rocky mountains and of the Sierra Nevada, ranging nearly
north and south, and present a very uniform character of abruptness,
rising suddenly from a narrow base of ten to twenty miles, and attaining
an elevation of two to five thousand feet above the level of the country.
They are grassy and wooded, showing snow on their summit peaks
during the greater part of the year, and affording small streams of water
from five to fifty feet wide, which lose themselves, some in lakes, some in
the dry plains, and some in a belt of alluvial soil at the base; for these
mountains have very uniformly this belt of alluvion, the wash and abrasion
of their sides, rich in excellent grass, fertile, and light and loose enough to
absorb small streams. Between these mountains are the arid plains which
receive and deserve the name of desert. Such is the general structure of
the interior of the Great Basin, more Asiatic than American in its character,
and much resembling the elevated region between the Caspian sea and
northern Persia.[3]

Frémont gives a very valuable account of the lakes, the rivers,
and the climate of the Great Basin. The explorer lays particular
emphasis on the importance of the Humboldt River in the
communications of America.

Its direction, nearly east and west, is the right course for that travel. It
furnishes a level unobstructed way for nearly three hundred miles, and a
continuous supply of the indispensable articles of water, wood, and grass.
Its head is towards the Great Salt lake, and consequently towards the
Mormon settlement, which must become a point in the line of emigration
to California and the lower Columbia. Its termination is within fifty miles

[1] J. C. Frémont, *Geog. Memo.* pp. 7–13.   [2] *Ibid.* p. 7.
[3] *Ibid.* pp. 7–8.

of the base of the Sierra Nevada, and opposite the Salmon Trout river pass[1]—a pass only seven thousand two hundred feet above the level of the sea, and less than half that above the level of the Basin, and leading into the valley of the Sacramento, some forty miles north of Nueva Helvetia.[2]

The greater part of Frémont's *Memoir*[3] is a lengthy geographical account of the Maritime region west of the Sierra Nevada, California proper, which he aptly compares with Italy. The concluding comparison with Italy is worthy of this great geographer.

California, below the Sierra Nevada, is about the extent of Italy, geographically considered in all the extent of Italy from the Alps to the termination of the peninsula. It is of the same length, about the same breadth, consequently the same area (about one hundred thousand square miles), and presents much similarity of climate and productions. Like Italy, it lies north and south, and presents some differences of climate and productions, the effect of difference of latitude, proximity of high mountains, and configuration of the coast. Like Italy, it is a country of mountains and vallies: different from it in its internal structure, it is formed for *unity*; its large rivers being concentric, and its large vallies appurtenant to the great central bay of San Francisco, within the area of those waters the dominating power must be found.

Geographically, the position of this California is one of the best in the world; lying on the coast of the Pacific, fronting Asia, on the line of an American road to Asia, and possessed of advantages to give full effect to its grand geographical position.[4]

This description shows that Frémont was not only a great explorer but also a geographer with a real understanding of the conception of a region as a natural unit.

Frémont's Last Expeditions. The fourth and fifth expeditions of the great explorer are of very little importance when compared with his earlier journeys and only require a brief mention. The object of the fourth expedition was to find out the best possible route for a trans-continental railway. In November, 1848, Frémont reached Pueblo and had planned to go west along the 37th parallel from the headwaters of the Rio Grande. He decided to set out in the winter, as he wished to see the worst possible conditions for travel. The expedition crossed the Sangre de Cristo Mountains by the Robidoux Pass and entered

---

[1] Afterwards called Truckee Pass.
[2] J. C. Frémont, *Geog. Memo.* pp. 10–11.
[3] *Ibid.* pp. 13–43.   [4] *Ibid.* p. 43.

the valley of the Rio Grande. The San Juan range, with peaks 14,000 feet in height, now blocked the westward march of the expedition. After terrible hardships, the party were forced to turn back. Eleven men and many animals were lost. The remnant of the expedition marched from Taos down the Rio Grande and then travelled by way of Tucson, and the Gila River.

The fifth and last expedition was carried out in 1853. The Government had determined that five distinct trans-continental routes be surveyed as a preliminary step towards the construction of railways. The command of these expeditions was given to officers of the regular army only. Frémont was overlooked and was bitterly disappointed. However, he decided to undertake an independent expedition, which would forestall the work of the official explorers. Frémont followed the same route as in 1848 and successfully crossed the San Juan Mountains by the Cochetope Pass. The expedition then reached the Uncompahgre River and by way of the Gunnison and Grand River reached the Green River in Utah. From here the party crossed the Wasatch Mountains and reached Parowan (a Mormon settlement) in February of 1854. Frémont then led his party in a south-westerly direction and crossed the Sierra Nevada by one of the southern passes.

Frémont took no more part in exploration. He was an unsuccessful candidate for the Presidency of the United States in 1856 and played a prominent part as a General in the Civil War. He died on July 13, 1890.

Frémont's contribution to geographical knowledge cannot be measured by a mere recital of his discoveries. It must be remembered that very little of his work was accomplished in regions not previously visited by civilised men. It is true that "He was not a 'Pathfinder'; he was a Pathmarker",[1] but he will always be remembered in the history of exploration because he was the first to write an adequate and accurate account of the general physical features of the region between the South Pass and the Pacific.[2] "It would be hard", says Nevins, "to over-

[1] A. Nevins, op. cit. II, 703.
[2] Frémont's accounts obviously could not be complete accounts. His work was completed by later explorers. Frémont's surveys of the Great

emphasize the zeal and conscientiousness which he gave to the work of mapping his routes, collecting specimens, noting geographical and topographical facts, and at midnight, often in the harshest weather, after a day of exhausting toil, taking his observations of the stars." [1] Frémont's descriptions of the routes across the continent are comparable with Lewis and Clark's accounts of the northern route. The narratives of Frémont with their descriptions of the best routes across the Great Basin and of the passes over the Sierra Nevada, combined with his glowing accounts of California, stimulated emigration to that country. The work of this great man is therefore closely connected with the acquisition of California by the United States. Frémont's surveys of the South Pass, the Great Salt Lake, the Humboldt River, and the Truckee Pass were all valuable additions to geographical knowledge, but there can be no doubt that his greatest scientific achievement was the discovery of the real nature of the Great Interior Basin of America.

Salt Lake were supplemented by the work of Captain H. Stansbury in the years 1849–50. Stansbury obtained much new information about the Lake itself and the surrounding region and returned by way of Bridger's Pass, south of South Pass. See H. Stansbury, *Exploration and Survey of the Valley of the Great Salt Lake of Utah* (1855). Also G. K. Warren, *Memoir*, pp. 57–9.

[1] A. Nevins, *op. cit.* pp. 703–4.

Chapter XIII

THE REPRESENTATION OF WESTERN AMERICA ON MAPS PUBLISHED BETWEEN 1800 AND 1850

Many of the maps of North America which were published in the eighteenth century reflect the geographical speculations of Baron Louis de la Hontan, who in 1683, when seventeen years old, had been sent to Canada in a company of French marines. In 1688 he made a journey from Green Bay to the Fox River, and then reached the Mississippi by way of the Fox-Wisconsin portage. La Hontan then claimed to have reached a mythical river which he named the Long. He said that he ascended this tributary of the Mississippi for many leagues and that Indians told him of a river in the far west that emptied itself into a salt lake of 300 leagues in extent. La Hontan's book was published in 1703,[1] and its combination of satire on European manners with accounts of mythical travels have led scholars to compare it with Swift's *Gulliver's Travels*. The book had a great vogue and its influence on geographical maps lasted throughout the century, the Long River being marked on a map by Vaugondy as late as 1783.

Cartographers endeavoured to connect La Hontan's imaginary western sea with the inlets discovered by Spanish explorers on the Pacific coast. J. N. de Lisle, in 1752, produced a map (Fig. 26) which shows, in the west of America, an immense inland sea connected with the Pacific Ocean by two narrow channels.[2] It was not until towards the end of the century, partly as the result of the journeys of Hearne and Mackenzie, that the inland sea was finally expunged from the maps.[3]

[1] Baron de Lahontan, *New Voyages to North-America*, London, 1703, ed. R. G. Thwaites (2 vols. 1905).
[2] J. N. de Lisle, *Explication de la Carte des Nouvelles Découvertes au Nord de la Mer du Sud* (1752).
[3] The following books contain useful accounts of the search for the inland sea and its representation on maps: L. J. Burpee, *The Search for the Western Sea* (1908); N. M. Crouse, *In Quest of the Western Ocean* (1928).

The maps of North America drawn by the geographers Winterbotham and Cary in 1795 and 1806 respectively, have already been discussed (Figs. 1 and 3). Both these maps indicate

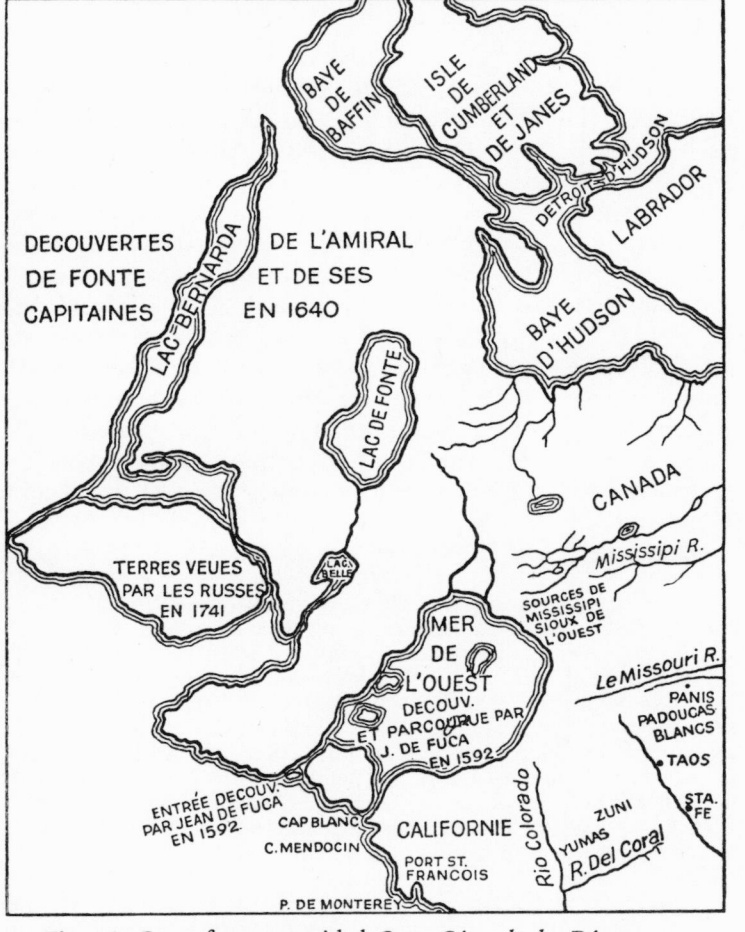

Fig. 26. Part of a map entitled *Carte Génerale des Découvertes de l'Amiral de Fonte*, J. N. de Lisle (1752).

the stage that exploration had reached by the beginning of the nineteenth century.

A map drawn in 1818 by William Rector and Roberdeau[1] (Fig. 27), entitled "Sketch of the Western part of the Continent of North America between Latitudes 35° and 52° N.", shows that the results of the expedition of Lewis and Clark were incorporated in the maps of the period. The courses of the Lewis and Clark forks of the Columbia are more or less correctly shown. Pike on his map had shown the Red River's sources as rising from a position where the Canadian's sources are known to be. Rector and Roberdeau follow Pike in this respect. Rector's map represents the Rio Grande as rising near the true source of the Green River. Rector's map also follows Lewis and Clark in the exaggerated drainage basin given to the Willamette River which is shown to rise near the Colorado. On this map the Colorado is considerably shorter than in nature, but the Gila is approximately correct. One large river flows into the Bay of San Francisco from the south-east. The map, although it does not indicate any idea of an interior basin, has one great merit. There is no indication of mythical rivers such as the Buenaventura. The map does not contain a very correct representation of the relief of the country west of the Rocky Mountains.

Schoolcraft, who discovered the source of the Mississippi,[2]

[1] This map is reproduced in G. K. Warren's *Memoir*, p. 22. On the map are the words, "This Map of an extent of country including more than twenty degrees of Latitude, and fifty of Longitude was originally drawn under the inspection of William Rector, Esquire, Surveyor of the United States for the territories of Missouri and Illinois, and was by him presented to the General Land Office, January 21st, 1818. It is probably the most correct Map of the country now extant. Signed Joseph Meigs, General Land Office. 21st Jan. 1818. Roberdeau U.S. Topl. Eng. del.".

[2] After Pike had explored the Upper Mississippi in 1805–6 (see vol. 1, *Expeditions of Z. M. Pike*, ed. Elliott Coues), no further work was done to discover the source of the great river until 1820. In that year an expedition under Governor Cass set out with the object of reaching the source of the Mississippi. H. R. Schoolcraft was a member of the party and wrote an account of the journey in *Narrative of Travels to the Sources of the Mississippi River, performed as a member of the expedition under Governor Cass in the year* 1820 (1821). In spite of Cass' expedition, "a veil of obscurity was still cast about the actual source of the Mississippi". The mystery was finally solved by Schoolcraft's expedition of 1831–2. This expedition is described in H. R. Schoolcraft's *Narrative of an Expedition through the*

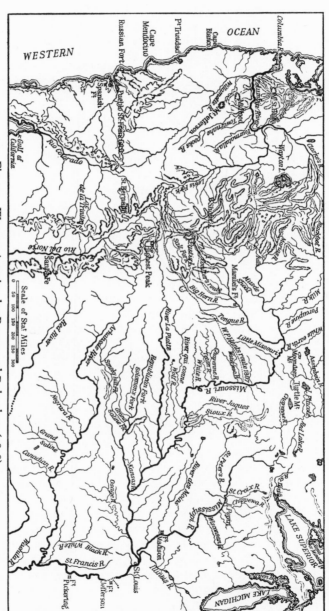

Fig. 27. Western America, by Rector and Roberdeau (1818).

states in his book written in 1834 that "American Geography may be said to have had three important problems to solve, in modern times. The first and second of these, related to the source of the Missouri, and to the course and termination of the Columbia. Both were substantially resolved by the expedition of Lewis and Clark, under the administration of Mr Jefferson.... The true source of the Mississippi, which forms the third topic of inquiry, was brought into discussion at the same period".[1] When the source of the Mississippi had been discovered by Schoolcraft's expedition of 1831–2, "It might seem, according to Mr Schoolcraft, that American geography had no more problems to solve".[2] Schoolcraft's statement illustrates the geographical ideas which prevailed at that time. It was not realised that the problem of the Great Basin had still to be made clear. The indications on the maps, at this period, of the region south of the Snake River, are drawn entirely from the imagination of the cartographers. Finley's map of North America, published in 1826, is an admirable example of this kind of cartography[3] (Fig. 28). On this map the author states that he includes "all the recent geographical discoveries", many of which were the discoveries of his fertile imagination! Two rivers, the Rio los Mongos and the Rio Timpanogos, flow from Lake Timpanogos across the Great Basin to the Pacific. The lake occupies the approximate position of the Great Salt Lake. Similarly the Rio Buenaventura, the mythical river for which Frémont vainly searched in 1843, flows across the Great Basin from Lake Salado to San Francisco. The course of the Colorado and the tributaries of the Mississippi are more correctly drawn than in 1818, but no real improvement in the representation of the area west of the Rockies had been made since the time of Lewis and Clark.

Upper Mississippi to Itasca Lake, the actual source of the river; embracing an exploratory trip through the St Croix and Burntwood (or Broule) Rivers; in 1832 (1834).

   [1] H. R. Schoolcraft, *Expedition to Itasca Lake*, pp. 7–8.
   [2] G. K. Warren, *Memoir*, p. 30.
   [3] A. Finley, Map of North America including all the recent Geographical Discoveries, from *New and General Atlas*, Philadelphia, 1826. The map is reproduced in G. K. Warren's *Memoir*, p. 30.

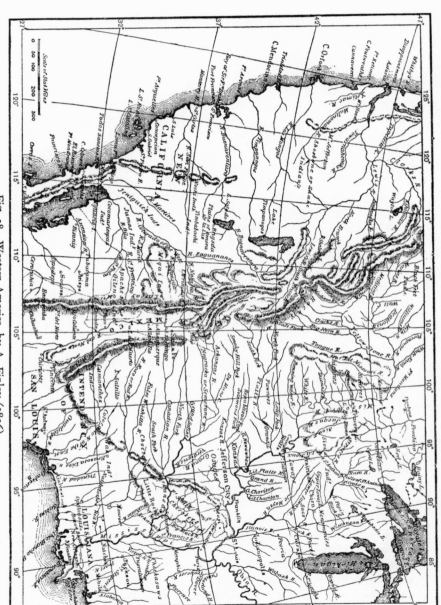

Fig. 28. Western America, by A. Finley (1826).

Maps similar in character to Finley's were published in Britain at this time. In 1829 a map of North America was constructed to illustrate a book by Hugh Murray.[1] This map shows two lakes, Lake Timpanogos and Lake Sale, on the western side of the Rockies. From Lake Timpanogos two rivers flow westward to the Pacific, one being the Sacramento, while from Lake Sale a river, the San Felipe, flows to Monterey. The courses of these rivers are marked tentatively by dotted lines. The Rio Buenaventura enters Lake Sale from the north-east and is apparently considered to be the upper stream of the river San Felipe.

James Stuart constructed a map to illustrate a book published in 1833.[2] The drainage shown is similar to that indicated on Murray's map. The rivers, although not named, are boldly marked. Arrowsmith in his Atlases of 1835 and 1844 drew a River Buenaventura, which flows from the centre of the Great Basin westwards to the Pacific.[3]

Albert Gallatin in 1836 compiled a map of western America for his work, *Synopsis of the Indian Tribes within the United States*[4] (Fig. 29). This map shows the results of the explorations of Ashley and Smith, and as it is apparently the first map to indicate the existence of a basin of interior drainage, is deserving of very high praise. The map had been neglected until Professor H. C. Dale discussed it in his book on the Ashley-Smith explorations. The map contains many features that appear in Bonneville's map of 1837 (Fig. 30), but Gallatin's map was comparatively unknown, while Bonneville's map was well advertised by the great Washington Irving. Gallatin's map shows a "Great Sandy Desert" occupying the Great Basin. The Great Salt Lake is shown with the Bear River flowing into it and there is no river flowing out of the lake. Ashley Lake is also shown in the Great Basin. There is a tolerable representation of the rivers of California. This map really represents the work of

[1] H. Murray, *Historical Account of Discoveries and Travels in North America, with Observations on Emigration* (2 vols. 1829).

[2] J. Stuart, *Three Years in North America* (2 vols. 2nd ed. 1833).

[3] J. Arrowsmith, *London Atlas of Universal Geography* (1835 and 1844). (Map of North America, no. 39.)

[4] Appeared in *American Antiquarian Society Transactions*, vol. II (1836).

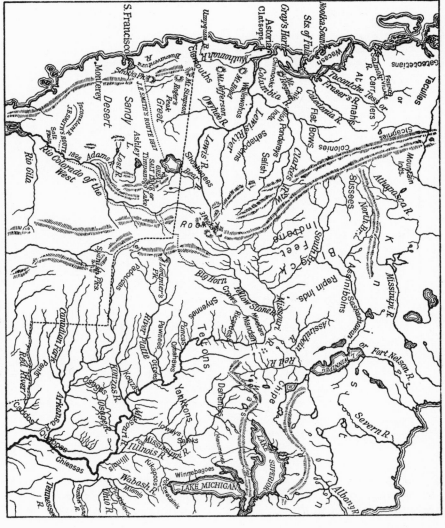

Fig. 29. Western America, by A. Gallatin (1836).

Ashley and Smith from whom Gallatin obtained his information. The course of the Colorado is well shown and Gallatin obtained this knowledge from Jedediah S. Smith.[1] Chittenden sums up the valuable discoveries recorded by the map in the following words:

That the sources of the Rio Grande del Norte were not above 39 degrees north latitude; that the sources of the Colorado of the West were as far north as 43 degrees; that Lake Timpanago, or Great Salt Lake, had no

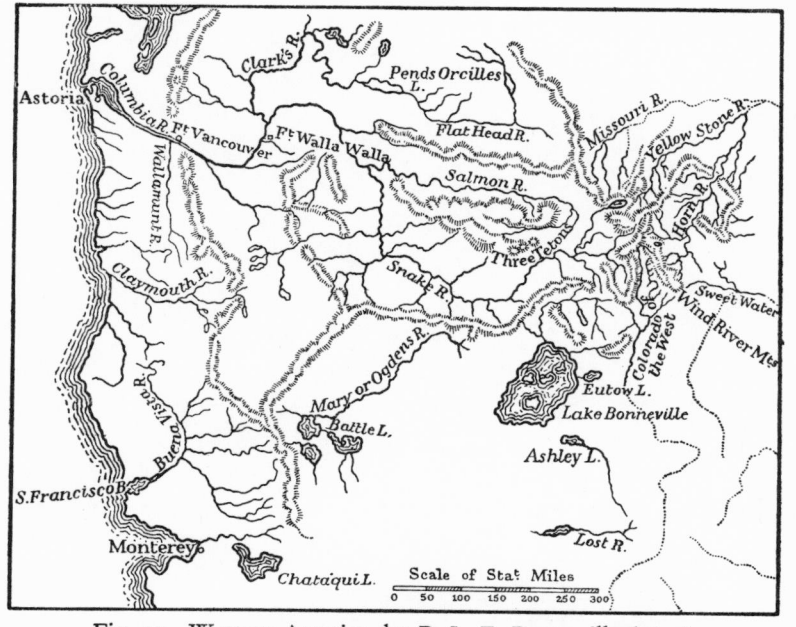

Fig. 30. Western America, by B. L. E. Bonneville (1837).

outlet to the Pacific ocean and no tributary on its west shore, but two important ones from the east; that there was another salt lake without an outlet about 80 miles south of the southernmost point of Great Salt Lake; that the course of the far-famed Buenaventura river, which was long supposed to drain some great central lake, was confined to the Pacific coast, and, far from being east and west, was in reality from north to south; that the Multanomah or Willamette river, long supposed to rise near

[1] For a full discussion see H. C. Dale, *Ashley-Smith Explorations*, pp. 304–6.

Great Salt Lake, was also a Pacific coast stream only; that the Owyhee river took its rise west of and at no great distance from the Great Salt Lake; and finally that the whole country between Great Salt Lake and the Sierra Nevada mountains was of sandy desert character.[1]

In view of what has been said about Gallatin's map, it is obvious that Bonneville's maps do not deserve the unstinted praise usually given to them. G. K. Warren, for example, referred to Bonneville's maps in the following words:

They are the first to correctly represent the hydrography of this region west of the Rocky mountains. Although the geographical positions are not accurate, yet the existence of the great interior basins, without outlets to the ocean, of Great Salt lake, of Mary's or Ogden's River, (named afterwards Humboldt by Captain Frémont), of the Mud lakes, and of Sevier river and lake *was determined* by Captain Bonneville's map, and they proved the non-existence of the Rio Buenaventura and of other hypothetical rivers. They reduced the Wallamuth or Multonomah (Willamette) to its proper length, and fixed approximately its source, and determined the general extent and direction of the Sacramento and San Joaquin rivers. The map of the sources of the Yellowstone is still the best original one of that region.[2]

The Great Salt Lake on this map is called Lake Bonneville. This title was never accepted by geographers, as Bonneville cannot claim to have discovered the lake, but his name has been given by geologists to the quaternary lake which once filled a large part of the Great Basin. Bonneville says in his letter to G. K. Warren (quoted *supra*, p. 172); "It was from my explorations and those of my party alone that it was ascertained that this lake (Great Salt Lake) had no outlet; that the California range *basined* all the waters of its eastern slope without further outlet; that the Buenaventura and all other California streams drained only the western slope. It was for this reason that Mr W. Irving named the salt lake after me, and he believed I was fairly entitled to it". Bonneville, although he is not entitled to make this claim, must, nevertheless, receive the credit for three important additions to geographical knowledge which he indicated on his map: (*a*) the position of the Humboldt and its lakes, (*b*) the indication of the San Joaquin River, and (*c*) a representation of

---

[1] H. M. Chittenden, *History of the American Fur Trade*, I, 307.
[2] G. K. Warren, *Memoir*, p. 33.

the country in the neighbourhood of the sources of the Big Horn and the Green River.

I. N. Nicollet, as a result of his explorations in 1836–40, published a map in 1843 of the basin of the upper Mississippi on the scale 1:200,000. This map was described by Warren[1] as "one of the greatest contributions ever made to American Geography", but it only concerns the region east of the Rocky Mountains, of which it presents an accurate representation.

The results of Frémont's work in the years 1842–4 were shown on a beautiful map drawn by Charles Preuss (published in 1845). This map is on a scale of 32 inches to a mile and only contains what was actually seen by the explorers. It is needless to repeat what was stated in the previous chapter of the importance of Frémont's contributions to American Geography. Frémont's map of 1848, the result of his third expedition, is described by Warren as "the most accurate map of that region extant".[2] Frémont's maps did, however, give rise to a somewhat erroneous idea of great ridges of mountains, forming a "rim" of the Great Basin on the north and the south. These two "rims" were supposed to stretch in an east to west direction.

The map of the Territory of the United States from the Mississippi to the Pacific[3] drawn by G. K. Warren in 1854 shows the extent of geographical knowledge at the end of the period covered by this book. The map is drawn on a scale of 1:3,000,000 and is an admirable production. It was definitely compiled from all the most reliable information available at the time. The method of compiling and drawing the map is explained at length by Warren.[4]

In his concluding chapter Warren gives some interesting information with regard to the development of geographical ideas about the continent. He explains that the current idea of the time about the relief of western America was the theory of the parallelism of the mountain ranges.

The idea has lately begun to prevail that this local parallelism is the characteristic of the great mountain mass throughout its whole extent.

[1] G. K. Warren, *Memoir*, p. 42. [2] *Ibid.* p. 50.
[3] The map is included in G. K. Warren's *Memoir*.
[4] G. K. Warren, *Memoir*, pp. 92–109.

Whether this idea has been true or not, it has been attended with some practicable advantages. Instead of one or two main summits for an overland route to pass, it shows us that we must expect many. On every route explored across the continent, at least four well-defined summits have been discovered, and on some of them many more. Some of these ridges enclose interior hydrographic basins. Others are traversed by rivers, but the passes thus made are generally impracticable, and, for the purposes of travel, might almost as well never have existed.[1]

On Warren's map, although "spaces are left blank, as in the southern portion of the Great Basin",[2] the general topography and drainage of the whole region are well known. The course of the Colorado is somewhat imperfectly drawn, and this omission was to be remedied by Major J. W. Powell in 1869–72.[3] An examination of Warren's map will show that the age of exploration is at an end and that the age of detailed survey is at hand.

[1] G. K. Warren, *Memoir*, p. 113.
[2] *Ibid.* p. 111.
[3] J. W. Powell, *Exploration of the Colorado River of the West*, issued under the direction of the Smithsonian Institute (1875). In 1869, Major J. W. Powell accomplished the descent of the Colorado from Green River to the mouth of the Virgin River, thus making a complete descent of the Grand Cañon. In 1871–2 Powell made a second descent of the river. The narrative part of the first journey has been reprinted unabridged in *First through the Grand Canyon*, ed. H. Kephart (1925).

Chapter XIV

CONCLUSION

It is impossible to understand the history of the United States without some knowledge of the exploration which was accomplished during the early part of the nineteenth century. The westward movement of the American people, which followed the Louisiana purchase, was carried out after the explorers had done their work as a necessary preliminary. The annexation of Texas in 1845, of the Oregon region in 1846, and of the Spanish south-west, after the war of 1848, were a natural result of exploration and subsequent settlement. The movement of western settlers followed so closely on the heels of the trappers and explorers, that the importance of exploration has not always been realised.

This book has attempted to relate the exploration of these years to Geography. The historical order of the discoveries was, in a sense, determined by geographical factors. The exploration of the region was partly accomplished by the trading pioneers of the fur trade. It can be said that exploration and trade resulted in the settlement of the region, particularly in Oregon, California, and the Salt Lake district. The history of the settlement of the region has not been discussed, although it must be realised that exploration and settlement are two closely related subjects. The two most important discoveries, from the point of view of settlement, were those of the South and the Truckee Passes. Through these passes and along the routes laid down by the explorers and trappers poured a great stream of migration to Oregon and to California. Between the years 1842 and 1846 large numbers of American pioneer settlers reached the Oregon country by way of the Oregon trail, while in later years thousands of emigrants followed the old trails that led them to the gold of California.[1] The Oregon trail, the

---

[1] For an account of the emigration to Oregon in 1845 and 1846 and for one of the best original descriptions of the Oregon trail, see Joel Palmer,

California trail, the Santa Fé trail, the Gila trail, and the Spanish trail all became routes of migration, because they were the routes which had been proved to be the most satisfactory, after a long period of exploration (Fig. 31).

The gold rush to California, in 1849, involved an immense increase in the number of settlers. It became essential that transcontinental railways should be constructed, to overcome the difficulties of communication with the west. The geographical knowledge of the west, although considerable, was not of sufficient accuracy for the immediate construction of railways. In 1853 the railway surveys were begun, and, as a result of the work of these surveys, the Pacific Railroad Reports were issued.[1] The modern means of communication, the railways, follow almost exactly the old trans-continental trails.[2] Land grants were made by the Federal Government of the United States in aid of the railway lines west of the Mississippi River. The Northern Pacific grant (1864) followed very closely the route of Lewis and Clark, the northern trans-continental route. The Union Pacific grant and the Kansas grant (1864) formed a central trans-continental route to California, while the Southern Pacific grant (1866) followed the route of the old Gila trail.[3]

At the beginning of the nineteenth century not only western

Journal of Travels over the Rocky Mountains to the mouth of the Columbia River made during the years 1845 *and* 1846 (1847) E.W.T. vol. xxx. R. B. Marcy, *The Prairie Traveler, a handbook for overland expeditions* (1859), contains useful maps and accounts of the different routes used by the emigrants to Oregon and California. W. J. Ghent, *The Road to Oregon* (1929), is a good secondary account of the history of the Oregon trail.

[1] *Reports of Explorations and Surveys, to Ascertain the most Practicable and Economical Route for a Railroad from the Mississippi River to the Pacific Ocean. Made under the Direction of the Secretary of War in* 1853–1856. U.S. Senate, 33rd Congress 2nd Session, Ex. Doc. no. 78. 12 vols. Washington, 1855–60.

[2] See E. C. Semple, *American History and its Geographic Conditions*, chap. xxvii, The Geographical Distribution of Railroads.

[3] For detailed accounts of modern railway routes see *Guidebooks of the Western United States*, U.S. Geol. Survey, Washington, 1916: Bulletin 611, Part A, *The Northern Pacific Route*, by M. R. Campbell and others; Bulletin 612, Part B, *The Overland Route*, by W. T. Lee, R. W. Stone, H. S. Gale and others; Bulletin 613, Part C, *The Santa Fé Route*, by N. H. Darton and others.

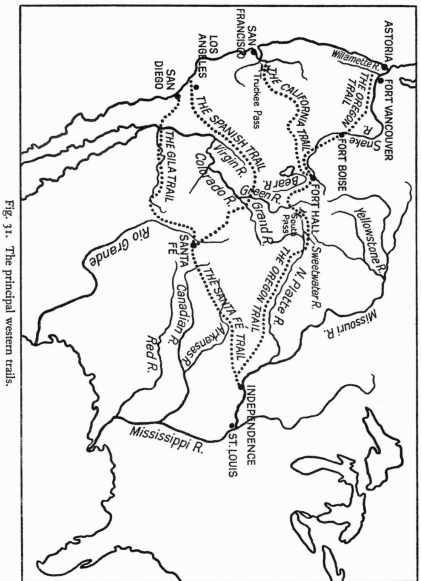

Fig. 31. The principal western trails.

America, but also the interior parts of Africa, Asia, and Australia were unknown. The exploration of Africa, of Asia, and of Australia have often been described and the explorers of these continents are well known. The exploration of America during this period has been frequently neglected in general works on exploration. European writers often forget that the inland exploration of a great part of the present United States is so recent, and do not realise the immense natural difficulties which confronted the original explorers.

BIBLIOGRAPHY

The following bibliography is a list of works cited in the footnotes of this book, and also contains the names of some of the other works consulted in its preparation, but it must not be regarded as a complete catalogue of books dealing with the subject. It has been thought better not to divide the bibliography into original and secondary sources, and it is hoped that the alphabetical arrangement of works cited will prove to be more useful to the reader than an elaborate classification. However, a division has been made into works dealing with the general geography of western America, and those which relate more particularly to the exploration of that area. Almost all the items contained in the first category are modern works, while those in the second include both original sources and secondary compilations.

The best collected bibliography of the printed original sources is that of H. R. Wagner, *The Plains and the Rockies, A Bibliography of original narratives of Travels and Adventure*, 1800–1865 (San Francisco, 1921). This book consists of a list of "books containing personal experiences of the authors", written and printed between 1800 and 1865, and, as it includes notes and particulars of the contents of each book cited, it is indispensable to the student of this period of American history.

G. K. Warren's *Memoir to accompany the Map of the Territory of the United States from the Mississippi River to the Pacific Ocean, giving a brief account of each of the exploring expeditions since* A.D. 1800, is still the most useful general summary of the history of the exploration of western America, but it was published in 1859 and must be supplemented by the results of modern scholarship. The work was printed as vol. XI of the *Reports of Explorations and Surveys, to Ascertain the most Practicable and Economical Route for a Railroad from the Mississippi River to the Pacific Ocean*. The only modern work which is solely concerned with the history of the exploration of western America is R. G. Thwaites' *A Brief History of Rocky Mountain Exploration* (1904), the greater part of which is devoted to a consideration of the work of Lewis and Clark. Cardinal Goodwin's *The Trans-Mississippi West, A History of its Acquisition and Settlement* (1803–1853) (1922) contains useful descriptions of the exploration of the west with bibliographies, but is more especially concerned with the history of American settlement and political negotiations west of the Mississippi. Katharine Coman's *Economic Beginnings of the Far West* (1925) is a valuable description of the exploration and settlement of the west and contains full bibliographies and useful illustrations and maps. H. M. Chittenden's *The History of the American Fur Trade of the Far West* (3 vols. 1902) is the best account of the fur trade and its relations with exploration, and contains much geographical matter. J. C. Bell's *Opening a Highway to the Pacific*, 1838–1846 (1921) gives a brief summary of

exploration, but the greater part of the book is devoted to the history of the American migration to and settlement of Oregon. Robert M. McElroy's *The Winning of the Far West* (1914) is a full account of the political events which resulted in a series of additions to the territory of the United States during the period 1829–67.

F. J. Turner's brilliant essays contained in his *The Frontier in American History* (1921), and F. L. Paxson's illuminating work, *The History of the American Frontier, 1763–1893* (1924), enable the reader to understand the exploration of western America in its proper perspective in American history as a whole. Both books are of great value to students of Historical Geography.

A. GENERAL GEOGRAPHICAL WORKS

BARTHOLOMEW, J. G. Atlas of Zoogeography. Prepared by J. G. Bartholomew, W. E. Clarke, and P. H. Grimshaw, being vol. v of Bartholomew's Physical Atlas. Edinburgh, 1911.

BAULIG, H. Écoulement fluvial et dénudation d'après les travaux de l'United States Geological Survey. Annales de Géographie, XIX (1910), 385–411.

BLODGET, LOUIS. Climatology of the United States. 1857.

BOWMAN, ISAIAH. Forest Physiography. New York, 1911.

BRIGHAM, A. P. The United States of America. London, 1927.

BROOKS, C. F. The Snowfall of the United States. Quarterly Journal of the Royal Meteorological Society, XXXIX (1913), 81–6.

FENNEMAN, N. M. Physiographic Divisions of the United States. Annals of the Association of American Geographers, VI (1915–16), 19–98. Revised and enlarged in XVIII (1928), 261–353.

—— Physiography of Western United States. New York, 1931.

FLINT, R. E. A Brief View of Rocky Mountain Structure. Journal of Geology, XXXII (1924), 410–31.

HARSHBERGER, J. W. Phytogeographic Survey of North America: (Vol. XIII of Die Vegetation der Erde, Ed. A. Engler and O. Drude.) Leipzig, 1911.

HENRY, A. J. Climatology of the United States. Bulletin Q, U.S. Weather Bureau. Washington, 1906.

JOERG, W. L. Subdivisions of North America into Natural Regions. A Preliminary Inquiry. Annals of the Association of American Geographers, IV (1913–14), 55–83.

KENDREW, W. G. The Climates of the Continents. 2nd ed. Oxford, 1927.

KINCER, J. B. Atlas of American Agriculture, Part II, Climate, Section A, Precipitation and Humidity. Washington, 1922.

LAUT, A. C. The Fur Trade of North America. New York, 1921.

LIVINGSTON, B. E. and SHREVE, F. The Distribution of Vegetation in the United States as related to the Climatic Conditions. Carnegie Institution of Washington, 1921.

RUSSELL, I. C. North America. London, 1904.

—— River Development. London, 1907. See especially chap. VIII, The Characteristics of American Rivers.

SHANTZ, H. L. and ZON, R. Atlas of American Agriculture, Part I, The Physical Basis of Agriculture, Section E, Natural Vegetation. Washington, 1924.

SHREVE, F. A Map of the Vegetation of the United States. Geographical Review, III (1917), 119.

UNITED STATES GEOLOGICAL SURVEY, BULLETINS. Washington, 1916.
   Bulletin 611. Guidebook of the Western United States, Part A, The Northern Pacific Route, by M. R. Campbell and others.

Bulletin 612. Guidebook of the Western United States, Part B., The Overland Route, by W. T. Lee, R. W. Stone, H. S. Gale and others.

Bulletin 613. Guidebook of the Western United States, Part C, The Santa Fé Route, by N. H. Darton and others.

UNITED STATES GEOLOGICAL SURVEY, WATER-SUPPLY PAPERS. NOS. 241–252. Surface Water-Supply of the United States, 1907–8. Prepared under the direction of M. O. Leighton. Washington, 1909–10.

Part VI, No. 246. Missouri River Basin, by R. Follansbee and J. E. Stewart.

Part VII, No. 247. Lower Mississippi Basin, by W. B. Freeman, W. A. Lamb and R. H. Bolster.

Part VIII, No. 248. Western Gulf of Mexico, by W. B. Freeman, W. A. Lamb and R. H. Bolster.

Part IX, No. 249. Colorado River Basin, by W. B. Freeman and R. H. Bolster.

Part X, No. 250. The Great Basin, by E. C. La Rue and F. F. Henshaw.

Part XI, No. 251. California, by W. B. Clapp and W. F. Martin.

Part XII, No. 252. North Pacific Coast, by J. C. Stevens and F. F. Henshaw.

VEGETATION. A Map of the Natural Vegetation of the United States. U.S. Dept. of Agriculture Year Book, 1921, p. 421. Reproduced in Economic Geography, II (1926), 469.

WARD, R. de C. The Climates of the United States. Boston, 1925.

WISSLER, C. The American Indian. 2nd ed. New York, 1922.

B. THE HISTORY OF EXPLORATION

ABEL, ANNIE H. A New Lewis and Clark Map. Geographical Review, I (1916), 329–49.

ADAMS, HENRY. History of the United States of America during the First Administration of Thomas Jefferson. 9 vols. New York, 1889–1911.

ARROWSMITH, J. London Atlas of Universal Geography. London, 1835. Map no. 39, a map of North America, shows the prevailing ideas as to the geography of western America.

ASHLEY, W. H. See under Dale.

ASTORIANS, Expedition of. See under Brackenridge, Bradbury, Cox, R., Dale, Franchère, and Irving.

BAKER, J. N. L. A History of Geographical Discovery and Exploration. London, 1931. This is the only general history of exploration which gives an adequate account of the explorers of the American West.

BANCROFT, H. H. The Works of. 39 vols. San Francisco, 1883–90.
   Vol. 17. History of Arizona and New Mexico, 1530–1888.
   Vols. 18–24. History of California, 1542–1890.
   Vol. 25. History of Nevada, Colorado and Wyoming, 1540–1888.
   Vol. 26. History of Utah, 1540–1886.
   Vols. 27, 28. History of the Northwest Coast, 1543–1846.
   Vols. 29, 30. History of Oregon, 1834–1888.
   Vol. 31. History of Washington, Idaho and Montana, 1845–1889.

BARBÉ-MARBOIS, F. Histoire de la Louisiane et de la cession de cette Colonie par la France. Paris, 1829.

BARTLETT, J. R. Personal Narrative of Explorations and Travels in Texas, New Mexico, California, Sonora, and Chihuahua connected with the U.S. and Mexican Boundary Commission during the years 1850–1853. London, 1854. 2 vols.

BELL, J. C. Opening a Highway to the Pacific, 1838–1846. New York, 1921.

BIEBER, R. P. The South-Western Trails to California in 1849. Mississippi Valley Historical Review, XII (1925), no. 3. Reprinted in The New Mexico Historical Review, I (1926), 92–4.

BIGELOW, JOHN. Memoir of the Life and Public Services of John Charles Frémont. New York, 1856.

BODLEY, T. George Rogers Clark. His Life and Public Services. New York, 1926.

BOLTON, H. E. Papers of Zebulon M. Pike, 1806–1807. American Historical Review, XIII (1908), 798–827.
—— Spanish Exploration in the Southwest, 1542–1706. New York, 1916.
—— Anza's California Expeditions. 5 vols. Berkeley, California, 1930.

BONNEVILLE, Captain. *See under* Irving.

BOONE, DANIEL. *See under* Bruce *and* Thwaites.

BRACKENRIDGE, H. M. Views of Louisiana. Pittsburg, 1814. The edition consulted was published at Baltimore in 1817.

—— Journal of a Voyage up the River Missouri in 1811. Baltimore, 1816. Reprinted in Early Western Travels, 1748–1846, vol. VI, ed. R. G. Thwaites. Cleveland, 1904. Brackenridge accompanied Manuel Lisa in pursuit of the Astorians, starting three weeks behind them.

BRADBURY, J. Travels in the Interior of America, 1809–1811. London, 1819. Reprinted in Early Western Travels, 1748–1846, vol. V, ed. R. G. Thwaites. Cleveland, 1904. Bradbury travelled with the Astorians from St Louis to the Arikara villages, and his book is the first description of the Missouri valley since the time of Lewis and Clark. It contains an admirable account of the Indian tribes.

BRUCE, H. A. Daniel Boone and the Wilderness Road. New York, 1910.

BURPEE, L. J. The Search for the Western Sea. London, 1908.

—— Journal de Larocque. Publications des Archives Canadiennes, no. 3. Ottawa, 1911.

CARSON, K. *See under* Cheetham.

CARVER, J. Travels Through the Interior Parts of North-America, in the years 1766, 1767, and 1768. London, 1778.

CARY, JOHN. New Universal Atlas, containing Distinct Maps of all the Principal States and Kingdoms throughout the World. From the latest and best authorities extant. London, 1808.

CATLIN, GEORGE. The North American Indians, being letters and notes on their manners, customs and conditions, written during eight years' travel amongst the wildest tribes of Indians in North America, 1832–1839. 2 vols. London, 1845.

CHANNING, EDWARD. A History of the United States. 6 vols. New York, 1905–25.

CHAPMAN, C. E. A History of California: The Spanish Period. New York, 1923.

CHEETHAM, F. T. Kit Carson. New Mexico Historical Review, I (1926), 375–99.

CHITTENDEN, H. M. The Yellowstone National Park. Historical and Descriptive. Cincinnati, 1895.

—— The History of the American Fur Trade of the Far West. 3 vols. New York, 1902.

—— Life, Letters and Travels of P. J. de Smet, S.J., 1801–1873. 4 vols. New York, 1905.

CLARK, GEORGE ROGERS. *See under* Bodley *and* James.

CLARK, WILLIAM. *See under* Abel, Coues, Hosmer, McMaster, Parker, Teggart, Thwaites *and* Wheeler.

COMAN, KATHARINE. Economic Beginnings of the Far West. How we won the land beyond the Mississippi. 2 vols. New York, 1925.

COUES, ELLIOTT. History of the Expedition under the Command of Lewis and Clark. 4 vols. New York, 1893.

COUES, ELLIOTT. The Expeditions of Zebulon Montgomery Pike. 3 vols. New York, 1895.
    Vol. I. Mississippi Voyage.
    Vol. II. Arkansaw Journey. Mexican Tour.
    Vol. III. Index, Maps.
—— New Light on the Early History of the Greater Northwest. 3 vols. New York, 1897. Contains the journals of Alexander Henry and David Thompson.
—— Forty Years a Fur Trader. The Personal Narrative of C. Larpenteur, 1833–1872. 2 vols. New York, 1899.
—— The Journal of Jacob Fowler. New York, 1899.
—— On the Trail of a Spanish Pioneer. The Diary and Itinerary of Francisco Garcés in his Travels through Sonora, Arizona and California. 2 vols. New York, 1900.
COX, ISAAC J. The Exploration of the Louisiana Frontier, 1803–1806. Annual Report of the American Historical Association for the Year 1904, pp. 149–74. Contains an account of the expeditions of Sibley, Dunbar and Freeman.
—— The Early Explorations of Louisiana. University of Cincinnati Studies, 1906.
COX, R. Adventures on the Columbia River. London, 1831.
CROUSE, N. M. In Quest of the Western Ocean. London, 1928.
DALE, H. C. The Ashley-Smith Explorations and the Discovery of a Central Route to the Pacific, 1822–1829. Cleveland, 1918. Contains Ashley's Journal 1824–1825, and the Journal of H. C. Rogers, member of the Company of J. S. Smith, 1826–1828.
—— Did the returning Astorians use the South Pass? Oregon Historical Society Quarterly, vol. XVII. Portland, 1916.
DE LISLE, J. N. Explication de la Carte des Nouvelles Découvertes au Nord de la Mer du Sud. Paris, 1752.
DE SMET, P. J., S.J. Letters and Sketches: with a Narrative of a Year's Residence among the Indian Tribes of the Rocky Mountains. Philadelphia, 1843. Reprinted in Early Western Travels, 1748–1846, vol. XXVII, ed. R. G. Thwaites. Cleveland, 1906.
—— Oregon Missions and Travels over the Rocky Mountains in 1845–46. New York, 1847. Reprinted in Early Western Travels, 1748–1846, vol. XXIX, ed. R. G. Thwaites. Cleveland, 1906.
—— See also under Chittenden.
DUNBAR, S. A History of Travel in America. 4 vols. Indianapolis, 1915.
DUNBAR, W. See under Cox, I. J.
DUNBAR, WILLIAM and Dr HUNTER. Observations made on the Washita River in Oct. 1804–Jan. 1805. Laid before the Senate by the President of the United States in February, 1806. Reprinted in Sir Richard Phillips' Collection of Modern and Contemporary Voyages and Travels, 1st series, vol. VI. London, 1807.
ELLIOT, T. C. (ed.). The Peter Skene Ogden Journals, 1825–1829. Oregon Hist. Soc. Quarterly, vols. X and XI. Portland, 1909–10.

EMERSON, F. W. A Geographical Interpretation of Missouri. Geographical Journal, XLI (1913), 39–48, 130–45.

EMORY, Major W. H. Notes of a Military Reconnaissance from Fort Leavenworth, in Missouri, to San Diego, in California, made in 1846–47. Washington, 1848.

FALCONER, THOMAS. Journal of the Royal Geographical Society. XIV (1844), 299–302, An analysis of the results of J. C. Frémont's first expedition.

FARNHAM, THOMAS J. Travels in the Great Western Prairies, the Anahuac and Rocky Mountains, and in the Oregon Territory. London, 1843. Reprinted in Early Western Travels, 1748–1846, vols. XXVIII–XXIX, ed. R. G. Thwaites. Cleveland, 1906.

FINLEY, A. New and General Atlas. Philadelphia, 1826.

FOWLER, J. See under Coues.

FRANCHÈRE, GABRIEL. Narrative of a voyage to the Northwest Coast, 1811–1814. New York, 1854. Reprinted in Early Western Travels, 1748–1846, vol. VI, ed. R. G. Thwaites. Cleveland, 1904.

FREEMAN, L. R. The Colorado River. London, 1923.

—— The Colorado. National Geographic Magazine, XLV (1924), 471–548.

FREEMAN, THOMAS. See under Cox, I. J.

FRÉMONT, J. C. Report of the Exploring Expedition to the Rocky Mountains in the year 1842, and to Oregon and North California in the years 1843–44 (28th Congress, 2d Session, Senate 174). Washington, 1845.

—— Geographical Memoir upon Upper California, in illustration of his Map of Oregon and California (30th Congress, 1st Session, Senate, 148). Washington, 1848.

—— See also under Bigelow, Falconer, Nevins and Smucker.

GALLATIN, A. Synopsis of the Indian Tribes within the United States East of the Rocky Mountains and in the British and Russian Possessions of North America. American Antiquarian Society Transactions, vol. II. Cambridge, 1836.

GASS, PATRICK. Journal. Philadelphia, 1810. First published in 1807.

—— See under Hosmer.

GHENT, W. J. The Road to Oregon. New York, 1929.

GOODWIN, Cardinal. The Trans-Mississippi West. A History of its Acquisition and Settlement (1803–1853). New York, 1922.

GREENHOW, R. The History of Oregon and California, and other Territories of the North-west Coast of America. Boston, 1844.

GREGG, J. Commerce of the Prairies. New York, 1845. Reprinted in Early Western Travels, 1748–1846, vols. XIX–XX, ed. R. G. Thwaites. Cleveland, 1905.

HAFEN, L. R. The Overland Mail, 1849–1868. Cleveland, 1926.

HEAWOOD, E. A History of Geographical Discovery in the Seventeenth and Eighteenth Centuries. Cambridge, 1912.

HENRY, ALEXANDER. See under Coues.

HIRST, F. W. Life and Letters of Thomas Jefferson. London, 1927.

HOSMER, J. K. History of the Expedition of Captains Lewis and Clark, 1804–5–6. Reprinted from the Biddle Edition of 1814 with Introduction and Index. 2 vols. Chicago, 1902.

—— (ed.). A Journal of the Lewis and Clark Expedition, by Sergeant P. Gass. Chicago, 1904.

HUMBOLDT, A. VON. Political Essay on the Kingdom of New Spain, translated by John Black. 3 vols. London, 1811.

HUNTER, Dr. See under Dunbar, W.

HUNTER, J. D. Memoirs of a Captivity among the Indians of North America from childhood to the age of nineteen, with anecdotes descriptive of their manners and customs. London, 1823.

IRVING, W. A Tour on the Prairies. London, 1835.

—— The Adventures of Captain Bonneville, U.S.A., in the Rocky Mountains and the Far West. Philadelphia, 1837.

—— Astoria; or, Enterprise Beyond the Rocky Mountains. London, 1839. (Published at Philadelphia, 1836.) "Irving's treatment of the subject has become classic", Chittenden.

JAMES, E. Account of an Expedition from Pittsburgh to the Rocky Mountains performed in the years 1819–1820 under the command of Major S. H. Long. 3 vols. London, 1823. Reprinted in Early Western Travels, 1748–1846. Vols. XIV–XVII, ed. R. G. Thwaites. Cleveland, 1905.

JAMES, J. A. The Life of George Rogers Clark. Chicago, 1928.

JEFFERSON, THOMAS. The Writings of, ed. H. A. Washington. Congress edition, 9 vols. Washington, 1853–4.

—— The Writings of, ed. P. L. Ford. 10 vols. New York, 1892–9.

—— See also under Hirst and Surface.

KENDALL, G. W. Narrative of the Texan Santa Fé Expedition, 1841. New York, 1844.

KEPHART, H. (ed.). First through the Grand Canyon (being a reprint of Major J. W. Powell's narrative of 1869). New York, 1925.

LA HONTAN, Baron LOUIS DE. See under Thwaites.

LAROCQUE. See under Burpee.

LARPENTEUR, C. See under Coues.

LEWIS, W. S. and PHILLIPS, P. C. The Journal of John Work, a Trader of the Hudson Bay Company. Cleveland, 1923.

LEWIS, Captain MERIWETHER. See under Abel, Coues, Hosmer, McMaster, Parker, Teggart, Thwaites, and Wheeler.

LONG, Major S. H. See under James, E.

LOUISIANA, an Account of, Being an Abstract of Documents in the Offices of the Departments of State and of the Treasury. Philadelphia, 1803. Reprinted in Old South Leaflets, v, no. 105, 89–116. Boston, n.d.

MACLEOD, W. M. The American Indian Frontier. New York, 1928.

McELROY, ROBERT M. The Winning of the Far West. A History of the Regaining of Texas, of the Mexican War and the Oregon Question; and of the Successive Additions to the Territory of the United States within the Continent of America: 1829–1867. New York, 1914.

McElroy, Robert M. The Pathway of Peace. An Interpretation of some British-American Crises. (Sir George Watson Lectures for 1926.) Cambridge, 1927.

McMaster, J. B. (ed.). History of the Expedition under the Command of Captains Lewis and Clark to the sources of the Missouri, then across the Rocky Mountains and down the River Columbia to the Pacific Ocean. A complete reprint of the Biddle edition, with an account of the Louisiana purchase and notes upon the route. 3 vols. D. Nutt, London, 1905.

Malloy, W. H. (ed.). Treaties, Conventions, International Acts, etc. between the United States of America and other Powers, 1776–1909. 2 vols. 61st Congress, 2nd Session, S. Doc. No. 357. Government Printing Office, Washington, 1910.

Maps. See under Abel, Arrowsmith, Cary, Finley, Gallatin, Murray, Nicollet, Parker, Stuart, and Warren.

Marcy, R. B. The Prairie Traveler, a handbook for overland expeditions. New York, 1859.

Michaux, André. The Journal of. (Travels into Kentucky, 1793–1796.) Reprinted in Early Western Travels, 1748–1846, vol. III, ed. R. G. Thwaites. Cleveland, 1904.

Murray, Hugh. Historical Account of Discoveries and Travels in North America, with Observations on Emigration. 2 vols. London, 1829. Contains a map which shows the geographical conceptions of the West at this period.

Nevins, A. Frémont, the West's Greatest Adventurer. 2 vols. New York, 1928.

Nicollet, J. N. Report intended to illustrate a map of the Hydrographical Basin of the Upper Mississippi River. Washington, 1843.

Nuttall, Thomas. A Journal of Travels into the Arkansa Territory during the year 1819, with occasional observations on the manners of the aborigines. Philadelphia, 1821. Reprinted in Early Western Travels, 1748–1846, vol. XIII, ed. R. G. Thwaites. Cleveland, 1905.

Ogden, P. S. See under Elliot.

Palmer, Joel. Journal of Travels over the Rocky Mountains to the mouth of the Columbia River made during the years 1845 and 1846. Cincinnati, 1847. Reprinted in Early Western Travels, 1748–1846, vol. XXX, ed. R. G. Thwaites. Cleveland, 1906.

Parker, M. S. Black Eagle Falls Dam, Great Falls, Montana. Trans. Amer. Soc. Civil Engineers, XXVIII (1892), pp. 56–68. Contains a reproduction of Lewis and Clark's map of the Great Falls of the Missouri.

Parkman, F. The Oregon Trail: Sketches of Prairie and Rocky Mountain Life. Centenary ed. Boston, 1925. First published in 1847.

Pattie, J. O. Personal Narrative of, during an Expedition from St Louis. Cincinnati, 1831. Reprinted in Early Western Travels, 1748–1846, vol. XVIII, ed. R. G. Thwaites. Cleveland, 1905.

Paxson, F. L. The History of the American Frontier, 1763–1893. New York, 1924.

PERRIN DU LAC, F. M. Voyage dans les deux Louisianes, et chez les nations sauvages du Missouri, par les États-Unis, l'Ohio et les Provinces qui le bordent, en 1801, 1802 et 1803. Paris, 1805. Reprinted in Sir Richard Phillips' Collection of Modern and Contemporary Voyages and Travels, 1st series, vol. VI. Translated from the French. London, 1807.

PIKE, Z. M. Papers of, 1806–1807, contributed by H. E. Bolton. American Historical Review, XII (1908), 798–827.

—— See also under Coues and Whiting.

POWELL, J. W. The Exploration of the Colorado River of the West and its Tributaries. Explored in 1869–1872, issued under the direction of the Smithsonian Institute. Washington, 1875.

—— See also under KEPHART.

READ, BENJAMIN M. Perils of the Santa Fé Trail in its Early Days (1822–1852). El Palacio, XIX (1925), 206–11.

ROBERTSON, J. A. Louisiana under the Rule of Spain, France, and the United States, 1785–1807. Social, Economic and Political Conditions of the Territory represented in the Louisiana Purchase. 2 vols. Cleveland, 1911.

ROSS, ALEXANDER. Adventures of the First Settlers on the Oregon or Columbia River, being a narrative of the expedition fitted out by J. J. Astor to establish the "Pacific Fur Company," 1810–1813. London, 1849. Reprinted in Early Western Travels, 1748–1846, vol. VII, ed. R. G. Thwaites. Cleveland, 1904. Contains a reliable account of events at Astoria.

—— Fur Hunters of the Far West. 2 vols. London, 1855.

RUXTON, G. F. Life in the Far West. London, 1849.

SCHOOLCRAFT, H. R. A View of the Lead Mines of Missouri, including Observations of Missouri and Arkansaw. New York, 1819.

—— Narrative of Travels to the Sources of the Mississippi River, performed as a member of the expedition under Governor Cass in the year 1820. Albany, 1821.

—— Narrative of an Expedition through the Upper Mississippi to Itasca Lake, the actual source of the river; embracing an exploratory trip through the St Croix and Burntwood (or Broule) Rivers; in 1832. New York, 1834.

—— Historical and Statistical Information respecting the Conditions and Prospects of the Indian Tribes. 5 vols. Philadelphia, 1853.

SEMPLE, E. C. American History and its Geographic Conditions. New York, 1903.

SIBLEY, JOHN. An Account of the Red River laid before the Senate by the President of the United States in February 1806. Reprinted in Sir Richard Phillips' Collection of Modern and Contemporary Voyages and Travels, 1st series, vol. VI. London, 1807.

—— See also under Cox, I. J.

SMET DE, P. J., S.J. See under de Smet and under Chittenden.

SMITH, J. S. See under Dale.

SMUCKER, S. M. The Life of Colonel J. C. Frémont. New York, 1856.

STANSBURY, H. Exploration and Survey of the Valley of the Great Salt Lake of Utah. Philadelphia, 1855.

STUART, JAMES. Three Years in North America. 2 vols. 2nd ed. Edinburgh, 1833. Contains a map which shows prevailing ideas of Western America.

SURFACE, G. T. Thomas Jefferson: a Pioneer Student of American Geography. Bulletin of the American Geographical Society, XLI (1909), 743–50.

TEGGART, F. J. Notes supplementary to any edition of Lewis and Clark. Annual Report of the American Historical Association for the Year 1908, I (1909), 185–95. This contains an account of the operations of the Spanish Compañia de Descubridores del Misuri. It also shows the relations of the achievements of Mackay and Evans to the later work of Lewis and Clark.

THOMAS, ALFRED B. The Yellowstone River, James Long and Spanish reaction to American intrusion into Spanish Dominions, 1818–1819. New Mexico Historical Review, IV (1929), 164–87.

THOMPSON, DAVID. *See under* Coues *and* Tyrrell.

THWAITES, R. G. A Brief History of Rocky Mountain Exploration. New York, 1904.

—— Daniel Boone. New York, 1903.

—— (ed.). The Original Journals of the Lewis and Clark Expedition, 1804–1806. 8 vols. New York, 1904–5.

—— (ed.). New Voyages to North-America by Baron de Lahontan (1703), 2 vols. Chicago, 1905.

—— (ed.). Early Western Travels, 1748–1846. 32 vols. Cleveland, 1904–1906.

TRUTEAU, J. B. Journal of Jean Baptiste Truteau on the Upper Missouri, "Première Partie," June 7, 1794–March 26, 1795. American Historical Review, XIX (1914), 299–333.

TURNER, F. J. The Rise of the New West, being vol. XIV of the History of the American Nation. New York, 1906.

—— The Frontier in American History. New York, 1921.

TYRRELL, J. B. David Thompson, a Great Geographer. Geographical Journal, XXXVII (1911), 49–58.

—— (ed.). David Thompson's Narrative of his Explorations in Western America, 1784–1812. Toronto, The Champlain Society, 1916.

UNITED STATES. Reports of Explorations and Surveys, to Ascertain the most Practicable and Economical Route for a Railroad from the Mississippi River to the Pacific Ocean. Made under the Direction of the Secretary of War in 1853–1856. U.S. Senate. 33rd Congress, 2d Session, Ex. Doc. no. 78. 12 vols. Washington, 1855–60. Vol. XI contains a memoir by G. K. Warren, *see under* Warren.

DE VERGENNES, M. Mémoire Historique et Politique sur la Louisiane. Paris, 1802.

VINTON, S. John Colter, Discoverer of Yellowstone Park. New York, 1926.

WAGNER, H. R. The Plains and the Rockies. A Bibliography of original narratives of Travels and Adventure, 1800–1865. San Francisco, 1921. An invaluable bibliography of "books containing personal experiences of the authors", written and printed between 1800 and 1865. Notes and partial digests of each book are contained in this volume.

—— Spanish Voyages to the Northwest Coast of America in the Sixteenth Century. San Francisco, 1929.

WARREN, G. K. Memoir to accompany the Map of the Territory of the United States from the Mississippi River to the Pacific Ocean, giving a brief account of each of the exploring expeditions since A.D. 1800, with a detailed description of the method adopted in compiling the general map. Printed as vol. XI of the Reports of Explorations and Surveys, to Ascertain the most Practicable and Economical Route for a Railroad from the Mississippi River to the Pacific Ocean. Senate, 33rd Congress, 2d Session, Ex. Doc. no. 78. Washington, 1859. *See under* United States.

WHEELER, O. D. The Trail of Lewis and Clark, 1804–1904. 2 vols. 2nd ed. New York, 1926.

WHITING, H. A Life of Z. M. Pike. Jared Sparks Library of American Biography, Old Series, xv (1845), 217–34.

WIED, PRINCE MAXIMILIAN OF. Travels in the Interior of North America. Translated from the German by H. E. Lloyd. London, 1843. Reprinted in Early Western Travels, 1748–1846. Vols. XXII–XXV, ed. R. G. Thwaites. Cleveland, 1906. Vol. XXV is a folio "atlas" containing a series of 81 illustrations reproduced from the original paintings of Charles Bodmer.

WILKES, Capt. CHARLES. Narrative of the United States Exploring Expedition, 1838–42. 5 vols. Philadelphia, 1845.

WINSOR, JUSTIN. Narrative and Critical History of America. 8 vols. London, 1888.

WINTERBOTHAM, W. Historical, Geographical, Commercial and Philosophical View of the American United States and of the European Settlement in America and the West Indies. 4 vols. New York, 1795.

WIZLIZENUS, A. Memoir of a Tour to Northern Mexico, connected with Colonel Doniphan's Expedition in 1846 and 1847. Washington, 1848.

WORK, JOHN. *See under* Lewis, W. S.

Index

Abert, Lake, 180
Abies grandis, 72 *footnote*
Abies nobilis, 72 *footnote*
Acadians, French, 16
Africa, 68, 207
Alaska, 3, 30
Allegheny Mountains (Alleghany, Alleghenies), 31, 140, 148, 150, 158
Alps, the, 189
Alvarez, Don Manuel, 45, 46
America, South, 176
American Falls, 58
American Fur Co., 54, 127
American Philosophical Society, 9, 106
American River, 139, 186
Anderson, Messrs Faulkner and, 45
Andes, the, 178, 178 *footnote*
Annian, Straits of, 5
Antelope, *see under* Prongbuck
Antelope Island, 185
Anza, Capt. J. B. de, 5, 6 *footnote*
Apache Cañon, 165
Appalachian Highlands, 27; type of folding, 30
Appalachians, 14, 30; southern, 30, 66
Arikara Indians, 91 *footnote*, 92, 93 *footnote*, 94, 128, 134
Arkansas River (Arkansa, Arkansaw), 30, 45, 50, 56, 85, 152, 154, 155, 156, 158, 159, 160, 163, 165, 182, 184, 185; Pike's description of, 56–7
Arkansas, State of, 168; Territory of, 121
Arrowsmith, J., 133, 198
Arteaga, 2
Artemisia, 58, 73, 149, 180
Ashley, General W. H., 102, 133, 135, 136, 137, 139, 141, 142, 170, 198, 200; Journals of, 134
Ashley Lake, 198
Asia, 184, 189, 207

Assiniboine Indians, 134
Assiniboine River, 4
aster, 48
Astor, J. J., 35, 102, 125, 127, 128, 130
Astoria, 130, 131; Fort, 127
Astorians, the, 91 *footnote*, 125, 130, 131, 132, 134, 141, 179; discovery of South Pass by, 131, 140–1
Atkinson, Col., 159
Atkinson, Fort, 47
Australia, 207

Bad lands, the, 67
Baker, J. N. L., quoted, 125 *footnote*, 178 *footnote*
Balboa, 1, 178, 178 *footnote*
Bald Peak, 136
Baranof Island, 3
Barbé-Marbois, M., 20, 23–4
Bartleson, 173
Basin, Great Interior, 33, 44, 59, 61, 62, 73, 75, 99, 103, 130, 132, 140, 145, 146, 170, 173, 174, 175, 177, 179, 180, 181, 184, 185, 186, 187, 188, 191, 196, 198, 201, 202, 203; climate of, 47–8; Frémont's descriptions of, 184–5, 188
Basin, Wyoming, 30
Basin and Range region, 33
Baton Rouge, 16
Bear, black (*Ursus americanus*), 89; grizzly, (*Ursus horribilis*), 86–9, 112, 123
Bear Lake, 132, 138
Bear River, 58, 60, 63, 130, 132, 135, 143, 150, 172, 173, 174, 177, 178, 198
Bear River Mountains, 48, 180
Beaver (*Castor canadensis*), 58, 77–9, 109, 111, 119, 135, 137, 139, 166, 171
Beaver Head, 114
Beckwith's route, 173

Belden, 173
Bell, Captain, 160, 161
Benton, Fort, 51, 53
Benton, Senator T. H., 174
Bent's Fort, 184, 185
Bering, Vitus, 3
Bidwell, 138, 173, 174
Bieber, R. P., quoted, 168, 169
Bigdry River, 111
Big Horn Mountains, 4, 129
Big Horn River, 53, 101, 121, 124, 129, 134, 135, 136, 141, 143, 167, 172, 202
Big Mountains, 30
Big Sandy River, 62, 135, 140, 141, 143, 147
Big Snowy Mountains, 30
Bighorn (*Ovis montana*), 85, 153 *footnote*
Bismarck, 110
Bison, *see under* Buffalo
Bitter Root Mountains, 70 *footnote*, 115, 119
Bitter Root River, 115, 120
Black Hills, 129
Black Mountains, 109 *footnote*
Blackfoot Indians, 91, 94, 124, 128, 133, 134, 148
Blackfoot River, 119
Blue Mountains, 58, 71, 130, 172, 179
Bodega (California), 41
Bodega Bay, 3
Bodega y Cuadra, 2
Boisé, Fort, 173, 179
Boisé River, 58
Bolton, H. E., quoted, 6 *footnote*
Bonneville, Capt. B. L. E., 78, 142, 170, 171, 172, 173, 201; expeditions of, 170–3; maps of Western America by, 172, 198, 201
Bonneville, Fort (Fort Nonsense), 171
Bonneville Lake, 59, 60, 201
Boone, Daniel, 15
Bowman, I, quoted, 57 *footnote*, 58 *footnote*, 62 *footnote*, 65 *footnote*, 70 *footnote*, 71 *footnote*

Boston, 3
Bozeman, 120
Bozeman Pass, 120
Brackenridge, H. M., 37, 92, 140
Brazos River, 56, 157
Brevel, M., 151
Bridger, Fort, 150 *footnote*
Bridger, James, 134, 135, 136, 170
Bridger Mountains, 30
Bridger's Pass, 136, 137, 150, 191 *footnote*
Broughton, 3, 4
Brown, Russell and Co., 46
Buenaventura River, 157, 170, 179, 180, 181, 182, 194, 196, 198, 200, 201
Buffalo (*Bos americanus*), 29, 68, 69, 77, 79, 79–84, 111, 112, 120, 145, 147, 152, 153, 153 *footnote*, 154, 155, 156; methods of hunting, 80–2; numbers of, 82–4
Buffon, 88
Burr, Colonel, 157

Cabrillo (Rodríguez), 2
Cajon Pass, 137, 168
Caldron Linn, 129, 130
California, 7, 57, 63, 72, 73, 102, 103, 104, 131, 137, 138, 140, 145, 150, 158, 165, 166, 167, 168, 169, 172, 173, 175, 177, 182, 183, 185, 187, 188, 191, 198, 204, 205; climate of, 48–9; compared with Italy, 189; Gulf of, 1, 118, 148, 149, 158; Indians of, 99; lower, 1–2; Mountains of, 171; upper, 5, 6
Californian coast ranges, 35
California trail, 61, 63, 150, 168, 174, 205
Campbell, Robert, 135 *footnote*
Canadian River, 56, 85, 160, 161, 165, 194
Cañon City, 156
Canton, 159
Cap Girardeau, 17
Cape Horn, 106
Cape of Good Hope, 106

Capitol Hill, 148
Cariacus columbianus, 123
Cariacus macrotis, 123
Carson, Kit, 148, 169, 174, 175, 181, 186
Carson Lake, 61, 171
Carson Pass, 174
Carson River, 62
Carson Sinks, 186
Carver, Jonathan, 5
Cary, John, 1, 1 *footnote*, 193; map of America by, 9, 13
Cascade Falls, 116, 118
Cascade Mountains, 34, 35, 39, 42, 58, 69, 88, 102, 116, 117, 118, 182, 185
Caspian Sea, 188
Catlin, G., 82–3
Cedros Island, 2
Central Lowlands, 27, 29
Centrocercus urophasianus, 123
Chaboneau, 110
Chama River, 167, 168
Charleston, 174
Charlevoix, Father, 4
Chayenne Indians, 121
Chihuahua, 156
Chiles, J. B., 173, 174 *footnote*
China, 127, 159
Chittenden, H. M., 59, 139, 171; on South Pass, 142; quoted, 131, 143, 162, 200
Chopunnish Camp, 119
Chopunnish Indians, 85, 95 *footnote*, 115
Choteau's Island, 45
Cimarron desert, 163
Cimarron River, 46, 56, 155, 160, 161, 165
Cincinnati, 174
Clark, George Rogers, 7, 106
Clark, William, 7, 25, 29, 31, 34, 51–2, 70, 81, 82, 84, 91, 94, 98, 101, 102, 103, 106, 107, 108, 114, 115, 116, 117, 118, 119, 120, 121, 122, 123, 124, 126, 127, 128, 132, 134, 135, 139, 140, 142, 145, 146,
147, 152, 191, 194, 196, 205; expedition of Lewis and, 105–23; Journal of Lewis and, quoted, 29, 37, 38, 39, 43–4, 45, 51–2, 70, 72, 73, 74, 75, 77–8, 80, 81, 82, 85, 86, 88, 89, 94, 95, 97–8, 108, 109, 110, 111, 112, 114, 115, 116, 117, 118, 119, 120, 121; map of Great Falls by, 112
Clark's fork, 58, 126, 133
Clark's Pass, 120
Clark's River, 70, 115, 118, 123, 145, 194
Clatsop, Fort, 116, 117, 118, 122
Clearwater River (Kooskooskee), 58, 59, 115, 118, 119
Coast Range, 122, 182
Cochetope Pass, 190
Collins, James L., report of, 45–7
Colorado desert, 167
Colorado Plateaux, 31, 33
Colorado River, 5, 6, 33, 63, 106, 129, 136, 137, 139, 142, 148, 156, 158, 166, 167, 170, 172, 183, 184, 194, 196, 200, 203, 203 *footnote*; basin of, 59, 62–3
Colorado River (of Texas), 56, 157
Colorado, State of, 31, 63, 73; forests of, 70; Mountains of, 44, 79, 154, 163
Columbia, the, 4
Columbia River, 2, 3, 4, 33, 34, 35, 42, 57, 58, 59, 73, 89, 95, 97, 102, 106, 111, 112, 115, 116, 118, 122, 123, 125, 126, 127, 128, 129, 130, 131, 132, 133, 135, 139, 140, 150, 159, 172, 177, 180, 183, 184, 196; Basin of, 98, 115; Great Falls of, 116; lower, 58, 188; plains of, 29; Plateaux, 33, 94
Colter, John, 91, 92, 121, 124, 124 *footnote*, 140
Colter's River, 140
Connelly, Dr H., 46
Cook, Captain James, 3, 8
Cooke, Col. P. St George, 169
Coppermine River, 5

Corondelet, 17
Cortés, 1, 158
Cottonwood, 101, 110, 116, 146; importance of, 50; uses of, 75
Cottonwood creek, 45, 47
Coues, Dr Elliott, 114, 115, 116, 140, 156; quoted, 98 *footnote*, 152–3 *footnote*
Council Bluffs, 109, 136, 159
Council Grove, 45, 74
Cowlitz River, 116
Crooks, 130
Crow Indians, 124, 129, 141, 148
Cumberland Gap, 150

Dale, Professor H. C., 122, 134, 141, 198; quoted, 135, 139
Dalles, the, 42, 58, 59, 116, 118, 179, 181
Darien, Isthmus of, 158
Dawson, Lewis, 89
Dearborn River, 112, 118
Death Valley, 62
de Cardenas, 167
Deschutes River (Fall River), 58, 132, 180
de Smet, P. J., 77, 95; on mosquitoes, 89–90
Des Moines River, 107
Dolores River, 168
Dominguez, Father, 6, 170
Drake, Francis, 2
Dubois, Fort, 108
Duchesne River, 136
Dunbar, William, 151, 152; expedition of, 152

Elk Head River, 183
Elk (*Cervus canadensis*), 85
Elk River, 5
El Paso, 156, 157
erodium circutarium, 48
Escalante, Father, 6, 170
Etruria, 18
Evans, John, 7, 107 *footnote*

Fall River, *see under* Deschutes

Farnham, T. J., quoted, 142, 145
Faulkner, Messrs, and Anderson, 45
Femme Osage district, 15
Fenneman, N. M., quoted, 31 *footnote*
Ferrelo, 2
Finley, A., map of Western America by, 196, 197
Fitzpatrick, Thomas, 134, 135, 141
Flathead House, 132
Flathead Indians, 95, 97, 133, 139
Flathead River (Clark's), 118
Flint, R. E., on structure of Rocky Mountains, 30 *footnote*
Floridas, the, 18, 19, 20, 21; boundaries of, 23 *footnote*; purchase of, 19 *footnote*
Fowler, Jacob, 88, 163
Fox River, 192
Fox-Wisconsin portage, 192
Franklin, 163, 165
Franklin Lake, 186
Fraser River, 5
Freeman, Thomas, 153
Frémont, John Charles, 25, 33, 103, 142, 143, 147, 148, 150, 168, 170, 175, 176, 177, 180, 181, 182, 183, 184, 185, 188, 189, 190, 191, 196, 201, 202; accounts of Humboldt River, 188–9; accounts of South Pass, 148–9; arrest of, 187; contributions to geographical knowledge, 190–1; crossing of Sierra Nevada by, 44, 181; description of California, 189; early career of, 174; first expedition of, 175–6; *Geog. Memoir* of, quoted, 34, 38, 41, 42, 47–9, 60, 61, 62, 63, 64, 71, 72, 73, 186, 187, 188, 189; last expeditions of, 189–90; map of Western America by, 202; on trade in buffalo skins, 83–4; political career of, 190; *Report* of, quoted, 40–1, 42, 54–5, 57–8, 59–60, 63, 69, 71, 73, 74, 75, 79–80, 82, 84, 96, 143, 146, 147, 148, 149, 174, 175, 176, 177, 178, 179, 180, 181, 182, 183, 184, 185;

Frémont, John Charles (*cont.*)
second expedition of, 177–185;
third expedition of, 185–9;
Frémont Peak, 176

Gallatin, A., 139, 198, 200, 201;
map of Western America by,
172, 198–201
Gallatin City, 120
Gallatin River, 53, 112, 120
Garcés, F., 5, 6
George, Fort (Astoria), 131
Ghent, W. J., quoted, 141
Gibbon's Pass (Gibson's), 102, 120
Gila River, 5, 63, 157, 166, 167,
169, 190, 194
Gila trail, 158, 165, 166, 167, 168,
169, 205
Gillespie, Lieut., 187
Glenn, Hugh, 163
Grand Cañon, 33, 63, 203 *footnote*
Grand River, 63, 142, 152, 154, 156,
167, 168, 190
Grappe, Francis, 151
Gray, Captain Robert, 4
Great Falls, the, of the Missouri, 51,
53, 88, 134
Great Gap, the, *see under* South
Pass
Great Interior Basin, *see under*
Basin
Great Plains, 27, 29, 31, 51; snow-
fall on, 43
Great St Bernard Pass, 148
Great Salt Lake, 47, 59, 60, 61, 125,
130, 133, 136, 137, 138, 139, 143,
150, 157, 166, 170, 171, 172, 177,
180, 181, 183, 185, 187, 191, 196,
198, 200, 201, 204; discovery
of, 135–6; Frémont's description
of, 59–60
Great Slave Lake, 5
Green Bay, 192
Green River, 63, 79, 129, 130, 131,
135, 136, 137, 139, 142, 143, 147,
148, 149, 167, 168, 171, 172, 177,
190, 194, 202, 203 *footnote*

Gregg, J., 74, 77, 79, 80, 83, 84, 85;
on the rainfall of the Plains, 40;
quoted, 162
Grimm, Baron de, 8
Gulf Plains, 30, 93
Gunnison River, 167, 190

Hall, Fort, 58, 145, 178
Haplocerus montanus (mountain
goat), 123, 153 *footnote*
Haplodon rufus, 123
Harney Lake, 132
Harshberger, J. W., on the origin
of the Prairies, 68; quoted, 68
footnote
Hayden, 142
Hearne, Samuel, 5, 10, 192
Heawood, E., quoted, 3 *footnote*
Heceta, 2
Hedin, Sven, 123
helianthus, 48
Henry, Andrew, 124, 128, 130, 134,
140
Henry Lake, 125
Henry River, 124
High Plains, 29
Highlands, Interior, 27, 30
Hood, Mount, 3, 118
Horse Creek, 171
Hot Springs, 152
Hudson's Bay Company, 4, 5, 125,
132, 133
Humboldt, A. von, 178 *footnote*
Humboldt Lake, 61
Humboldt River (Ogden's or
Mary's River), 61, 133, 143, 150,
170, 171, 172, 173, 174, 186, 191,
201; Frémont's description of,
61–2; importance of, 188–9
Hunt, William P., 52, 128, 130
Hunter, George, 151, 152; expedi-
tion of, 152
Hunter, John D., 53, 54 *footnote*; on
Missouri and Platte, 53–4

Iberville, 16
Idaho, State of, 23, 24

Illinois, Spanish (upper Louisiana), 6, 17
Illinois Country, 98
Illinois, State of, 121
Independence, 40, 142, 165
Indians, cultural regions of, 92–9
Interior Basin, *see under* Basin
Interior Highlands, 27, 30
Interior Plains, 27
Interior Plateaux, 50, 102
Intermontane Plateaux, 27, 33
Irving, Washington, 52, 53, 88, 99, 128 *footnote*, 170, 198, 201; description of the Columbia by, 59
Italy, 189

Jackson, D. E., 138
James, Dr, 160
James' Peak, 160
Jefferson, Mount, 118
Jefferson River, 52, 112, 114, 119, 120, 140
Jefferson, Thomas, 7, 8, 9, 13, 19, 19 *footnote*, 20, 105, 106, 107, 121, 152; account of Ledyard by, 8; account of Louisiana by, 17, 21–3; quoted, 19–20, 105, 106–7, 121–2
John Day's River, 58, 132
Jordan River, 60
Jordan River (Asia), 61
Jornada River, 46
Joseph, Mount, 138
Juan de Fuca Strait, 3, 35
Julesburg, 150 *footnote*

Kansa Indians, 93 *footnote*, 161
Kansas City, 163, 165, 177, 179
Kansas grant, 205
Kansas River, 40, 50, 53, 55, 107, 109 *footnote*, 131, 148, 149, 154, 162, 175
Kearney, Fort, 175
Kearny, General S. W., 169, 187
Kearny's trail, 169
Kentucky, 14

Kern, E. M., 186
Kern River, 186
King, 142
King's River (Tulares Lake River), 186
Klamath Lake, 179; upper, 187
Klamath Mountains, 35, 41
Klamath River, 132
Kooskooskee River (Clearwater), 97, 115, 116, 118, 119

La Hontan, Baron L. de, 192
La Lande, 162
Lane, W. C., Governor of New Mexico, 45, 47
Laramie, Fort, 55 *footnote*, 69, 148, 150 *footnote*, 175, 176
Laramie Plains, 177
Laramie's Fork, 54
Larocque, 120 *footnote*
Lassen's Fort, 187
Lassen's Pass, 64
Lassen's Road, 174
Laurentian Upland, 27
La Vérendrye, Sieur de (P. G. de Varennes), 4
Leavenworth, Colonel, 134
Lecuyer, 7
Ledyard, John, 8, 105
Lemhi Creek, 114
Lemhi Pass, 102, 114, 115
Lemhi River, 114, 132
Lewis, Meriwether, 7, 25, 29, 31, 34, 51–2, 70, 84, 91, 94, 98, 101, 102, 103, 105, 106, 107, 108, 111, 114, 115, 118, 119, 120, 121, 122, 123, 124, 126, 127, 128, 132, 134, 135, 139, 140, 142, 145, 146, 147, 152, 191, 194, 196, 205; character of, 121–2; discovers the Great Falls, 112; expedition of Lewis and Clark, 105–23; Journal of, quoted, 29, 37, 38, 39, 43–4, 45, 51–2, 70, 72, 73, 74, 75, 77–8, 80, 81, 82, 85, 86, 88, 89, 94, 95, 97–8, 108, 109, 110, 111, 112, 114, 115, 116, 117, 118, 119, 120, 121

Lewis and Clark Pass, 102, 112, 115, 119
Lewis fork, 124, 126
Lewis River, 97, 123, 194
Lisa, Fort, 159
Lisa, Manuel, 91, 124, 128, 148
Lisle, J. N. de, 192
Little Belt Mountains, 30
Little Colorado River, 63
Little Missouri River, 9, 110
Little Sandy River, 145, 147, 148, 149
Livingston, B. E., 65, 65 footnote
Livingston (Montana), 120
Livingston, Robert R., 19, 21, 24
Livingstone, David, 123
Llano-Estacado, 29
Lo Lo Pass, 70 footnote, 115, 119, 133
Long, Major S. H., 53, 56, 103, 151, 158, 159, 160, 161, 169, 176; expedition of, 158–61
Long River, 192
Long's Mountains, 145
Long's Peak, 160, 176
Los Angeles, 6, 35, 63, 137, 138, 168
Los Angeles range, 35
Louis XV, 14
Louisiana, 6, 9, 13, 14, 15, 16 footnote, 18, 19, 20, 21, 23, 24, 31, 103, 105, 107, 121, 152; boundaries of, 21–4; French and Spanish settlement in, 16–18; purchase of, 18–21, 20 footnote, 21, 107, 151, 204
Louisiana, upper, 6, 16, 17, 21, 108; products of, 18
Louisiana, lower, 16; products of, 18
Lowlands, Central, 27, 29
Lynx rufus fasciatus, 123

McElroy, R. M., 20 footnote
Mackay, James, 7
Mackenzie, Alexander, 5, 10, 176, 192
Mackenzie River, 5
McKnight, 162
Madison River, 53, 112, 124
Maine, 30

Malgares, 154
Malheur Lake, 132
Malheur River, 173
Mandan, Fort, 110, 117, 122
Mandan Indians, 93, 93 footnote, 94, 111, 121; villages of, 7, 101, 108
Maria's River, 53, 111, 114, 119, 120
Marmot, the Prairie (Cynomys ludovicianus), 86, 123
Mary's Lake, 179, 180
Mary's River (Humboldt), 133, 170, 201; see also under Humboldt
Meares, Captain Robert, 3, 3 footnote
Mediterranean, the, 38; lands, 99
Mendocino, Cape, 2, 48
Menzies, Cape, 5
Merced River, 171
Mexican Mountains (Rocky Mountains), 31, 155
Mexico, 103, 157, 158, 167, 185; Bay of, 23; Gulf of, 50, 149, 158, 176
Michaux, André, 9, 105
Michigan, State of, 66
Milk River, 101
Minnesota River, 5, 107
Minnesota, State of, 66
Minnetaree Indians, 120
Mississippi River, 5, 7, 9, 14, 15, 16, 17, 19, 20, 21, 22, 29, 30, 31, 41, 56, 66, 67, 68, 77, 101, 105, 107, 143, 149, 151, 152, 153, 155, 157, 158, 159, 163, 174, 183, 192, 194, 196, 202, 205; basin, American settlement in, 14–15; lower, 16; upper 202; Territory of, 14
Missouri River, 4, 6, 7, 8, 9, 15, 16, 29, 40, 50, 51, 55, 57, 59, 63, 67, 68, 75, 77, 81, 82, 83, 88, 92, 93, 94, 95, 101, 102, 105, 106, 107, 110, 111, 118, 119, 120, 121, 122, 124, 128, 129, 131, 134, 143, 145, 153, 159, 162, 163, 165, 172, 174, 196; navigation of, 51–2, 74; traders, 40; three forks of, 112; upper, 50–3, 135

Missouri Fur Co., 124, 125, 135
Missouri, State of, 45, 46, 121, 173
Missouri, Territory of, 121
M'Kenzie, Donald, 132
Mobille River, 23
Mohave desert, 62, 74, 137, 168
Mohave Indians, 96 footnote, 138
Mohave River, 137, 183
Mojave, 6
Mono Lake, 61
Monroe, James, 19, 20, 21, 24
Mont Blanc, 176
Montana, State of, 30; rainfall of, 39
Monterey, 138, 171, 187, 198
Monterey Bay, 2
Montreal, 127, 128
Mormon Battalion, 169
Mormon settlement, 103, 188, 190
Mormons, the, 150, 178 footnote,
    188
Morsignona River (Des Moines),
    107
Mosquito, 89–90
Mud Lake, 180, 201
Muddy Fork, 177
Muddy Pass, 183
Multanomah (Multnomah, Multo-
    nomah), see under Willamette
Murphy, 173
Murray, H., 198
Muscle Shell River, 172
Mussell Shell Creek, 110

Napoleon, 18, 19, 20, 20 footnote, 21,
    105
Natchitoches, 151, 156
Nebraska River (Platte), 53, 54, 75
    footnote, 129; see also under Platte
Nebraska, State of, 29
Nevada, State of, 73, 186
Nevins, A., quoted, 178 footnote,
    190
New Mexico, 5, 6, 30, 31, 45, 71, 96,
    152, 161, 162, 169; Pike on, 157
New Orleans, 14, 15, 16, 19, 20, 21
New York, 127
Nez Percé, Fort, 133

Nez Perces Pass, 115
Nicollet, I. N., 174, 202
Niobrara River, 7, 77
Nootka Sound, 2, 3, 8, 127
North-West Fur Co., 5, 110, 125,
    131, 132
Nova Scotia, 16
Nueva Helvetia (New Helvetia),
    42, 182, 189

Ogden, Peter Skene, 132, 133, 135
    footnote, 170; expeditions of,
    132–3
Ogden Sinks, 173
Ogden's River, see under Humboldt
Ohio River, 14, 19, 159, 163
Ohio, State of, 14
Olympic Mountains, 3, 35
Olympus, Mount, 3 footnote
Omaha Indians, 93 footnote, 161
Ordway, Sergeant, 120
Oregon coast ranges, 35
Oregon River, 5, 59, 106, 107, 149
Oregon, State of, 23, 24, 72, 103,
    132, 142, 143, 145, 147, 150, 179,
    183, 204
Oregon trail, 33, 54, 58, 60, 63, 130,
    131, 142, 150, 168, 173, 177, 204,
    204–5 footnote
Osage, Fort, 171
Osage Indians, 55, 93 footnote;
    villages of, 153
Osage River, 55, 153, 154
Otoe Indians, 53
Ouachita Highlands, 30
Owen's Lake, 61, 62, 186
Owen's River, 62, 186
Owyhee River, 201
Ozark Plateau, 30, 56

Pacific Border Region, 34, 35; cli-
    mate of, 38, 39, 41, 48–9
Pacific Fur Co., 125, 127
Pacific Mountain System, 27, 34
Pacific Railroad Reports, 205
Padouca River (Kansas), 107
Palermo, 182

Palmer, Joel, quoted, 142, 145, 146, 147
Pani River (Platte), 107; see also under Platte
Papillion creek, 75 footnote
Parkman, F., quoted, 55 footnote
Parowan, 190
Pattie, J. O., 166, 167, 168, 169
Pattie, S., 166, 168, 169
Pawkee Indians, 95
Pawnee Fork, 154
Pawnee Indians, 93 footnote, 94, 154; villages of, 55 footnote
Peace River, 5
Pecos River, 50, 56, 165
Perdigo River, 23
Pérez, Juan, 2, 3 footnote
Perrin du Lac, F. M., 16 footnote
Persia, northern, 188
Petite Prairie, 17
Philadelphia, 106
Picea sitchensis, 72 footnote
Pierre, Fort, 53
Pike, Zebulon, M., 25, 31, 55, 68, 79, 82, 94, 96, 102, 151, 153, 154, 155, 156, 160, 162, 169, 194; expedition of, 153–8; his description of the Arkansas, 56–7; his description of the Prairies, 67–8; Journal of, quoted, 31, 56–7, 67–8, 84, 154, 155, 156, 157, 158
Pike's Peak (Grand Peak), 31, 69, 155, 160, 176, 177
Pilot Peak, 185
Pima Indians, villages of, 169
Pinckney, Thomas, 15
pinus colorado, 71
Pinus lambertiana, 72 footnote
pinus monophyllus, 73
Pitt River, 64, 132, 173
Pittsburgh, 14, 159
Plains, Coastal, 27; Great, 27, 29, 31, 51, 67, snowfall on, 43; Gulf, 30, 93; High, 29; Interior, 27
Plateaux, Interior, 50, 102; Intermontane, 27
Platte River (Nebraska, Pani), 6, 7,

9, 50, 53–5, 74, 75 footnote, 107, 109, 129, 131, 136, 137, 142, 143, 145, 149, 152, 159, 160, 161, 162, 171, 172, 175, 176, 183, 184; Farnham's description of, 145; North, 54, 80, 143, 145, 176, 184; South, 80, 145, 155, 160, 175
Point Concepcion, 48
Point Coupée, 16
Portneuf River, 58, 132, 133, 172, 178
Powder River, 136
Powell, Major J. W., 167, 203, 203 footnote
Prairie Marmot, see under Marmot
"Prairie Schooner", 54
Prairies, 27, 67, 69; Frémont's description of, 69
Preuss, Charles, 175, 202
Priest rapids, 59
Prongbuck (Antilocapra americana), 84–5, 153 footnote
Provot (Provost), Étienne, 134, 135 footnote, 141
Pseudotsuga douglasi, 72 footnote
Pueblo (Colorado), 155, 163, 189
Puget Sound valley, 35
Pursley (Purcell), James, 162
Pyramid Lake, 61, 180

Rainier, Mount, 3, 118
Raynal, 88
Rector, W., 194
Red River, 16, 50, 56, 85, 107, 151, 153, 155, 156, 159, 160, 161, 167, 194
Republican River, 154
Ricara Indians, 121
Rio Buenaventura, 198, 200, 201; see also under Buenaventura
Rio de los Americanos, 182
Rio del Norte, 57, 156
Rio Grande, 5, 30, 50, 56, 57, 63, 156, 163, 166, 169, 189, 190, 194, 200
Rio los Mongos, 196
Rio Timpanogos, 196
Roberdeau, 194

Robidoux Pass, 189
Rocky Mountains, 4, 9, 24, 29, 30, 31, 40, 41, 50, 53, 54, 57, 65, 69, 73, 75, 86, 89, 96, 101, 102, 110, 111, 114, 115, 118, 119, 122, 125, 129, 133, 135, 140, 141, 142, 143, 145, 146, 147, 149, 150, 155, 157, 159, 160, 170, 174, 176, 179, 181, 182, 183, 184, 188, 194, 196, 198, 201, 202; forests of, 70; northern, 30; rainfall of, 38–9; snowfall on, 44; southern, 30, 33; structure of, 30–3; system of, 27
Rocky Mountains Fur Co., 133, 135, 139, 141; operations of, 133–40
Rodríguez (Cabrillo), 2
Rogers, H. G., 137; Journal of, 134
Ross, Alexander, 132
Roubidoux, Don A., 46
Roxby, Professor P. M., 26

Sacramento River, 63, 139, 173, 181, 182, 187, 189, 198, 201; Frémont's description of, 63–4
St André, 17
St Charles, 17
St Helens, Mount, 3, 116, 118
St Louis, 6, 15, 17, 21, 45, 51, 54, 55, 74, 102, 108, 121, 128, 130, 131, 137, 139, 149, 151, 153, 158, 159, 162, 163, 175, 176, 184
St Peter's River (Minnesota), 107
St Vrain, 175
St Vrain's Fort, 177
Ste Généviève, 17
Salado, Lake, 196
Sale, Lake, 198
Salmo gairdneri, 123
Salmon River, 58, 114, 115, 132
Salmon Trout River, 42, 61, 62, 186, 186 footnote
Salmon Trout River Pass (Truckee Pass), 189
Salt Lake, see under Great Salt Lake
Salt Lake City, 168

San Antonio River, 157
San Diego, 63, 137, 166, 167; Bay of, 2
San Domingo, 18, 19
San Felipe River, 198
San Francisco, 3, 35, 41, 69, 184; Bay of, 2, 6, 63, 181, 182, 183, 189, 194
San Gabriel (Los Angeles), 6, 137, 138
San Ildefonso, treaty of, 18, 19 footnote, 23
San Joaquin River, 63, 137, 171, 182, 201
San Juan Mountains, 190
San Juan River, 63, 167
San Lorenzo, 2
San Miguel, 47
San Pedro, 137
Sand Hill Pass, 156
Sandy River, 136
Sangre de Cristo Mountains (Great White Mountains), 156, 189
Sangre de Cristo Pass, 163
Santa Barbara Channel, 2
Santa Barbara Mountains, 48
Santa Fé, 5, 6, 46, 57, 63, 85, 94, 102, 156, 157, 158, 162, 163, 165, 166, 167, 168, 170, 183; Mountains of, 74; trail, 45, 56, 57, 74, 158, 162–5, 166, 168, 169, 205
Santa Rosalia (Mount Olympus), 3 footnote
Saskatchewan River, 125
Schoolcraft, H. R., 194–6, 194 footnote; expedition of, 196; on problems of American geography, 194–6
Scott's bluffs, 55
Semoulin, M. de, 8
Senora, 158
Sevier Lake, 6, 60, 136, 140
Sevier River, 60, 63, 137, 168, 170, 183, 201
Shasta Indians, 132
Shasta, Mount, 132
Shasta River, 139

Shoshone Indians (Snake), 95, 114, 115; woman, 110; *see also under* Snake Indians
Shreve, F., 65, 65 *footnote*
Shreveport, 151
Sibley, Dr John, expedition of, 151, 151–2
Sierra Blanca, 176
Sierra-Cascade Mountains, 34, 35, 41, 71
Sierra Nevada, 34, 35, 42, 44, 48, 49, 61, 62, 63, 69, 73, 98, 103, 138, 140, 150, 171, 172, 173, 175, 179, 182, 184, 185, 186, 187, 188, 189, 190, 191, 201; as a climatic divide, 42; forests of, 71–2; rainfall of, 38; routes across, 173–4 snowfall on, 44;
Simplon Pass, 148
Sioux Indians, 4, 53, 94, 109, 110
Siskyou Pass, 139
Sitka, 3
Smith, Captain, 41
Smith, Fort, 163
Smith, Jedediah S., 102, 134, 137, 138, 140, 166, 170, 198, 200; Journals of, 134
Smoky Hill Fork, 154, 184
Smucker, S. M., quoted, 175
Smyrna, 182
Snake Indians, 110, 112, 133; *see also under* Shoshone
Snake River, 33, 38, 57, 58, 59, 73, 78, 96, 116, 124, 125, 129, 130, 132, 133, 139, 143, 172, 178, 179, 180, 196
Snake River brigade, 133
Sonora Pass, 173, 174
Sonoran district, 33
South Pass, 33, 35, 54, 61, 62, 102, 131, 135, 136, 139, 140, 141, 142, 150 *footnote*, 167, 171, 175, 176, 179, 181, 183, 190, 191, 204; and distribution of buffalo, 79, 147; and snowfall, 44, 145–6; and vegetation, 70–1, 146–7; dis-

covery of, 134–5, 140–50; trails through, 149–50
Southern Pacific grant, 205
Spanish Illinois (upper Louisiana), 6, 17
Spanish River, 129
Spanish trail, 35, 63, 158, 165, 168, 169, 182, 183
Sparks, Captain, 151, 153
Spokane River, 58
Spyre, Mr, 46
Sublette, W. L., 138
Sublettes, the, 134
Summer, Lake, 180
Sumner, Colonel, 47
Superior, Lake, 4
Sutter, Capt., 182
Sutter's Fort, 182, 186, 187
Stanislaus, Mount, 138
Stanislaus River, 138
Stanley, H. M., 123
Stansbury, H., 142, 191 *footnote*
Stein, Sir Aurel, 123
Stevens, Elisha, 173
Stony Mountains, 9
Stuart, James, 198
Stuart, Robert, 130, 131
Sweetwater River, 54, 131, 135, 136, 141, 143, 145, 146, 147, 148, 171, 172, 176
Swift (member of Long's expedition), 160
Swift's *Gulliver's Travels*, 192

Table Rock, 148
Tacouche Tesse River, 5
Tahoe, Lake, 61, 174, 181
Talleyrand, 21
Taos, 57, 168, 190
Tehachapi Pass, 137, 182 *footnote*
Tennessee, 14
Teton Indians, 110
Tetons, the three, 129, 131, 139
Texas, 74, 156, 157, 204; central, 29
Thomas, A. B., quoted, 6 *footnote*
Thompson, David, 125, 126, 131

Three Forks (of Missouri River), 91, 95, 124
Thuja gigantea, 72 *footnote*
Thwaites, R. G., quoted, 161, 167
Timpanogos, Lake, 157, 196, 198, 200
Timpanogos, Rio, 196
Tlamath Lake, 179
Tonquin, the, 127
Toussaint l'Ouverture, 19
Trail Creek (Jefferson River), 114
Traveler's-rest Creek, 118, 119, 120
Truckee desert, 173
Truckee Pass, 35, 63, 150, 173, 174, 186, 189, 191, 204
Truckee River, 173, 174, 186; name of, 174 *footnote*
Trudeau, Z., 6
Truteau, J. B., 6
Tsuga mertensiana, 72 *footnote*
Tucson, 190
Tulare Lake, 186
Tulare Lake River, 186
Turner, F. J., quoted, 150
Twisted Hair, 115, 119

Uinta Mountains, 136
Uinta River, 136, 183
Ulloa, Francisco de, 1
Umatilla River, 58, 130
Umpqua River, 139
Uncompahgre River, 190
Union, Fort, 53
Union Pacific grant, 205
Union Pacific Railway, 84, 136, 150
Union Pass, 102, 129, 130
Utah Lake, 6, 60, 137, 140, 141, 157, 170, 182, 183, 185
Utah, State of, 190

Vancouver, Fort, 59, 132, 133, 139, 142, 179
Vancouver, George, 3, 3 *footnote*
Vancouver Island, 3
Varennes, P. G de, *see under* La Vérendrye

Vaugondy, 192
Vera Cruz, 162
Vergennes, M. de, 16 *footnote*, 18
Virgin, Thomas, 137
Virgin River, 63, 137, 168, 183
Vizcaíno, 2

Waldo, McCoy and Co., 46
Walker, Joseph, 171, 173, 174, 174 *footnote*, 182, 185, 186, 187
Walker Lake, 171, 173, 186
Walker Pass, 171, 173, 174, 182 *footnote*, 186
Walker River, 62, 171, 173, 186
Wallamuth River, *see under* Willamette
Walla-Walla, Fort, 133, 172, 177, 179
Walla-Walla River, 58, 118, 130, 179
Walla-Walla Indians, 118
Ward, R. de C., quoted, 36 *footnote*, 37 *footnote*, 38 *footnote*
Warner's Pass, 166
Warren, G. K., 172 *footnote*, 194 *footnote*, 196 *footnote*, 201, 202; his ideas on Western America, 202–3; his map of Western America, 202, 203
Wasatch Mountains (Wahsatch), 30, 168, 180, 183, 190
Washington (D.C.), 20, 21, 107, 121, 148, 159
Washington, State of, 23, 24, 72, 73
Washita River, 151, 152
Weber River, 60
Weber's fork, 178
Weiser River, 130
Westport, 165
Wheeler, 142
White, J. G., 140 *footnote*
White River, 16 *footnote*, 83
Whiting, H., quoted, 157–8
Wilkes, Charles, 177
Wilkinson, Lieut., 56, 154, 155
Willamette River (Multonomah, Multnomah, Multanomah or

Willamette River (*cont.*)
  Wallamuth), 35, 58, 116, 118,
    139, 194, 200, 201
Wind River, 129, 135, 141, 172
Wind River Mountains, 129, 131,
    142, 143, 145, 146, 148, 175, 176
Windsor River, 111
Winterbotham, W., map of Western
    America by, 9, 193
Wisconsin, State of, 66
Wisdom River, 120
Wissler, C., quoted, 99 *footnote*
Wolfskill, W., 166, 168, 169

Work, John, 132, 133
Wyoming Basin, 30, 31, 33, 44,
    143
Wyoming, State of, 63; central, 31;
    snowfall in, 44

Yankton Indians, 109
Yellowstone Park, 57
Yellowstone River, 9, 53, 57, 111,
    119, 120, 121, 124, 129, 134, 136,
    155, 158, 159, 167, 172, 201
Yosemite, 171
Young, Brigham, 178 *footnote*

D1207409